THE SHOES OF FORTUNE

BY THE SAME AUTHOR.

JOHN SPLENDID.
THE TALE OF A POOR GENTLEMAN AND THE
LITTLE WARS OF LORN.

THE NEW ROAD.

THE DAFT DAYS.

THE LOST PIBROCH.
AND OTHER SHEILING STORIES.

FANCY FARM.

DOOM CASTLE.
A ROMANCE.

GILIAN THE DREAMER.
HIS FANCY, HIS LOVE AND ADVENTURE.

CHILDREN OF TEMPEST.
A TALE OF THE OUTER ISLES.

JAUNTY JOCK, AND OTHER STORIES.

WILLIAM BLACKWOOD AND SONS,
EDINBURGH AND LONDON.

THE

SHOES OF FORTUNE

HOW THEY BROUGHT TO MANHOOD, LOVE,
ADVENTURE AND CONTENT, AS ALSO INTO
DIVERS PERILS ON LAND AND SEA IN FOREIGN
PARTS AND IN AN ALIEN ARMY, PAUL GREIG
OF THE HAZEL DEN IN SCOTLAND, ONE TIME
PURSER OF *THE SEVEN SISTERS* BRIGANTINE
OF HULL, AND LATE LIEUTENANT IN THE
REGIMENT D'AUVERGNE, ALL AS WRIT BY HIM
AND NOW FOR THE FIRST TIME SET FORTH

BY

NEIL MUNRO

WILLIAM BLACKWOOD AND SONS
EDINBURGH AND LONDON
MCMXXIII

CONTENTS

CONTENTS

CONTENTS

THE SHOES OF FORTUNE

CHAPTER I

NARRATES HOW I CAME TO QUIT THE STUDY OF LATIN AND THE LIKE, AND TAKE TO HARD WORK IN A MOORLAND COUNTRY

IT is an odd thing, chance—the one element to baffle the logician and make the scheming of the wisest look as foolish in the long run as the sandy citadel a child builds upon the shore without any thought of the incoming tide. A strange thing, chance; and but for chance I might this day be the sheriff of a shire, my head stuffed with the tangled phrase and sentiment of interlocutors, or maybe no more than an advocate overlooked, sitting in John's Coffee-house in Edinburgh—a moody soured man with a jug of claret, and cursing the inconsistencies of preferment to office. I might have been that, or less, if it had not been for so trifling a circumstance as the burning of an elderly woman's batch of scones. Had Mistress Grant a more attentive eye to her Culross griddle, what time the scones for her lodgers' breakfast were a-baking forty years ago, I would never have fled furth my native land in a mortal terror of the gallows : had her griddle, say, been higher on the swee-chain by a link or two, Paul Greig would never have foregathered with Dan Risk, the blackguard skipper of a notorious craft ; nor pined in a foreign jail ; nor connived, unwitting, at a prince's murder ; nor marched the weary leagues of France and fought there on a beggar's wage. And this is not all that hung that long-gone day upon a woman's stair-head gossip to the neglect of her *cuisine*, for had this woman been more diligent at her baking I had probably never seen my Isobel with a lover's eye.

Well, here's one who can rarely regret the past except that it is gone. It was hard, it was cruel often ; dangers the most curious and unexpected beset me, and I got an insight to deep villainies whereof man may be capable ; yet on my word, if I had the parcelling out of a second life for myself, I think I would have it not greatly differing from the first, that seems in God's providence like to end in the parish where it started, among kent and friendly folk. I would not swear to it, yet I fancy I would have Lucky Grant again gossiping on her stair-head and her scones burned black, that Mackellar, my fellow-lodger, might make me once more, as he used to do, the instrument of his malcontent.

I mind, as it were yesterday, his gloomy look at the platter that morn's morning. " Here they are again ! " cried he, " fired to a cinder ; it's always that with the old wife, or else a heart of dough. For a bawbee I would throw them in her face."

"Well, not so much as that," said I, "though it is mighty provoking."

"I'm not thinking of myself," said he, always glooming at the platter with his dark, wild Hielan' eye. "I'm not thinking of myself," said he, "but it's something by way of an insult to you, that had to complain of Sunday's haddocks."

"Oh, as to them," quo' I, "they did brawly for me; 'twas you put your share in your pocket and threw it away on the Green. Besides the scones are not so bad as they look"—I broke one and ate; "they're owre good at least for a hungry man like me to send back where they came from."

His face got red. "What's that rubbish about the haddocks and the Green?" said he. "You left me at my breakfast when you went to the Ram's Horn Kirk."

"And that's true, Jock," said I; "but I think I have made no' so bad a guess. You were feared to affront the landlady by leaving her ancient fish on the ashet, and you egged me on to do the grumbling."

"Well, it's as sure as death, Paul," said he shamefacedly, "I hate to vex a woman. And you're a thought wrong in your guess"—he laughed at his own humour as he said it—"for when you were gone to your kirk I transferred my share of the stinking fish to your empty plate."

He jouked his head, but scarcely quick enough, for my Sallust caught him on the ear. He replied with a volume of Buchanan the historian, the man I like because he skelped the Lord's anointed, James the

First, and for a time there was war in Lucky Grant's parlour room, till I threw him into the recess bed, snibbed the door, and went abroad into the street, leaving my room-fellow for once to utter his own complaints.

I went out with the itch of battle on me, and that was the consequence of a woman's havering while scones burned, and likewise my undoing, for the High Street when I came to it was in the yeasty ferment of encountering hosts, their cries calling poor foolish Paul Greig like a trumpet.

It had been a night and morning of snow, though I and Mackellar, so high in Lucky Grant's chamber in Crombie's Land, had not suspected it. The dull drab streets, with their crazy, corbelled gable-ends, had been transformed by a silent miracle of heaven into something new and clean; where noisome gutters were wont to brim with slops there was the napkin of the Lord.

For ordinary I hated this town of my banishment; hated its tun-bellied Virginian merchants, so constantly airing themselves upon the Tontine piazza and seeming to suffer from prosperity as from a disease; and felt no great love of its women— always so much the madame to a drab-coated lad from the moorlands; suffered from its greed and stifled with the stinks of it. "Gardyloo! Gardyloo! Gardyloo!" Faith! I hear that evening slogan yet, and see the daunderers on the Rottenrow skurry like rats into the closes to escape the cascades from the attic windows. And while I think I loved learning (when it was not too ill to come by), and was doing

not so bad in my Humanities, the carven gateway of
the college in my two sessions of a scholar's fare
never but scowled upon me as I entered.

But the snow that morning made of the city a
place wherein it was good to be young, warm-clad,
and hardy. It silenced the customary traffic of the
street, it gave the morning bells a song of fairydom
and the valleys of dream ; up by-ordinary tall and
clean-cut rose the crow-stepped walls, the chimney
heads, and steeples, and I clean forgot my constant
fancy for the hill of Ballageich and the heather all
about it. And war raged. The students faced
'prentice lads and the journeymen of the crafts with
volleys of snowballs ; the merchants in the little
booths ran out tremulous and vainly cried the watch.
Charge was made and counter-charge ; the air was
thick with missiles, and close at hand the silver bells
had their merry sweet chime high over the city of
my banishment drowned by the voices taunting and
defiant.

Merry was that day, but doleful was the end of it,
for in the fight I smote with a snowball one of the
bailies of the burgh, who had come waving his three-
cocked hat with the pomp and confidence of an
elected man and ordering an instant stoppage of our
war : he made more ado about the dignity of his
office than the breakage of his spectacles, and I was
haled before my masters, where I fear I was not so
penitent as prudence would advise.

Two days later my father came in upon Dawson's
cart to convoy me home. He saw the Principal he

saw the regents of the college, and up, somewhat dashed and melancholy, he climbed to my lodging. Mackellar fled before his face as it had been the face of the Medusa.

"Well, Paul," said my father, "it seems we made a mistake about your birthday."

"Did you ?" said I, without meaning, for I knew he was ironical.

"It would seem so, at any rate," said he, not looking my airt at all, but sideways to the window and a tremor in his voice. "When your mother packed your washing last Wednesday and slipped the siller I was not supposed to see into a stocking-foot, she said, ' Now he's twenty and the worst of it over.' Poor woman! she was sadly out of her reckoning. I'm thinking I have here but a bairn of ten. You should still be at the dominie's."

"I was not altogether to blame, father," I cried. "The thing was an accident."

"Of course, of course," said he soothingly. "Was't ever otherwise when the devil joggled an elbow ? Whatever it was, accident or design, it's a session lost. Pack up, Paul, my very young boy, and we'll e'en make our way quietly from this place where they may ken us."

He paid the landlady her lawing, with sixpence over for her motherliness, whereat she was ready to greet, and he took an end of my blue kist down the stairs with me, and over with it like a common porter to the carrier's stance.

A raw, raining day, and the rough highways over the hoof with slush of melted snow, we were a chittering pair as we drove under the tilt of the cart that came to the Mearns to meet us, and it was a dumb and solemn home-coming for me.

Not that I cared much myself, for my lawyership thus cracked in the shell, as it were. I had been often seized with the notion that six feet of a moorlander, in a lustre gown and a horse-hair wig and a blue shalloon bag for the fees, was a wastry of good material. But it was the dad and her at home I thought of, and could put my neck below the cartwheel for distressing. I knew what he thought of as he sat in the cart corner, for many a time he had told me his plans ; and now they were sadly marred. I was to get as much as I could from the prelections of Professor Reid, work my way through the furrows of Van Eck, Van Muyden, and the Pandects, then go to Utrecht or Groningen for the final baking, and come back to the desk of Coghill and Sproat, Writers to the Signet, in Spreull's Land of Edinburgh ; run errands between that dusty hole and the taverns of Salamander Land, where old Sproat (that was my father's doer) held long sederunts with his clients, to write a thesis finally, and graduate at the art of making black look—not altogether white perhaps, but a kind of dirty grey. I had been even privileged to try a sampling of the lawyer's life before I went to college, in the chambers of MacGibbon of Lanark town, where I spent a summer (that had been more profitably passed in my father's fields), backing letters, fair-copying drafts of lease and process, and indexing the letter-book. The last I hated least of all, for I could have a half-sheet of foolscap between the pages, and under MacGibbon's very nose try my hand at something sombre in the manner of the old ancient ballads of the Border. Doing that same once, I gave a wild cry and up with my inky hand and shook it. "Eh! eh!" cried MacGibbon, thinking I had gone mad. "What ails ye?" "He struck me with his sword!" said I like a fool, not altogether out of my frenzy; and then the snuffy old body came round the corner of the desk, keeked into the letter-book where I should have been doing his work, and saw that I was wasting good paper with clinking trash. "Oh, sirs! sirs! I never misused a minute of my youth in the like of that!" said he, sneering, and the sneer hurt. "No, I daresay not," I answered him. "Perhaps ye never had the inclination—nor the art."

I have gone through the world bound always to say what was in me, and that has been my sore loss more than once; but to speak thus to an old man, who had done me no ill beyond demonstrating the general world's attitude to poetry and men of sentiment, was the blackest insolence. He was well advised to send me home for a leathering at my father's hands. And I got the leathering, too, though it was three months after. I had been off in the interim upon a sloop ship out of Ayr.

But here I am havering, and the tilted cart with my father and me in it toiling on the mucky way through the Mearns; and it has escaped couping into the Earn at the ford, and it has landed us at the gate of home; and in all that weary journey never a word, good or ill, from the man that loved me and my mother before all else in a world he was well content with.

Mother was at the door ; that daunted me.

"Ye must be fair starving, Paul," quoth she softly with her hand on my arm, and I daresay my face was blae with cold and chagrin. But my father was not to let a disgrace well merited blow over just like that.

"Here's our little Paul, Katrine," said he, and me towering a head or two above the pair of them and a black down already on my face. "Here's our little Paul. I hope you have not put by his bibs and daidlies, for the wee man's not able to sup the good things of this life clean yet."

And that was the last word of reproof I heard for my folly from my father Quentin Greig.

CHAPTER II

FOR the most part of a year I toiled and moiled like any crofter's son on my father's poor estate, and dreary was the weird I had to dree, for my being there at all was an advertisement to the countryside of what a fool was young Paul Greig. "The Spoiled Horn" was what they called me in the neighbourhood (I learned it in the taunt of a drunken packman), for I had failed at being the spoon I was once designed for, and there was not a ne'er-do-weel peasant nor a bankrupt portioner came craving some benefit to my father's door but made up for his deference to the laird by his free manner with the laird's son. The extra tenderness of my mother (if that were possible) only served to swell my rebel heart, for I knew she was but seeking to put me in a better conceit of myself, and I found a place whereof I had before been fond exceedingly assume a new complexion. The rain seemed to fall constantly that year, and the earth in spring was sodden and sour. Hazel Den House appeared sunk in the rotten leafage of the winter long after the lambs came home and the snipe went drumming on the marsh, and the rookery in the holm plantation was busy with scolding parents tutoring their young. A solemn house at its best—it is so yet, sometimes I think, when my wife is on a jaunt at her sister's and Walter's bairns are bedded—it was solemn beyond all description that spring, and little the better for the coming of summer weather. For then the trees about it, that gave it over long billows of un-timbered countryside an aspect of dark importance, by the same token robbed it (as I thought then) of its few amenities. How it got the name of Hazel Den I cannot tell, for autumn never browned a nut there. It was wych elm and ash that screened Hazel Den House; the elms monstrous and gro-tesque with knotty growths: when they were in their full leaf behind the house they hid the valley of the Clyde and the Highland hills, that at bleaker seasons gave us a sense of companionship with the wide world beyond our infield of stunted crops. The ash towered to the number of two score and three towards the south, shutting us off from the view there, and working muckle harm to our kitchen-garden. Many a time my father was for cutting them down, but mother forbade it, though her syboes suffered from the shade and her roses grew leggy and unblooming. "That," said she, "is the want of constant love: flowers are like bairns; ye must be aye thinking of them kindly to make them thrive." And indeed there might be something in the notion, for her apple-ringie and Dutch Admiral, jonquils, gillyflowers, and peony-roses throve marvellously, better then they did anywhere in the shire of Renfrew while she lived and tended them and have never been quite the same since she died, even with a paid gardener to look after them.

A winter loud with storm, a spring with rain-rot in the fallen leaf, a summer whose foliage but made our home more solitary than ever, a short autumn of stifling heats—that was the year the Spoiled Horn tasted the bitterness of life, the bitterness that comes from the want of an aim (that is better than the best inheritance in kind) and from a consciousness that the world mistrusts your ability. And to cap all, there was no word about my returning to the prelections of Professor Reid, for a reason which I could only guess at then, but learned later was simply the want of money.

My father comported himself to me as if I were doomed to fall into a decline, as we say, demanding my avoidance of night airs, preaching the Horatian virtues of a calm life in the fields, checking with a reddened face and a half-frightened accent every turn of the conversation that gave any alluring colour to travel or adventure. Notably he was dumb, and so was my mother, upon the history of his family. He had had four brothers : three of them I knew were dead and their tombs not in Mearns kirkyard; one of them, Andrew, the youngest, still lived : I feared it might be in a bedlam, by the avoidance they made of all reference to him. I was fated, then, for Bedlam or a galloping consumption—so I appre-hended dolefully from the mystery of my folk ; and the notion sent me often rambling solitary over the autumn moors, cultivating a not unpleasing melancholy and often stringing stanzas of a solemn complexion that I cannot recall nowadays but with a laugh at my folly.

A favourite walk of mine in these moods was along the Water of Earn, where the river chattered and sang over rocks and shallows or plunged thundering in its linn as it did ere I was born and shall do when I and my story are forgotten. A pleasant place, and yet I nearly always had it to myself alone.

I should have had it always to myself but for one person—Isobel Fortune from the Kirkillstane. She seemed as little pleased to meet me there as I was to meet her, though we had been brought up in the same school together; and when I would come suddenly round a bend of the road and she appeared a hundred yards off, I noticed that she half stopped and seemed, as it were, to swither whether she should not turn and avoid me. It would not have surprised me had she done so, for, to tell the truth, I was no very cheery object to contemplate upon a pleasant highway, with the bawbee frown of a poetic gloom upon my countenance and the most curt of salutations as I passed. What she did there all her lone so often mildly puzzled me, till I concluded she was on a tryst with some young gentleman of the neighbourhood; but as I never saw sign of him, I did not think myself so much the marplot as to feel bound to take another road for my rambling. I was all the surer 'twas a lover she was out to meet, because she reddened guiltily each time that we encountered (a fine and sudden charm to a countenance very striking and beautiful, as I could not but observe even then when weightier affairs engaged me); but it seemed I was all in error, for long after she maintained she was, like myself, indulging a sentimental humour that she found go very well in tune with the noise of Earn Water.

As it was her habit to be busily reading when we thus met, I had little doubt as to the ownership of a book that one afternoon I found on the road not long after passing her. It was—of all things in the world!—Hervey's "Meditations."

"It's an odd graveyard taste for a lass of that stamp," thought I, hastening back after her to restore the book, and when I came up to her she was—not red this time, but wan to the very lips, and otherwise in such confusion that she seemed to tremble upon her legs.

"I think this is yours, Isobel," says I : we were too well acquaint from childhood for any address more formal.

"Oh, thank you, Paul," said she hastily. "How stupid of me to lose it!" She took it from me ; her eye fell (for the first time, I felt sure) upon the title of the volume, and she bit her lip in a vexation. I was all the more convinced that her book was but a blind in her rambles, and that there was a lover somewhere ; and I think I must have relaxed my silly black frown a little, and my proud melancholy permitted a faint smile of amusement. The flag came to her face then.

"Thank you," said she very dryly, and she left

me in the middle of the road, like a stirk. If it had been no more than that, I should have thought it a girl's tantrum; but the wonder was to come, for before I had taken three steps on my resumed way I heard her run after me. I stopped, and she stopped, and the notion struck me like a rhyme of song that there was something inexpressibly pleasant in her panting breath and her heaving bosom, where a pebble brooch of shining red gleamed like an eye between her breasts.

"I'm not going to tell you a lie about it, Master Paul," she said, almost like to cry; "I let the book fall on purpose."

"Oh, I could have guessed as much as that, Isobel," said I, wondering who in all the world the fellow was. Her sun-bonnet had fallen from her head in her running, and hung at her back on its pink ribbons, and a curl or two of her hair played truant upon her cheek and temple. It seemed to me the young gentleman she was willing to let a book drop for as a signal of her whereabouts was lucky enough.

"Oh! you could have guessed!" she repeated, with a tone in which were dumbfounderment and annoyance; "then I might have saved myself the trouble." And off she went again, leaving me more the stirk than ever and greatly struck at her remorse of conscience over a little sophistry very pardonable in a lass caught gallivanting. When she was gone and her frock was fluttering pink at the turn of the road, I was seized for the first time with a notion that a girl like that some way set off, as we say, or suited with, a fine landscape.

Not five minutes later I met young David Borland of the Driepps, and there—I told myself—the lover was revealed! He let on he was taking a short cut for Polnoon, so I said neither buff nor sty as to Mistress Isobel.

The cool superiority of the gentleman, who had, to tell the truth, as little in his head as I had in the heel of my shoe, somewhat galled me, for it cried "Spoiled Horn!" as loud as if the taunt were bawled, so my talk with him was short. There was but one topic in it to interest me.

" Has the man with the scarred brow come yet ? " he asked curiously.

I did not understand.

" Then he's not your length yet said he, with the manifest gratification of one who has the han'selling of great news. " Oh! I came on him this morning outside a tavern in the Gorbals, bargaining loudly about a saddle horse for Hazel Den. I'll warrant Hazel Den will get a start when it sees him."

I did not care to show young Borland much curiosity in his story, and so it was just in the few words he gave it to me that I brought it home to our supper-table.

My father and mother looked at each other as if I had told them a tragedy. The supper ended abruptly. The evening worship passed unusually fast, my father reading the Book as one in a dream, and we went to our beds nigh an hour before the customary time.

CHAPTER III

OF THE COMING OF UNCLE ANDREW WITH A SCARRED FOREHEAD AND A BRASS-BOUND CHEST, AND HOW I TOOK AN INFECTION

IT was a night—as often happens in the uplands of our shire in autumn weather—of vast and brooding darkness: the world seemed to swound in a breathless oven, and I had scarcely come to my chamber when thunder broke wild upon the world and torrential rain began to fall. I did not go to bed, but sat with my candle extinguished and watched the lightning show the landscape as if it had been flooded by the gleam of moon and star.

Between the roar of the thunder and the blatter of the rain there were intervals of an astounding stillness of an ominous suspense, and it seemed oddly to me, as I sat in my room, that more than I was awake in Hazel Den House. I felt sure my father and mother sat in their room, still clad and whispering; it was but the illusion of a moment—something felt by the instinct and not by reason—and then a louder, nearer peal of thunder dispelled the notion, and I made to go to bed.

I stopped like one shot, with my waistcoat half undone.

There was a sound of a horse's hoofs coming up the loan, with the beat of them in mire sounding soft enough to make me shiver at the notion of the rider's discomfort in that appalling night, and every now and then the metal click of shoes, showing the animal over-reached himself in the trot.

The rider drew up at the front; a flash of the lightning and the wildest thunder-peal of the night seemed to meet among our outhouses, and when the roll of the thunder ceased I heard a violent rapping at the outer door.

The servants would be long ere they let this late visitor out of the storm, I fancied, and I hurried down; but my father was there in the hall before me, all dressed, as my curious intuition had informed me, and his face strange and inscrutable in the light of a shaded candle. He was making to open the door. My appearance seemed to startle him. He paused, dubious and a trifle confused.

" I thought you had been in bed long ago," said he, " and——"

His sentence was not finished, for the horseman broke in upon it with a masterful rataplan upon the oak, seemingly with a whip-head or a pistol butt, and a cry, new to my ear and uncanny, rose through the beating rain.

With a sigh the most distressing I can mind of, my father seemed to reconcile himself to some fate he would have warded off if he could. He unbolted and threw back the door.

Our visitor threw himself in upon us as if we held the keys of paradise—a man like a rake for lankiness,

as was manifest even through the dripping wrap-
rascal that he wore ; bearded cheek and chin in a
fashion that must seem fiendish in our shaven country ; with a wild and angry eye, the Greig mole
black on his temple, and an old scar livid across his
sunburned brow. He threw a three-cocked hat upon
the floor with a gesture of insolent possession.

" Well, I'm damned ! " cried he, " but this is a
black welcome to one's poor brother Andy," and
scarcely looked upon my father standing with the
shaded candle in the wind. " What's to drink ?
Drink, do you hear that Quentin ? Drink—drink
—d-r-i-n-k. A long strong drink too, and that's
telling you, and none of the whey that I'm hearing's
running through the Greigs now, that once was a
reputable family of three bottles and a rummer to
top all."

" Whist, whist, man ! " pleaded father tremu-
lously, all the man out of him as he stood before
this drunken apparition.

" Whist ! quo' he. Well stap me ! do you no' ken
the lean pup of the litter ? " hiccoughed our visitor,
with a sort of sneer that made the blood run to my
head, and for the first time I felt the great, the
splendid joy of a good cause to fight for.

" You're Andrew," said my father simply, putting
his hand upon the man's coat sleeve in a sympathy
for his drenchen clothes.

That kindly hand was jerked off rudely, an act as
insolent as if he had smitten his host upon the
mouth : my heart leaped, and my fingers went at his
throat. I could have spread him out against the

wall, though I knew him now my uncle ; I could have given him the rogue's quittance with a black face and a protruding tongue. The candle fell from my father's hand ; the glass shade shattered ; the hall of Hazel Den House was plunged in darkness, and the rain drave in through the open door upon us three struggling.

"Let him go, Paul," whispered my father, who I knew was in terror of frightening his wife, and he wrestled mightily with an arm of each of us.

Yet I could not let my uncle go, for with the other arm he held a knife, and he would perhaps have died for it had not another light come on the stair and my mother's voice risen in a pitiful cry.

We fell asunder on a common impulse, and the drunken wanderer was the first to speak.

"Katrine," said he ; "it's always the old tale with Andy, you see ; they must be misunderstanding me," and he bowed with a surprising gentlemanliness that could have made me almost think him not the man who had fouled our house with oaths and drawn a knife upon us in the darkness. The blade of the same, by a trick of legerdemain, had gone up the sleeve of his dripping coat. He seemed all at once sobered. He took my good mother by the hand as she stood trembling and never to know clearly upon what elements of murder she had come.

"It is you, Andrew," said she, bravely smiling. "What a night to come home in after twenty years ! I'm wae to see you in such a plight. And your horse ? " said she again, lifting her candle and peering into the darkness of the night. "I must cry up Sandy to stable your horse."

I'll give my uncle the credit of a confusion at his own forgetfulness.

"Good Lord! Katrine," said he, "if I did not clean forget the brute, a fiddle-faced, spavined, spatter-dasher of a Gorbals mare, no' worth her corn; but there's my bit kistie on her hump."

The servant was round soon at the stabling of the mare, and my mother was brewing something of what the gentleman had had too much already, though she could not guess that; and out of the dripping night he dragged in none of a rider's customary holsters but a little brass-bound chest.

"Yon night I set out for my fortune, Quentin," said he, "I did not think I would come back with it a bulk so small as this; did you? It was the sight of the quiet house and the thought of all it contained that made me act like an idiot as I came in. Still, we must just take the world as we get it, Quentin; and I knew I was sure of a warm welcome in the old house, from one side of it if not from the other, for the sake of lang syne. And this is your son, is it?" he went on, looking at my six feet of indignation not yet dead. "Split me if there's whey in that piece! You near jammed my hawze that time! Your Uncle Andrew's hawze, boy. Are you not ashamed of yourself?"

"Not a bit," said I between my teeth; "I leave that to you."

He smiled till his teeth shone white in his black beard, and "Lord!" cried he, "I'm that glad I came. It was but the toss of a bawbee, when I came to Leith last week, whether I should have a try at the old doocot, or up Blue Peter again and off to the Indies. I hate ceiled rooms—they mind me of the tomb; I'm out of practice at sitting doing nothing in a parlour and saying grace before meat, and—I give you warning, Quentin—I'll be damned if I drink milk for supper. It was the notion of milk for supper and all that means that kept me from calling on Katrine—and you—any sooner. But I'm glad I came to meet a lad of spirit like young Andy here."

"Not Andy," said my father. "Paul is his name."

My uncle laughed.

"That was ill done of you, Quentin," said he; "I think it was as little as Katrine and you could do to have kept up the family name. I suppose you reckoned to change the family fate when you made him Paul. H'm! You must have forgotten that Paul the Apostle wandered most, and many ways fared worst of all the rest. I haven't forgotten my Bible, you see, Quentin."

We were now in the parlour room; a servant lass was puffing up a new-lighted fire; my uncle, with his head in the shade, had his greatcoat off, and stood revealed in shabby garments that had once been most genteel; and his brass-bound fortune, that he seemed averse from parting with a moment, was at his feet. Getting no answer to what he had said of the disciples, he looked from one to the other of us and laughed slyly.

"Take off your boots, Andy," said my father. "And where have you been since—since—the Plantations?"

"Stow that, Quentin!" cried my uncle, with an oath and his eye on me. "What Plantations are you blethering about? And where have I been? Ask me rather where have I not been. It makes me dizzy even to think of it: with rotten Jesuits and Pagan gentlemen; with France and Spain, and with filthy Lascars, lying Greeks, Eboe slaves, stinking niggers, and slit-eyed Chinese! Oh! I tell you I've seen things in twenty years. And places, too: this Scotland, with its infernal rain and its grey fields and its rags, looks like a nightmare to me yet. You may be sure I'll be out of it pretty fast again."

"Poor Scotland!" said father ambiguously.

There must be people in the world who are oddly affected by the names of places, peoples, things that have never come within their own experience. Till this day the name of Barbadoes influences me like a story of adventure; and when my Uncle Andrew—lank, bearded, drenched with storm, stood in our parlour glibly hinting at illimitable travel, I lost my anger with the tipsy wretch and felt a curious glow go through my being.

CHAPTER IV

I COME UPON THE RED SHOES

UNCLE ANDREW settled for the remainder of his time into our domestic world at Hazel Den as if his place had been kept warm for him since ever he went away. For the remainder of his time, I say, because he was to be in the clods of Mearns kirkyard before the hips and haws were off the hedges; and I think I someway saw his doom in his ghastly countenance the first morning he sat at our breakfast table, contrite over his folly of the night before, as you could see, but carrying off the situation with worldly *sang froid*, and even showing signs of some affection for my father.

His character may be put in two words—he was a lovable rogue; his tipsy bitterness to the goodman his brother may be explained almost as briefly: he had had a notion of Katrine Oliver, and had courted her before ever she met my father, and he had lost her affection through his own folly. Judging from what I would have felt myself in the like circumstances, his bitterest punishment for a life ill spent must have been to see Katrine Oliver's pitying kindness to him now, and the sight of that douce and loving couple finding their happiness in each other must have been a constant sermon to him upon repentance.

Yet, to tell the truth, I fear my Uncle Andrew was not constituted for repentance or remorse. He had slain a man honestly once, and had suffered the Plantations, but beyond that (and even that included, as he must ever insist) he had been guilty of no mean act in all his roving career. Follies—vices—extremes—ay, a thousand of them; but for most his conscience never pricked him. On the contrary, he would narrate with gusto the manifold jeopardies his own follies brought him into; his wan face, nigh the colour of a shroud, would flush, and his eyes dance humorously as he shocked the table when we sat at meals, our spoons suspended in the agitation created by his wonderful histories.

Kept to a moderation with the bottle, and with the constant influence of my mother, who used to feed the rogue on vegetables and, unknown to him, load his broth with simples as a cure for his craving, Uncle Andrew was, all things considered, an acquisition to Hazel Den House. Speaking for myself, he brought the element of the unusual and the unexpected to a place where routine had made me sick of my own society; and though the man in his sober senses knew he was dying on his feet, he was the cheeriest person of our company sequestered so remote in the moors. It was a lesson in resignation to see yon merry eyes loweing like lamps over his tombstone cheeks, and hear him crack a joke in the flushed and heaving interludes of his cough.

It was to me he ever directed the most sensational

of his extraordinary memorials. My father did not like it; I saw it in his eye. It was apparent to me that a remonstrance often hung on the tip of his tongue. He would invent ridiculous and unnecessary tasks to keep me out of reach of that alluring *raconteur*, and nobody saw it plainer than Uncle Andrew, who but laughed with the mischievousness of a boy.

Well, the long and short of it was just what Quentin Greig feared—the Spoiled Horn finally smit with a hunger for the road of the Greigs. For three hundred years—we could go no further back, because of a bend sinister—nine out of ten of that family had travelled that road, that leads so often to a kistful of sailor's shells and a death with boots on. It was a fate in the blood, like the black hair of us, the mole on the temple, and the trick of irony. It was that ailment my father had feared for me; it was that kept the household silent upon missing brothers (they were dead, my uncle told me, in Trincomalee, and in Jamaica, and a yard in the Borough of London); it was that inspired the notion of a lawyer's life for Paul Greig.

Just when I was in the deepmost confidence of Uncle Andrew, who was by then confined to his bed and suffering the treatment of Doctor Clews, his stories stopped abruptly and he began to lament the wastry of his life. If the thing had been better acted I might have been impressed, for our follies never look just like what they are till we are finally on the broad of our backs and the Fell Sergeant's step is at the door. But it was not well acted; and when the wicked Uncle Andrew groaned over the very ploys he had a week ago exulted in, I recognised some of my mother's commonest sentiments in his sideways sermon. She had got her quondam Andy, for lang syne's sake, to help her keep her son at home ; and he was doing his best, poor man, but a trifle late in the day.

" Uncle Andrew," said I, never heeding his homily, "tell me what came of the pock-marked tobacco planter when you and the negro lay in the swamp for him ? "

He groaned hopelessly.

" A rotten tale, Paul, my lad," said he, never looking me in the face ; " I rue the day I was mixed up in that affair."

" But it was a good story so far as it went, no further gone than Wednesday last," I protested.

He laughed at that, and for half an hour he put off the new man of my mother's bidding, and we were on the old naughty footing again. He concluded by bequeathing to me for the twentieth time the brass-bound chest, and its contents that we had never seen nor could guess the nature of. But now for the first time he let me know what I might expect there.

" It's not what Quentin might consider much," said he, "for there's not a guelder of money in it, no, nor so little as a groat, for as the world's divided ye can't have both the money and the dance, and I was aye the fellow for the dance. There's scarcely anything in it, Paul, but the trash—ahem !—that is the very fitting reward of a life like mine."

"And still and on, uncle," said I, "it is a very good tale about the pock-marked man."

"Ah! You're there, Greig!" cried the rogue, laughing till his hoast came to nigh choke him. "Well, the kist's yours, anyway, such as it is; and there's but one thing in it—to be strict, a pair— that I set any store by as worth leaving to my nephew."

"It ought to be spurs," said I, "to drive me out of this lamentable countryside and to where a fellow might be doing something worth while."

"Eh!" he cried, "you're no' so far off it, for it's a pair of shoes."

"A pair of shoes!" I repeated, half inclined to think that Uncle Andrew was doited at last.

"A pair of shoes, and perhaps in some need of the cobbler, for I have worn them a good deal since I got them in Madras. They were not new when I got them, but by the look of them they're not a day older now. They have got me out of some unco' plights in different parts of the world, for all that the man who sold them to me at a bonny penny called them the Shoes of Sorrow; and so far as I ken, the virtue's in them yet."

"A doomed man's whim," thought I, and professed myself vastly gratified by his gift.

He died next morning. It was Candlemas Day. He went out at last like a crusie wanting oil. In the morning he had sat up in bed to sup porridge that, following a practice I had made before his reminiscences concluded, I had taken in to him myself. Tremendous long and lean the upper part of him looked, and the cicatrice upon his brow made his ghastliness the more appalling. When he sat against the bolsters he could see through the window into the holm field, and, as it happened, what was there but a wild young roe-deer driven down from some higher part of the country by stress of winter weather, and a couple of mongrel dogs keeping him at bay in an angle of the fail dyke.

I have seldom seen a man more vastly moved than Uncle Andrew looking upon this tragedy of the wilds. He gasped as though his chest would crack, a sweat burst on his face.

"That's—that's the end o't, Paul, my lad!" said he. "Yonder's your roving uncle, and the tykes have got him cornered at last. No more the heather and the brae; no more—no more—no more——"

Such a change came on him that I ran and cried my mother ben, and she and father were soon at his bedside.

It was to her he turned his eyes, that had seen so much of the spacious world of men and women and all their multifarious interests, great and little. They shone with a light of memory and affection, so that I got there and then a glimpse of the Uncle Andrew of innocence and the Uncle Andrew who might have been if fate had had it otherwise.

He put out his hand and took hers, and said goodbye.

"The hounds have me, Katrine," said he. "I'm at the fail dyke corner."

"I'll go out and whistle them off, uncle," said I, fancying it all a doited man's illusion, though the look of death was on him; but I stood rebuked in the frank gaze he gave me of a fuller comprehension than mine, though he answered me not.

And then he took my father's hand in his other, and to him too he said farewell.

"You're there, Quentin!" said he; "and Katrine —Katrine—Katrine chose by far the better man. God be merciful to poor Andy Greig, a sinner." And these were his last words.

CHAPTER V

A SPOILED TRYST, AND OTHER THINGS THAT FOL-
LOWED ON THE OPENING OF THE CHEST

THE funeral was over before I cared to examine my
bequest, and then I went to it with some reluctance,
for if a pair of shoes was the chief contents of the
brass-bound chest, there was like to be little else
except the melancholy relics of a botched life. It
lay where he left it on the night he came—under the
foot of his bed—and when I lifted the lid I felt as if
I was spying upon a man through a keyhole. Yet,
when I came more minutely to examine the contents,
I was disappointed that at the first reflection nothing
was there half so pregnant as his own most casual
tale to rouse in me the pleasant excitation of
romance.

A bairn's caul—that sailor's trophy that has kept
many a mariner from drowning only that he might
die a less pleasant death; a broken handcuff, whose
meaning I cared not to guess at; a pop or pistol; a
chap-book of country ballads, that possibly solaced
his exile from the land they were mostly written
about; the batters of a Bible, with nothing between
them but his name in his mother's hand on the inside

of the board ; a traveller's log or itinerary, covering a period of fifteen years, extremely minute in its detail and well written ; a broken sixpence and the pair of shoes.

The broken sixpence moved my mother to tears, for she had had the other half twenty years ago, before Andrew Greig grew ne'er-do-weel ; the shoes failed to rouse in her or in my father any interest whatever. If they could have guessed it, they would have taken them there and then and sunk them in the deepest linn of Earn.

There was little kenspeckle about them saving their colour, which was a dull dark red. They were of the most excellent material, with a great deal of fine sewing thrown away upon them in parts where it seems to me their endurance was in no wise benefited, and an odd pair of silver buckles gave at your second glance a foreign look to them.

I put them on at the first opportunity : they fitted me as if my feet had been moulded to them, and I sat down to the study of the log-book. The afternoon passed, the dusk came. I lit a candle, and at midnight, when I reached the year of my uncle's escape from the Jesuits of Spain, I came to myself gasping, to find the house in an alarm, and that lanthorns were out about Earn Water looking for me, while all the time I was *perdu* in the dead uncle's chamber in the baron's wing, as we called it, of Hazel Den House. I pretended I had fallen asleep ; it was the first and the last time I lied to my mother, and something told me she knew I was deceiving her. She looked at the red shoes on my feet.

"Ugly brogues!" said she; "it's a wonder to me you would put them on your feet. You don't know who has worn them."

"They were Uncle Andy's," said I, complacently looking at them, for they fitted like a glove; the colour was hardly noticeable in the evening, and the buckles were most becoming.

"Ay! and many a one before him, I'm sure," said she, with distaste in her tone, "I don't think them nice at all, Paul," and she shuddered a little.

"That's but a freit," said I; "but it's not likely I'll wear much of such a legacy." I went up and left them in the chest, and took the diary into my own room and read Uncle Andrew's marvellous adventures in the trade of rover till it was broad daylight.

When I had come to the conclusion it seemed as if I had been in the delirium of a fever, so tempestuous and unreal was that memoir of a wild loose life. The sea was there, buffeting among the pages in rollers and breakers; there were the chronicles of a hundred ports, with boozing kens and raving lazarettos in them; far out isles and cays in nameless oceans, and dozing lagoons below tropic skies; a great clash of weapons and a bewildering deal of political intrigue in every part of the Continent from Calais to Constantinople. My uncle's narrative in life had not hinted at one half the marvel of his career, and I read his pages with a rapture, as one hears a noble piece of music, fascinated to the uttermost, and finding no moral at the end beyond that the world we most of us live in with innocence and ignorance is a crust over tremendous depths. And then I burned the book. It went up in a grey smoke on the top of the fire that I had kept going all night for its perusal; and the thing was no sooner done than I regretted it, though the act was dictated by the seemly enough idea that its contents would only distress my parents if they came to their knowledge.

For days—for weeks—for a season—I went about, my head humming with Uncle Andy's voice recounting the most stirring of his adventures as narrated in the log-book. I had been infected by almost his first words the night he came to Hazel Den House, and made a magic chant of the mere names of foreign peoples; now I was fevered indeed; and when I put on the red shoes (as I did of an evening, impelled by some dandyism foreign to my nature hitherto), they were like the seven-league boots for magic, as they set my imagination into every harbour Uncle Andy had frequented and made me a guest at every inn where he had met his boon companions.

I was wearing them the next time I went on my excursion to Earn side and there met Isobel Fortune, who had kept away from the place since I had smiled at my discovery of her tryst with Hervey's "Meditations." She came upon me unexpectedly, when the gentility of my shoes and the recollection of all that they had borne of manliness was making me walk along the road with a very high head and an unusually jaunty step.

She seemed struck as she came near, with her

face displaying her confusion, and it seemed to me she was a new woman altogether—at least, not the Isobel I had been at school with and seen with an indifferent eye grow up like myself from pinafores. It seemed suddenly scandalous that the like of her should have any correspondence with so ill-suited a lover as David Borland of the Dreipps.

For the first time (except for the unhappy introduction of Hervey's "Meditations") we stopped to speak to each other. She was the most bewitching mixture of smiles and blushes, and stammering now and then, and vastly eager to be pleasant to me, and thinks I, "My lass, you're keen on trysting when it's with Borland."

The very thought of the fellow in that connection made me angry in her interest; and with a mischievous intention of spoiling his sport if he hovered, as I fancied, in the neighbourhood, or at least of delaying his happiness as long as I could, I kept the conversation going very blithe indeed.

She had a laugh, low and brief, and above all sincere, which is the great thing in laughter, that was more pleasant to hear than the sound of Earn in its tinkling hollow among the ferns: it surprised me that she should favour my studied and stupid jocosities with it so frequently. Here was appreciation! I took, in twenty minutes, a better conceit of myself, than the folks at home could have given me in the twelve months since I left the college, and I'll swear to this date 'twas the consciousness of my fancy shoes that put me in such good key.

She saw my glance to them at last complacently,

and pretended herself to notice them for the first time.

She smiled—little hollows came near the corners of her lips; of a sudden I minded having once kissed Mistress Grant's niece in a stair-head frolic in Glasgow High Street, and the experience had been pleasant enough.

"They're very nice," said Isobel.

"They're all that," said I, gazing boldly at her dimples. She flushed and drew in her lips.

"No, no!" I cried, "'twas not them I was thinking of; but their neighbours. I never saw you had dimples before."

At that she was redder than ever.

"I could not help that, Paul," said she; "they have been always there, and you are getting very audacious. I was thinking of your new shoes.'

"How do you know they're new?"

"I could tell," said she, "by the sound of your footstep before you came in sight."

"It might not have been my footstep," said I, and at that she was taken back.

"That is true," said she, hasty to correct herself. "I only thought it might be your footstep, as you are often this way."

"It might as readily have been David Borland's. I have seen him about here." I watched her as closely as I dared: had her face changed, I would have felt it like a blow.

"Anyway, they're very nice, your new shoes," said she, with a marvellous composure that betrayed nothing.

"They were uncle's legacy," I explained, "and had travelled far in many ways about the world; far —and fast."

"And still they don't seem to be in such a hurry as your old ones," said she, with a mischievous air. Then she hastened to cover what might seem a rudeness. "Indeed, they're very handsome, Paul, and become you very much, and—and—and——"

"They're called the Shoes of Sorrow; that's the name my uncle had for them," said I, to help her to her own relief.

"Indeed, and I hope it may be no more than a by-name," she said gravely.

The day had the first rumour of spring: green shoots thrust among the bare bushes on the river side, and the smell of new turned soil came from a field where a plough had been feiring ; above us the sky was blue, in the north the land was pleasantly curved against silver clouds.

And one small bird began to pipe in a clump of willows, that showered a dust of gold upon us when the little breeze came among the branches. I looked at all and I looked at Isobel Fortune, so trim and bonny, and it seemed there and then good to be a man and my fortunes all to try.

"Sorrow here or sorrow there, Isobel," I said, "they are the shoes to take me away sooner or later from Hazel Den."

She caught my meaning with astounding quickness.

"Are you in earnest?" she asked soberly, and I thought she could not have been more vexed had it been David Borland.

"Another year of this," said I, looking at the vacant land, "would break my heart."

"Indeed, Paul, and I thought Earn-side was never so sweet as now," said she, vexed like, as if she was defending a companion.

"That is true, too," said I, smiling into the very depths of her large dark eyes, where I saw a pair of Spoiled Horns as plainly as if I looked in sunny weather into Linn of Earn. "That is true, too. I have never been better pleased with it than to-day. But what in the world's to keep me? It's all bye with the college—at which I'm but middling well pleased; it's all bye with the law—for which thanks to Heaven! and, though they seem to think otherwise at Hazel Den House, I don't believe I've the cut of a man to spend his life among rowting cattle and dour clay land."

"I daresay not; it's true," said she stammeringly, with one fast glance that saw me from the buckles of my red shoes to the underlids of my eyes. For some reason or other she refused to look higher, and the distant landscape seemed to have charmed her after that. She drummed with a toe upon the path; she bit her nether lip; upon my word, the lass had tears at her eyes! I had, plainly, kept her long enough from her lover.

"Well, it's a fine evening; I must be going," said I stupidly, making a show at parting, and an ugly sense of annoyance with David Borland stirring in my heart.

"But it will rain before morning," said she, making to go too, but always looking to the hump of

Dungoyne that bars the way to the Hielands. "I think, after all, Master Paul, I liked the old shoon better than the new ones."

"Do you say so?" I asked, astonished at the irrelevance that came rapidly from her lips, as if she must cry it out or choke. "And how comes that?"

"Just because—" said she, and never a word more, like a woman, nor fair good-e'en nor fair good-day to ye, but off she went, and I was the stirk again.

I looked after her till she went out of sight, wondering what had been the cause of her tirravee. She fair ran at the last, as if eager to get out of my sight; and when she disappeared over the brae that rose from the river-side there was a sense of deprivation within me. I was clean gone in love and over the lugs in it with Isobel Fortune.

CHAPTER VI

MY DEED ON THE MOOR OF MEARNS

NEXT day I shot David Borland of the Driepps.

It was the seventh of March, the first day I heard the laverock that season, and it sang like to burst its heart above the spot where the lad fell with a cry among the rushes. It rose from somewhere in our neighbourhood, aspiring to the heavens, but chained to earth by its own song; and even yet I can recall the eerie influence of that strange conjunction of sin and song as I stood knee-deep in the tangle of the moor with the pistol smoking in my hand.

To go up to the victim of my jealousy as he lay ungainly on the ground, his writhing over, was an ordeal I could not face.

"Davie, Davie!" I cried to him over the thirty paces; but I got no reply from yon among the rushes. I tried to wet my cracking lips with a tongue like a cork, and "Davie, oh, Davie, are ye badly hurt?" I cried, in a voice I must have borrowed from ancient time when my forefathers fought with the forest terrors.

I listened and I better listened, but Borland still lay there at last, a thing insensate like a gangrel's pack, and in all the dreary land there was nothing living but the laverock and me.

The bird was high—a spot upon the blue; his song, I am sure, was the song of his kind, that has charmed lovers in summer fields from old time—a melody rapturous, a message like the message of the evening star that God no more fondly loves than that small warbler in desert places—and yet there and then it deaved me like a cry from hell. No heavenly message had the lark for me: he flew aloft there into the invisible, to tell of this deed of mine among the rushes. Not God alone would hear him tell his story: they might hear it, I knew, in shepherds' cots; they might hear it in an old house bowered dark among trees; the solitary witness of my crime might spread the hue and cry about the shire; already the law might be on the road for young Paul Greig.

I seemed to listen a thousand years to that tell-tale in the air; for a thousand years I scanned the blue for him in vain, yet when I looked at my pistol again the barrel was still warm.

It was the first time I had handled such a weapon.

A senseless tool it seemed, and yet the crooking of a finger made it the confederate of hate; though it, with its duty done, relapsed into a heedless silence, I, that owned it for my instrument, must be wailing in my breast, torn head to foot with thunders of remorse.

I raised the hammer, ran a thumb along the flint, seeing something fiendish in the jaws that held it; I lifted up the prime-cap, and it seemed some miracle of Satan that the dust I had put there in the peace of my room that morning in Hazel Den should have disappeared. "Truefitt," on the lock; a silver shield and an initial graven on it; a butt with a dragon's grin that had seemed ridiculous before, and now seemed to cry "Cain." Lord! that an instrument like this in an unpractised hand should cut off all young Borland's earthly task, end his toil with plough and harrow, his laugh and story.

I looked again at the shapeless thing at thirty paces. "It cannot be," I told myself; and I cried again, in the Scots that must make him cease his joke, "I ken ye're only lettin' on, Davie. Get up oot o' that and we'll cry quits."

But there was no movement; there was no sound; the tell-tale had the heavens to himself.

All the poltroon in me came a-top and dragged my better man round about, let fall the pistol from my nerveless fingers and drove me away from that place. It was not the gallows I thought of (though that too was sometimes in my mind), but of the frightful responsibility I had made my burden, to send a human man before his Maker without a preparation, and my bullet hole upon his brow or breast, to tell for ever through the roaring ring of all eternity that this was the work of Paul Greig. The rushes of the moor hissed me as I ran blindly through them; the tufts of heather over Whiggit Knowe caught at me to stop me; the laverock seemed to follow overhead, a sergeant of provost determined on his victim.

My feet took me, not home to the home that was mine no more, but to Earn-side, where I felt the water crying in its linn would drown the sound of the noisy laverock; and the familiar scene would blot for a space the ugly sight from my eyes. I leant at the side to lave my brow, and could scarce believe that this haggard countenance I saw look up at me from the innocent waters was the Spoiled Horn who had been reflected in Isobel's eyes. Over and over again I wet my lips and bathed my temples; I washed my hands, and there was on the right forefinger a mark I bear to this day where the trigger guard of the pistol in the moments of my agony had cut me to the bone without my knowing it.

When my face looked less like clay and my plans were clear, I rose and went home.

My father and mother were just sitting to supper, and I joined them. They talked of a cousin to be married in Drymen at Michaelmas, of an income in the leg of our mare, of Sabbath's sermon, of things that were as far from me as I from heaven, and I heard them as one in a dream, far-off. What I was hearing most of the time was the laverock setting the hue and cry of Paul Greig's crime around the world and up to the Throne itself, and what I was seeing was the vacant moor, now in the dusk, and a lad's remains awaiting their discovery. The victuals choked me as I pretended to eat; my father noticed nothing, my mother gave a glance, and a fright was in her face.

I went up to my room and searched a desk for some verses that had been gathering there in my twelve months' degradation, and particularly for one no more than a day old with Isobel Fortune for its theme. It was all bye with that! I was bound to be glancing at some of the lines as I furiously tore them up and threw them out of the window into the bleaching-green; and oh! but the black sorrows and glooms that were there recorded seemed a mockery in the light of this my terrible experience. They went by the window, every scrap: then I felt cut off from every innocent day of my youth, the past clean gone from me for ever.

The evening worship came.

"*If I take the wings of the morning and dwell in the uttermost ends of the sea.*"

My father, peering close at the Book through his spectacles, gave out the words as if he stood upon a pulpit, deliberate—too deliberate for Cain his son, that sat with his back to the window shading his face from a mother's eyes. They were always on me, her eyes, throughout that last service; they searched me like a torch in a pit, and wae, wae was her face!

When we came to pray and knelt upon the floor, I felt as through my shut eyes that hers were on me even then, exceeding sad and troubled. They followed me like that when I went up, as they were to think, to my bed, and I was sitting at my window in the dark half an hour later when she came up after me. She had never done the like before since I was a child.

"Are ye bedded, Paul?" she whispered in the dark.

I could not answer her in words, but I stood to my feet and lit a candle, and she saw that I was dressed.

"What ails ye to-night?" she asked trembling.

"I'm going away, mother," I answered.

"There's something wrong?" she queried in great distress.

"There's all that!" I confessed. "It'll be time for you to ken about that in the morning, but I must be off this night."

"Oh, Paul, Paul!" she cried, "I did not like to see you going out in these shoes this afternoon, and I ken't that something ailed ye."

"The road to hell suits one shoe as well's another," said I bitterly; "where the sorrow lies is that ye never saw me go out with a different heart. Mother, mother, the worst ye can guess is no' so bad as the worst ye've yet to hear of your son."

I was in a storm of roaring emotions, yet her next words startled me.

"It's Isobel Fortune of the Kirkillstane," she said, trying hard to smile with a wan face in the candle light.

"It was—poor dear! Am I not in torment when I think that she must know it?"

"I thought it was that that ailed ye, Paul," said she, as if she were relieved. "Look; I got this a little ago on the bleaching-green—this scrap of paper in your write and her name upon it. Maybe I should not have read it." And she handed me part of that ardent ballad I had torn less than an hour ago.

I held it in the flame of her candle till it was

gone, our hands all trembling, and "That's the end appointed for Paul Greig," said I.

"Oh, Paul, Paul, it cannot be so unco'!" she cried in terror, and clutched me at the arm.

"It is—it is the worst."

"And yet—and yet—you're my son, Paul. Tell me."

She looked so like a reed in the winter wind, so frail and little and shivering in my room, that I dared not tell her there and then. I said it was better that both father and she should hear my tale together, and we went into the room where already he was bedded but not asleep. He sat up staring at our entry, a night-cowl tassel dangling on his brow.

"There's a man dead——" I began, when he checked me with a shout.

"Stop, stop!" he cried, and put my mother in a chair. "I have heard the tale before with my brother Andy, and the end was not for women's ears."

"I must know, Quentin," said his wife, blanched to the lip but determined, and then he put his arm about her waist. It seemed like a second murder to wrench those tender hearts that loved me, but the thing was bound to do.

I poured out my tale at one breath and in one sentence, and when it ended my mother was in her swound.

"Oh, Paul!" cried the poor man, his face like a clout; "black was the day she gave you birth!"

CHAPTER VII

QUENTIN GREIG LOSES A SON, AND I SET OUT
WITH A HORSE AS ALL MY FORTUNE

He pushed me from the chamber as I had been a
stranger intruding, and I went to the trance door
and looked out at the stretching moorlands lit by an
enormous moon that rose over Cathkin Braes, and
an immensity of stars. For the first time in all my
life I realised the heedlessness of nature in human
affairs the most momentous. For the moon swung
up serene beyond expression; the stars winked
merrily: a late bird glid among the bushes and
perched momentarily on a bough of ash to pipe
briefly almost with the passion of the spring. But
not the heedlessness of nature influenced me so
much as the barren prospect of the world that the
moon and stars revealed. There was no one out
there in those deep spaces of darkness I could claim
as friend or familiar. Where was I to go? What
was I to do? Only the beginnings of schemes came
to me—schemes of concealment and disguise, of
surrender even—but the last to be dismissed as soon
as it occurred to me, for how could I leave this house
the bitter bequest of a memory of the gallows-tree?

Only the beginnings, I say, for every scheme ran tilt against the obvious truth that I was not only without affection or regard out there, but without as much as a crown of money to purchase the semblance of either.

I could not have stood very long there when my father came out, his face like clay, and aged miraculously, and beckoned me to the parlour.

"Your mother—my wife," said he, "is very ill, and I am sending for the doctor. The horse is yoking. There is another woman in Driepps who— God help her!—will be no better this night, but I wish in truth her case was ours, and that it was you who lay among the heather."

He began pacing up and down the floor, his eyes bent, his hands continually wringing, his heart bursting, as it were, with sighs and the dry sobs of the utmost wretchedness. As for me, I must have been clean gyte (as the saying goes), for my attention was mostly taken up with the tassel of his nightcap that bobbed grotesquely on his brow. I had not seen it since, as a child, I used to share his room.

"What! what!" he cried at last piteously, "have ye never a word to say? Are ye dumb?" He ran at me and caught me by the collar of the coat and tried to shake me in an anger, but I felt it no more than I had been a stone.

"What did ye do it for? What in heaven's name did ye quarrel on?"

"It was—it was about a girl," I said, reddening even at that momentous hour to speak of such a thing to him.

"A girl!" he repeated, tossing up his hands. "Keep us! Hoo lang are ye oot o' daidlies? Well! well!" he went on, subduing himself and prepared to listen. I wished the tassel had been any other colour than crimson, and hung fairer on the middle of his forehead; it seemed to fascinate me. And he, belike, forgot that I was there, for he thought, I knew, continually of his wife, and he would stop his feverish pacing on the floor, and hearken for a sound from the room where she was quartered with the maid. I made no answer.

"Well, well!" he cried again fiercely, turning upon me. "Out with it; out with the whole hellish transaction, man!"

And then I told him in detail what before my mother I had told in a brief abstract.

How that I had met young Borland coming down the breast of the brae at Kirkillstane last night and——

"Last night!" he cried. "Are ye havering? I saw ye go to your bed at ten, and your boots were in the kitchen."

It was so, I confessed. I had gone to my room but not to bed, and had slipped out by the window when the house was still, with Uncle Andrew's shoes.

"Oh, lad!" he cried, "it's Andy's shoes you stand in sure enough, for I have seen him twenty years syne in the plight that you are in this night. Merciful heaven! what dark blotch is in the history of this family of ours that it must ever be embroiled in crimes of passion and come continually to broken ends of fortune? I have lived stark honest and humble, fearing the Lord; the covenants have I kept, and still and on it seems I must beget a child of the Evil One!"

And how, going out thus under cover of night, I had meant to indulge a boyish fancy by seeing the light of Isobel Fortune's window. And how, coming to the Kirkillstane, I met David Borland leaving the house, whistling cheerfully.

"Oh, Paul, Paul!" cried my father, "I mind of you an infant on her knees that's ben there, and it might have been but yesterday your greeting in the night wakened me to mourn and ponder on your fate."

And how Borland, divining my object there, and himself new out triumphant from that cheerful house of many daughters, made his contempt for the Spoiled Horn too apparent.

"You walked to the trough-stane when you were a twelvemonth old," said my father with the irrelevance of great grief, as if he recalled a dead son's infancy.

And how, maddened by some irony of mine, he had struck a blow upon my chest, and so brought my challenge to something more serious and gentlemanly than a squalid brawl with fists upon the highway.

I stopped my story; it seemed useless to be telling it to one so much preoccupied with the thought of the woman he loved. His lips were open, his eyes were constant on the door.

But "Well! Well!" he cried again eagerly, and I resumed.

Of how I had come home, and crept into my guilty chamber and lay the long night through, torn by grief and anger, jealousy and distress. And how evading the others of the household as best I could that day, I had in the afternoon at the hour appointed gone out with Uncle Andrew's pistol.

My father moaned—a waefu' sound!

And found young Borland up on the moor before me with such another weapon, his face red by-ordinary, his hands and voice trembling with passion.

"Poor lad, poor lad!" my father cried, blurting the sentiment as he had been a bairn.

How we tossed a coin to decide which should be the first to fire, and Borland had won the toss, and gone to the other end of our twenty paces with vulgar menaces and "Spoiled Horn" the sweetest of his epithets.

"Poor lad! he but tried to bluster down the inward voice that told him the folly o't," said father.

And how Borland had fired first. The air was damp. The sound was like a slamming door.

"The door of hope shut up for him, poor dear," cried father.

And how he missed me in his trepidation that made his hand that held the pistol so tremble that I saw the muzzle quiver even at twenty paces.

"And then you shot him deliberately!" cried my father.

"No, no," I cried at that, indignant. "I aimed without a glance along the barrel: the flint flashed; the prime missed fire, and I was not sorry, but

Borland cried 'Spoiled Horn' braggingly, and I cocked again as fast as I could, and blindly jerked the trigger. I never thought of striking him. He fell with one loud cry among the rushes."

"Murder, by God !" cried my father, and he relapsed into a chair, his body all convulsed with horror.

I had told him all this as if I had been in a delirium, or as if it were a tale out of a book, and it was only when I saw him writhing in his chair and the tassel shaking over his eyes, I minded that the murderer was me. I made for the door ; up rose my father quickly and asked me what I meant to do.

I confessed I neither knew nor cared.

"You must thole your assize," said he, and just as he said it the clatter of the mare's hoofs sounded on the causey of the yard, and he must have minded suddenly for what object she was saddled there.

"No, no," said he, "you must flee the country. What right have you to make it any worse for her ?"

"I have not a crown in my pocket," said I.

"And I have less," he answered quickly. "Where are you going ? No, no, don't tell me that; I'm not to know. There's the mare saddled, I meant Sandy to send the doctor from the Mearns, but you can do that. Bid him come here as fast as he can."

"And must I come back with the mare ?" I asked, reckless what he might say to that, though my life depended on it.

"For the sake of your mother," he answered, "I would rather never set eyes on you or the beast again; she's the last transaction between us, Paul Greig." And then he burst in tears, with his arms about my neck.

Ten minutes later I was on the mare, and galloping, for all her ailing leg, from Hazel Den as if it were my own loweing conscience. I roused Dr. Clews at the Mearns, and gave him my father's message. "Man," said he, holding his chamber light up to my face, "man, ye're as gash as a ghaist yersel'." "I may well be that," said I, and off I set, with some of Uncle Andy's old experience in my mind, upon a ride across broad Scotland

CHAPTER VIII

I RIDE BY NIGHT ACROSS SCOTLAND, AND MEET A
MARINER WITH A GLEED EYE

THAT night was like the day, with a full moon
shining. The next afternoon I rode into Borrow-
stounness, my horse done out and myself sore from
head to heel; and never in all my life have I seen a
place with a more unwelcome aspect, for the streets
were over the hoof in mud; the natives directed me
in an accent like a tinker's whine; the Firth of
Forth was wrapped in a haar or fog that too closely
put me in mind of my prospects. But I had no
right to be too particular, and in the course of an
hour I had sold the mare for five pounds to a man of
much Christian profession, who would not give a
farthing more on the plea that she was likely stolen.

The five pounds and the clothes I stood in were
my fortune: it did not seem very much, if it was to
take me out of the reach of the long arm of the
doomster; and thinking of the doomster I minded of
the mole upon my brow, that was the most kenspeckle thing about me in the event of a description
going about the country, so the first thing I bought
with my fortune was a pair of scissors. Going into

a pend close in one of the vennels beside the quay, I clipped off the hair upon the mole and felt a little safer.   I was coming out of the close, pouching the scissors, when a man of sea-going aspect, with high boots and a tarpaulin hat, stumbled against me and damned my awkwardness.

"You filthy hog," said I, exasperated at such manners, for he was himself to blame for the encounter ; "how dare you speak to me like that ?"

He was a man of the middle height, sturdy on his bowed legs in spite of the drink obvious in his face and speech, and he had a roving gleed black eye.   I had never clapped gaze on him in all my life before.

"Is that the way ye speak to Dan Risk, ye swab ?" said he, ludicrously affecting a dignity that ill suited with his hiccough.   "What's the good of me being a skipper if every linen-draper out of Fife can cut into my quarter on my own deck ?"

"This is no' your quarter-deck, man, if ye were sober enough to ken it," said I ; "and I'm no linen-draper from Fife or anywhere else."

And then the brute, with his hands thrust to the depth of his pockets, staggered me as if he had done it with a blow of his fist.

"No," said he, with a very cunning tone, "ye're no linen-draper perhaps, but—ye're maybe no sae decent a man, young Greig."

It was impossible for me to conceal even from this tipsy rogue my astonishment and alarm at this.   It seemed to me the devil himself must be leagued against me in the cause of justice.   A cold sweat came on my face and the palms of my hands.   I opened my mouth and meant to give him the lie but I found I dare not do so in the presence of what seemed a miracle of heaven.

"How do you ken my name's Greig?" I asked at the last.

"Fine that," he made answer, with a grin; "and there's mony an odd thing else I ken."

"Well, it's no matter," said I, preparing to quit him, but in great fear of what the upshot might be; "I'm for off, anyway."

By this time it was obvious that he was not so drunk as I thought him at first, and that in temper and tact he was my match even with the glass in him.

"Do ye ken what I would be doing if I was you?" said he seemingly determined not to let me depart like that, for he took a step or two after me.

I made no reply, but quickened my pace and after me he came, lurching and catching at my arm; and I mind to this day the roll of him gave me the impression of a crab.

"If it's money ye want——" I said at the end of my patience.

"Curse your money!" he cried, pretending to spit the insult from his mouth. "Curse your money; but if I was you, and a weel-kent skipper like Dan Risk—like Dan Risk of the *Seven Sisters*—made up to me out of a redeeculous good nature and nothing else, I would gladly go and splice the rope with him in the nearest ken."

"Go and drink with yourself, man," I cried; "there's the money for a chappin of ale, and I'll forego my share of it."

I could have done nothing better calculated to infuriate him. As I held out the coin on the palm of my hand he struck it up with an oath and it rolled into the syver. His face flamed till the neck of him seemed a round of seasoned beef.

"By the Rock o' Bass!" he roared, "I would clap ye in jyle for less than your lousy groat."

Ah, then, it was in vain I had put the breadth of Scotland between me and that corpse among the rushes : my heart struggled a moment, and sank as if it had been drowned in bilge. I turned on the man what must have been a gallows face, and he laughed, and, gaining his drunken good nature again he hooked me by the arm, and before my senses were my own again he was leading me down the street and to the harbour. I had never a word to say.

The port, as I tell, was swathed in the haar of the east, out of which tall masts rose dim like phantom spears ; the clumsy tarred bulwarks loomed like walls along the quay, and the neighbourhood was noisy with voices that seemed unnatural coming out of the haze. Mariners were hanging about the sheds, and a low tavern belched others out to keep them company. Risk made for the tavern, and at that I baulked.

"Oh, come on!" said he. "If I'm no' mistaken Dan Risk's the very man ye're in the need of. You're wanting out of Scotland, are ye no'?"

"More than that ; I'm wanting out of myself," said I, but that seemed beyond him.

"Come in anyway, and we'll talk it over."

That he might help me out of the country seemed possible if he was not, as I feared at first, some agent of the law and merely playing with me, so I entered the tavern with him.

"Two gills to the coffin-room, Mrs. Clerihew," he cried to the woman in the kitchen. "And slippy aboot it, if ye please, for my mate here's been drinking buttermilk all his life, and ye can tell't in his face."

"I would rather have some meat," said I.

"Humph!" quo' he, looking at my breeches. "A lang ride!" He ordered the food at my mentioning, and made no fuss about drinking my share of the spirits as well as his own, while I ate with a hunger that was soon appeased, for my eye, as the saying goes, was iller to satisfy than my appetite.

He sat on the other side of the table in the little room that doubtless fairly deserved the name it got of coffin, for many a man, I'm thinking, was buried there in his evil habits; and I wondered what was to be next.

"To come to the bit," said he at last, looking hard into the bottom of his tankard in a way that was a plain invitation to buy more for him. "To come to the bit, you're wanting out of the country?"

"It's true," said I; "but how do you know? And how do you know my name, for I never saw you to my knowledge in all my life before?"

"So much the worse for you; I'm rale weel liked by them that kens me. What would ye give for a passage to Nova Scotia?"

"It's a long way," said I, beginning to see a little clearer.

"Ay," said he, "but I've seen a gey lang rope too, and a man danglin' at the end of it."

Again my face betrayed me. I made no answer.

"I ken all aboot it," he went on. "Your name's Greig; ye're from a place called the Hazel Den at the other side o' the country; ye've been sailing wi' a stiff breeze on the quarter all night, and the clime o' auld Scotland's one that doesna suit your health, eh? What's the amount?" said he, and he looked towards my pocket. "Could we no' mak' it halfers?"

"Five pounds," said I, and at that he looked strangely dashed.

"Five pounds," he repeated incredulously. "It seems to have been hardly worth the while." And then his face changed, as if a new thought had struck him. He leaned over the table and whispered with the infernal tone of a confederate, "Doused his glim, eh?" winking with his hale eye, so that I could not but shiver at him, as at the touch of slime.

"I don't understand," said I.

"Do ye no'?" said he, with a sneer; "for a Greig ye're mighty slow in the uptak'. The plain English o' that, then, is that ye've killed a man. A trifle like that ance happened to a Greig afore."

"What's your name?" I demanded.

"Am I no tellin' ye?" said he shortly. "It's just Daniel Risk; and where could you get a better? Perhaps ye were thinkin' aboot swappin' names wi' me ; and by the Bass, it's Dan's family name would suit very weel your present position," and the scoundrel laughed at his own humour.

"I asked because I was frightened it might be Mahoun," said I.   "It seems gey hard to have ridden through mire for a night and a day, and land where ye started from at the beginning.   And how do ye ken all that ?"

"Oh!" he said, "kennin's my trade, if ye want to know.   And whatever way I ken, ye needna think I'm the fellow to make much of a sang aboot it.   Still and on, the thing's frowned doon on in this country, though in places I've been it would be coonted to your credit.   I'll take anither gill ; and if ye ask me, I would drench the butter-milk wi' something o' the same, for the look o' ye sittin' there's enough to gie me the waterbrash.   Mrs. Clerihew— here!"   He rapped loudly on the table, and the drink coming in I was compelled again to see him soak himself at my expense.   He reverted to my passage from the country, and "Five pounds is little enough for it," said he ; "but ye might be eking it oot by partly working your passage."

"I didn't say I was going either to Nova Scotia or with you," said I, "and I think I could make a better bargain elsewhere."

"So could I, maybe," said he, fuming of spirits till I felt sick.   "And it's time I was doin' something for the good of my country."   With that he rose to his feet with a look of great moral resolution, and made as if for the door, but by this time I understood him better.

"Sit down, ye muckle hash!" said I, and I stood over him with a most threatening aspect.

"By the Lord!" said he, "that's a Greig anyway!"

"Ay!" said I, "ye seem to ken the breed. Can I get another vessel abroad besides yours?"

"Ye can not," said he, with a promptness I expected, "unless ye wait on the *Sea Pyat*. She leaves for Jamaica next Thursday; and there's no' a spark of the Christian in the skipper o' her, one Macallum from Greenock."

For the space of ten minutes I pondered over the situation. Undoubtedly I was in a hole. This brute had me in his power so long as my feet were on Scottish land, and he knew it. At sea he might have me in his power too, but against that there was one precaution I could take, and I made up my mind.

"I'll give you four pounds—half at leaving the quay and the other half when ye land me."

"My conscience wadna' aloo me," protested the rogue; but the greed was in his face, and at last he struck my thumb on the bargain, and when he did that I think I felt as much remorse at the transaction as at the crime from whose punishment I fled.

"Now," said I, "tell me how you knew me and heard about—about——"

"About what?" said he, with an affected surprise. "Let me tell ye this, Mr. Greig, or whatever your name may be, that Dan Risk is too much of the gentleman to have any recollection of any unpleasantness ye may mention, now that he has made the bargain wi' ye. I ken naethin' aboot ye, if ye please: whether your name's Greig or Mackay or Habbie Henderson, it's new to me, only ye're a likely lad for a purser's berth in the *Seven Sisters*." And refusing to say another word on the topic that so interested me, he took me down to the ship's side, where I found the *Seven Sisters* was a brigantine out of Hull, sadly in the want of tar upon her timbers and her mainmast so decayed and worm-eaten that it sounded boss when I struck it with my knuckles in the by-going.

Risk saw me doing it. He gave an ugly smile.

"What do ye think o' her? said he, showing me down the companion.

"Mighty little," I told him straight. "I'm from the moors," said I, "but I've had my feet on a sloop of Ayr before now; and by the look of this craft I would say she has been beeking in the sun idle till she rotted down to the garboard strake."

He gave his gleed eye a turn and vented some appalling oaths, and wound up with the insult I might expect—namely, that drowning was not my portion.

"There was some brag a little ago of your being a gentleman," said I, convinced that this blackguard was to be treated to his own fare if he was to be got on with at all. "There's not much of a gentleman in the like of that."

At this he was taken aback. "Well," said he, "don't you cross my temper; if my temper's crossed it's gey hard to keep up gentility. The ship's sound enough, or she wouldn't be half a dizen times round the Horn and as weel kent in Halifax as one o' their ain dories. She's guid enough for your—for our business, if ye please, Mr. Greig; and here's my mate Murchison."

Another tarry-breeks of no more attractive aspect came down the companion.

"Here's a new hand for ye," said the skipper humorously.

The mate looked me up and down with some contempt from his own height of little more than five feet four, and peeled an oilskin coat off him. I was clad myself in a good green coat and breeches with fine wool rig-and-fur hose, and the buckled red shoon and the cock of my hat I daresay gave me the look of some importance in tarry-breeks' eyes. At any rate, he did not take Risk's word for my identity, but at last touched his hat with awkward fingers after relinquishing his look of contempt.

"Mr. Jamieson?" said he questioningly, and the skipper by this time was searching in a locker for a bottle of rum he said he had there for the signing of agreements. "Mr. Jamieson," said the mate, "I'm glad to see ye. The money's no' enough for the job, and that's letting ye know. It's all right for Dan here wi' neither wife nor family, but——"

"What's that, ye idiot?" cried Risk turning about in alarm. "Do ye tak' this callan for the owner? I tell't ye he was a new hand."

"A hand!" repeated Murchison, aback and dubious.

"Jist that; he's the purser."

Murchison laughed. "That's a new ornament on the auld randy; he'll be to keep his keekers on the manifest, like?" said he as one who cracks a good joke. But still and on he scanned me with a suspicious eye, and it was not till Risk had taken him aside later in the day and seemingly explained, that he was ready to meet me with equanimity. By that time I had paid the skipper his two guineas, for the last of his crew was on board, every man Jack of them as full as the Baltic, and staggering at the coamings of the hatches not yet down, until I thought half of them would finally land in the hold.

CHAPTER IX

WHEREIN THE "SEVEN SISTERS" ACTS STRANGELY, AND I SIT WAITING FOR THE MANACLES

AN air of westerly wind had risen after meridian and the haar was gone, so that when I stood at the break of the poop as the brigantine crept into the channel and flung out billows of canvas while her drunken seamen quarrelled and bawled high on the spars, I saw, as I imagined, the last of Scotland in a pleasant evening glow. My heart sank. It was not a departure like this I had many a time anticipated when I listened to Uncle Andy's tales; here was I with blood on my hands and a guinea to start my life in a foreign country; that was not the worst of it either, for far more distress was in my mind at the reflection that I travelled with a man who was in my secret. At first I was afraid to go near him once our ropes were off the pawls, and I, as it were, was altogether his, but to my surprise there could be no pleasanter man than Risk when he had the wash of water under his rotten barque. He was not only a better-mannered man to myself, but he became, in half an hour of the Firth breeze, as sober as a judge. But for the roving gleed eye, and what I had seen of him on shore, Captain Dan Risk might have passed for a model of all the virtues. He called me Mr.

Greig and once or twice (but I stopped that) Young Hazel Den, with no irony in the appellation, and he was at pains to make his mate see that I was one to be treated with some respect, proffering me at our first meal together (for I was to eat in the cuddy,) the first of everything on the table, and even making some excuses for the roughness of the viands. And I could see that whatever his qualities of heart might be, he was a good seaman, a thing to be told in ten minutes by a skipper's step on a deck and his grip of the rail, and his word of command. Those drunken barnacles of his seemed to be men with the stuff of manly deeds in them, when at his word they dashed aloft among the canvas canopy to fist the bulging sail and haul on clew or gasket, or when they clung on greasy ropes and at a gesture of his hand heaved cheerily with that "yo-ho" that is the chant of all the oceans where keels run.

Murchison was a saturnine, silent man, from whom little was to be got of edification. The crew numbered eight men, one of them a black deaf mute, with the name of Antonio Ferdinando, who cooked in a galley little larger than the Hazel Den kennel. It was apparent that no two of them had ever met before, such a career of flux and change is the seaman's, and except one of them, a fellow Horn, who was foremast man, a more villainous gang I never set eyes on before or since. If Risk had raked the ports of Scotland with a fine bone comb for vermin, he could not have brought together a more unpleasant-looking crew. No more than two of them brought a bag on board, and so ragged was their appearance that I felt ashamed to air my own good clothes on the same deck with them.

Fortunately it seemed I had nothing to do with them nor they with me; all that was ordered for the eking out of my passage, as Risk had said, was to copy the manifest, and I had no sooner set to that than I discerned it was a gowk's job just given me to keep me in employ in the cabin. Whatever his reason, the man did not want me about his deck. I saw that in an interlude in my writing, when I came up from his airless den to learn what progress old rotten-beams made under all her canvas.

It had declined to a mere handful of wind, and the vessel scarcely moved, seemed indeed steadfast among the sea-birds that swooped and wheeled and cried around her. I saw the sun just drop among blood-red clouds over Stirling, and on the shore of Fife its pleasant glow. The sea swung flat and oily, running to its ebb, and lapping discernibly upon a recluse promontory of land with a stronghold on it.

"What do you call yon, Horn?" I said to the seaman I have before mentioned, who leaned upon the taffrail and watched the vessel's greasy wake, and I pointed to the gloomy buildings on the shore.

"Blackness Castle," said he, and he had time to tell no more, for the skipper bawled upon him for a shirking dog, and ordered the flemishing of some ropes loose upon the forward deck. Nor was I exempt from his zeal for the industry of other folks for he came up to me with a suspicious look, as if he feared I had been hearing news from his foremast man, and "How goes the manifest, Mr. Greig?" says he.

" Oh, brawly, brawly!" said I, determined to begin with Captain Daniel Risk as I meant to end.

He grew purple, but restrainèd himself with an effort. "This is not an Ayr sloop, Mr. Greig," said he; "and when orders go on the *Seven Sisters* I like to see them implemented. You must understand that there's a pressing need for your clerking, or I would not be so soon putting you at it."

"At this rate of sailing," says I, "I'll have time to copy some hundred manifests between here and Nova Scotia."

" Perhaps you'll permit me to be the best judge of that," he replied in the English he ever assumed with his dignity, and seeing there was no more for it, I went back to my quill.

It was little wonder, in all the circumstances, that I fell asleep over my task with my head upon the cabin table whereon I wrote, and it was still early in the night when I crawled into the narrow bunk that the skipper had earlier indicated as mine.

Weariness mastered my body, but my mind still roamed; the bunk became a coffin quicklimed, and the murderer of David Borland lying in it; the laverock cried across Earn Water and the moors of Renfrew with the voice of Daniel Risk. And yet the strange thing was that I knew I slept and dreamed, and more than once I made effort, and dragged myself into wakefulness from the horrors of my nightmare. At these times there was nothing to hear but the plop of little waves against the side of the ship, a tread on deck, and the call of the watch.

I had fallen into a sleep more profound than any that had yet blessed my hard couch, when I was suddenly wakened by a busy clatter on the deck, the shriek of ill-greased davits, the squeak of blocks, and the fall of a small-boat into the water. Another odd sound puzzled me : but for the probability that we were out over Bass I could have sworn it was the murmur of a stream running upon a gravelled shore. A stream—heavens ! There could be no doubt about it now ; we were somewhere close in shore, and the *Seven Sisters* was lying to. The brigantine stopped in her voyage where no stoppage should be ; a small boat plying to land in the middle of the night ; come ! here was something out of the ordinary, surely, on a vessel seaward bound. I had dreamt of the gallows and of Dan Risk as an informer. Was it a wonder that there should flash into my mind the conviction of my betrayal ? What was more likely than that the skipper, secure of my brace of guineas, was selling me to the garrison of Blackness ?

I clad myself hurriedly and crept cautiously up the companion ladder, and found myself in overwhelming darkness, only made the more appalling and strange because the vessel's lights were all extinguished. Silence large and brooding lay upon the *Seven Sisters* as she lay in that obscuring haar that had fallen again ; she might be Charon's craft pausing mid-way on the cursed stream, and waiting for the ferry cry upon the shore of Time. We were still in the estuary or firth, to judge by the bickering burn and the odours off-shore, above all the odour

of rotting brake ; and we rode at anchor, for her
bows were up-water to the wind and tide, and above
me, in the darkness, I could hear the idle sails
faintly flapping in the breeze and the reef-points all
tap-tapping. I seemed to have the deck alone, but
for one figure at the stern ; I went back, and found
that it was Horn.

"Where are we ? " I asked, relieved to find there
the only man I could trust on board the ship.

"A little below Blackness," said he shortly with
a dissatisfied tone.

"I did not know we were to stop here," said I,
wondering if he knew that I was doomed.

"Neither did I," said he, peering into the void of
night. "And whit's mair, I wish I could guess the
reason o' oor stopping. The skipper's been ashore
mair nor ance wi' the lang-boat forward there, and
I'm sent back here to keep an e'e on lord kens what
except it be yersel'."

"Are ye indeed ? " said I, exceedingly vexed.
"Then I ken too well, Horn, the reason for the
stoppage. You are to keep your eye on a man
who's being bargained for with the hangman."

"I would rather ken naithin' about that," said he,
"and onyway I think ye're mista'en. Here they're
comin' back again."

Two or three small boats were coming down on
us out of the darkness ; not that I could see them,
but that I heard their oars in muffled rowlocks.

"If they want me," said I sorrowfully, " they can
find me down below," and back I went and sat me
in the cabin, prepared for the manacles.

CHAPTER X

THE STRUGGLE IN THE CABIN, AND AN EERIE SOUND OF RUNNING WATER

THE place stank with bilge and the odour of an ill-trimmed lamp smoking from a beam; the fragments of the skipper's supper were on the table, with a broken quadrant; rats scurried and squealed in the bulkheads, and one stared at me from an open locker, where lay a rum-bottle, while beetles and slaters travelled along the timbers. But these things compelled my attention less than the sky-lights that were masked internally by pieces of canvas nailed roughly on them. They were not so earlier in the evening; it must have been done after I had gone to sleep, and what could be the object? That puzzled me extremely, for it must have been the same hand that had extinguished all the deck and mast lights, and though black was my crime darkness was unnecessary to my betrayal.

I waited with a heart like lead.

I heard the boats swung up on the davits, the squeak of the falls, the tread of the seamen, the voice of Risk in an unusually low tone. In the bows in a little I heard the windlass click and the chains rasp in the hawse-holes ; we were lifting the anchor.

For a moment hope possessed me. If we were weighing anchor then my arrest was not imminent at least ; but that consolation lasted briefly when I thought of the numerous alternatives to imprisonment in Blackness

We were under weigh again ; there was a heel to port, and a more rapid plop of the waters along the carvel planks. And then Risk and his mate came down.

I have seldom seen a man more dashed than the skipper when he saw me sitting waiting on him, clothed and silent. His face grew livid ; round he turned to Murchison and hurried him with oaths to come and clap eyes on this sea-clerk. I looked for the officer behind them, but they were alone, and at that I thought more cheerfully I might have been mistaken about the night's curious proceedings.

"Anything wrang ?" said Risk, affecting nonchalance now that his spate of oaths was by, and he pulled the rum out of the locker and helped himself and his mate to a swingeing caulker.

"Oh, nothing at all," said I, "at least nothing that I know of, Captain Risk. And are we—are we—at Halifax already ?"

"What do you mean ?" said he. And then he looked at me closely, put out the hand unoccupied by his glass and ran an insolent dirty finger over my new-clipped mole. "Greig, Greig," said he, "Greig to a hair ! I would have the wee shears to that again, for its growin'."

"You're a very noticing man," said I, striking down his hand no way gently, and remembering that he had seen my scissors when I emerged from the Borrowstouness close after my own barbering.

"I'm all that," he replied, with a laugh, and all the time Murchison, the mate, sat mopping his greasy face with a rag, as one after hard work, and looked on us with wonder at what we meant. "I'm all that," he replied, "the hair aff the mole and the horse-hair on your creased breeches wad hae tauld ony ane that ye had ridden in a hurry and clipped in a fricht o' discovery."

"Oh, oh!" I cried, "and that's what goes to the makin' o' a Mahoun!"

"Jist that," said he, throwing himself on a seat with an easy indifference meant to conceal his vanity. "Jist observation and a knack o' puttin' twa and twa thegether. Did ye think the skipper o' the *Seven Sisters* was fleein' over Scotland at the tail o' your horse?"

"The Greig mole's weel kent, surely," said I, astonished and chagrined. "I jalouse it's notorious through my Uncle Andy?"

Risk laughed at that. "Oh, ay!" said he, "when Andy Greig girned at ye it was ill to miss seein' his mole. Man, ye might as well wear your name on the front o' your hat as gae aboot wi' a mole like that—and—and that pair o' shoes."

The blood ran to my face at this further revelation of his astuteness. It seemed, then, I carried my identity head and foot, and it was no wonder a half-eyed man like Risk should so easily discover me.   I looked down at my feet, and sure enough, when I thought of it now, it would have been a stupid man who, having seen these kenspeckle shoes once, would ever forget them.

"My uncle seems to have given me good introductions," said I.

"They struck mysel' as rather dandy for a ship," broke in the mate, at last coming on something he could understand.

"And did *you* know Andy Greig, too ?" said I.

"Andy Greig," he replied.   "Not me !"

"Then, by God, ye hinna sailed muckle aboot the warld!" said the skipper.   "I hae seen thae shoes in the four quarters and aye in a good companionship."

"They appear yet to retain that virtue," said I, unable to resist the irony.   "And, by the way, Captain Risk, now that we have discussed the shoes and my mole, what have we been waiting for at Blackness ?"

His face grew black with annoyance.

"What's that to you ?" he cried.

"Oh, I don't know," I answered indifferently. "I thought that now ye had got the best part o' your passage money ye might hae been thinking to do something for your country again.   They tell me it's a jail in there, and it might suggest itself to you as providing a good opportunity for getting rid of a very indifferent purser."

It is one thing I can remember to the man's credit that this innuendo of treachery seemed to make him frantic. He dashed the rum-glass at his feet and struck at me with a fist like a jigot of mutton, and I had barely time to step back and counter. He threw himself at me as he had been a cat; I closed and flung my arms about him with a wrestler's grip, and bent him back upon the table edge, where I might have broken his spine but for Murchison's interference. The mate called loudly for assistance; footsteps pounded on the cuddy-stair, and down came Horn. Between them they drew us apart, and while Murchison clung to his captain, and plied him into quietness with a fresh glass of grog, Horn thrust me not unkindly out into the night, and with no unwillingness on my part.

It was the hour of dawn, and the haar was gone.

There was something in that chill grey monotone of sky and sea that filled me with a very passion of melancholy. The wind had risen, and the billows ran frothing from the east; enormous clouds hung over the land behind us, so that it seemed to roll with smoke from the eternal fires. Out from that reeking pit of my remorse—that lost Scotland where now perhaps there still lay lying among the rushes, with the pees-weep's cry above it, the thing from which I flew, our ship went fast, blown upon the frothy billows, like a ponderous bird, leaving a wake of hissing bubbling brine, flying, as it seemed, to a world of less imminent danger, yet unalluring still. I looked aloft at the straining spars; they seemed to prick the clouds between the swelling sails; the ropes and shrouds stretched infinitely into a region very grey and chill. Oh, the pallor! oh, the cold

and heartless spirit of the sea in that first dawning
morn!

"It's like to be a good day," said Horn, breaking
in upon my silence, and turning to him I saw his
face exceeding hollow and wan. The watch lay forward, all but a lad who seemed half-dozing at the
helm; Risk and his mate had lapsed to silence in
the cuddy.

"You're no frien', seemingly, o' the pair below!"
said Horn again, whispering, and with a glance
across his shoulder at the helm.

"It did not look as if I were, a minute or two
ago," said I. "Yon's a scoundrel, and yet I did him
an injustice when I thought he meant to sell me."

"I never sailed with a more cheat-the-widdy
crew since I followed the sea," said Horn, "and
whether it's the one way or the other, sold ye are."

"Eh?" said I, uncomprehending.

He looked again at the helm, and moved over to a
water-breaker further forward, obviously meaning
that I should follow. He drew a drink of water for
himself, drank slowly, but seemed not to be much in
the need for it from the little he took, but he had got
out of ear-shot of the man steering.

"You and me's the gulls this time, Mr. Greig,"
said he, whispering. "This is a doomed ship."

"I thought as much from her rotten spars," I
answered. "So long as she takes me to Nova
Scotia I care little what happens to her."

"It's a long way to Halifax," said he. "I wish I
could be sure we were likely even to have Land's
End on our starboard before waur happens. Will

ye step this way, Mr. Greig?" and he cautiously led the way forward. There was a look-out humming a stave of song somewhere in the bows, and two men stretched among the chains, otherwise that part of the ship was all our own. We went down the fo'c'sle scuttle quietly, and I found myself among the carpenter's stores, in darkness, divided by a bulk-head door from the quarters of the sleeping men. Rats were scurrying among the timbers and squealing till Horn stamped lightly with his feet and secured stillness.

"Listen!" said he.

I could hear nothing but the heavy breathing of a seaman within, and the wash of water against the ship's sides.

"Well?" I queried, wondering.

"Put your lug here," said he, indicating a beam that was dimly revealed by the light from the lamp swinging in the fo'c'sle. I did so, and heard water running as from a pipe somewhere in the bowels of the vessel.

"What's that?" I asked.

"That's all," said he and led me aft again.

The dawn by now had spread over half the heavens; behind us the mouth of the Firth gulped enormous clouds, and the fringe of Fife was as flat as a bannock; before us the sea spread chill, leaden, all unlovely. "My sorrow!" says I, "if this is travelling, give me the high-roads and the hot noon."

Horn's face seemed more hollow and dark than ever in the wan morning. I waited his explanation.

" I think ye said Halifax, Mr. Greig ? " said he. " I signed on, mysel', for the same port, but you and me's perhaps the only ones on this ship that ever hoped to get there. God give me grace to get foot on shore and Dan Risk will swing for this ! "

Somebody sneezed behind us as Horn thus rashly expressed himself: we both turned suddenly on the rail we had been leaning against, expecting that this was the skipper, and though it was not Risk, it was one whose black visage and gleaming teeth and rolling eyes gave me momentarily something of a turn.

It was the cook Ferdinando. He had come up behind on his bare feet, and out upon the sea he gazed with that odd eerie look of the deaf and dumb, heedless of us, it seemed, as we had been dead portions of the ship's fabric, seeing but the salt wave, the rim of rising sun, blood-red upon the horizon, communing with an old familiar.

" A cauld mornin', cook," said Horn, like one who tests a humbug pretending to be dumb, but Ferdinando heard him not.

" It might have been a man wi' all his faculties," said the seaman whispering," and it's time we werena seen thegether. I'll tell ye later on."

With that we separated, he to some trivial duty of his office, I, with a mind all disturbed, back to my berth to lie awake, tossing and speculating on the meaning of Horn's mystery.

CHAPTER XI

THE SCUTTLED SHIP

WHEN I went on deck next morning there was something great ado. We were out of sight of land, sailing large, as the old phrase went, on a brisk quarter breeze with top-sails atrip, and the sky a vast fine open blue. The crew were gathered at the poop, the pump was clanking in the midst of them, and I saw they were taking spells at the cruellest labour a seaman knows.

At first I was noway troubled at the spectacle ; a leak was to be expected in old rotten-beams, and I went forward with the heart of me not a pulse the faster.

Risk was leaning over the poop-rail, humped up and his beard on his hands ; Murchison, a little apart, swept the horizon with a prospect-glass, and the pump sent a great spate of bilge-water upon the deck. But for a man at the tiller who kept the ship from yawing in the swell that swung below her counter the *Seven Sisters* sailed at her sweet will , all the interest of her company was in this stream of stinking water that she retched into the scuppers. And yet I could not but be struck by the half-hearted manner in which the seamen wrought; they were visibly shirking; I saw it in the slack muscles, in the heedless eyes.

Risk rose and looked sourly at me as I went up. "Are ye for a job?" said he. "It's more in your line perhaps than clerkin'."

"What, at the pumps? Is the old randy geyzing already?"

"Like a washing-boyne," said he. "Bear a hand like a good lad! we maun keep her afloat at least till some other vessel heaves in sight."

In the tone and look of the man there was something extraordinary. His words were meant to suggest imminent peril, and yet his voice was shallow as that of a burgh bellman crying an auction sale, and his eyes had more interest in the horizon that his mate still searched with the prospect-glass than in the spate of bilge that gulped upon the deck.

Bilge did I say? Heavens! it was bilge no more, but the pure sea-green that answered to the clanking pump. It was no time for idle wonder at the complacence of the skipper; I flew to the break and threw my strength into the seaman's task. "Clank-click, clank-click"—the instrument worked reluctantly as if the sucker moved in slime, and in a little the sweat poured from me.

"How is she now, Campbell?" asked Risk, as the carpenter came on deck.

"Three feet in the hold," said Campbell airily, like one that had an easy conscience.

"Good lord, a foot already!" cried Risk, and then in a tone of sarcasm, "Hearty, lads, hearty there! A little more Renfrewshire beef into it, Mr. Greig, if you please."

At that I ceased my exertion, stood back straight and looked at the faces about me. There was only one man in the company who did not seem to be amused at me, and that was Horn, who stood with folded arms, moodily eying the open sea.

"You seem mighty joco about it," I said to Risk, and I wonder to this day at my blindness that never read the whole tale in these hurried events.

"I can afford to be," he said quickly; "if I gang I gang wi' clean hands," and he spat into the sea-water streaming from the pump where the port-watch now were working with as much listlessness as the men they superseded.

To the taunt I made no reply, but moved after Horn who had gone forward with his hands in his pockets.

"What does this mean, Horn?" I asked him. "Is the vessel in great danger?"

"I suppose she is," said he bitterly, "but I have had nae experience o' scuttled ships afore."

"Scuttled!" cried I, astounded, only half grasping his meaning.

"Jist that," said he. "The job's begun. It began last night in the run of the vessel as I showed ye when ye put your ear to the beam. After I left ye, I foun' half a dizen cords fastened to the pump stanchels; ane of them I pulled and got a plug at the end of it; the ithers hae been comin' oot since as it suited Dan Risk best, and the *Seven Sisters* is doomed to die o' a dropsy this very day. Wasn't I the cursed idiot that ever lipped drink in Clerihew's coffin-room!"

"If it was that," said I, "why did you not cut the cords and spoil the plot?"

"Cut the cords! Ye mean cut my ain throat; that's what wad happen if the skipper guessed my knowledge o' his deevilry. And dae ye think a gallows job o' this kind depends a'thegither on twa or three bits o' twine? Na, na, this is a very business-like transaction, Mr. Greig, and I'll warrant there has been naethin' left to chance. I wondered at them bein' sae pernicketty about the sma' boats afore we sailed when the timbers o' the ship hersel' were fair ganting. That big new boat and sails frae Kirkcaldy was a gey odd thing in itsel' if I had been sober enough to think o't. I suppose ye paid your passage, Mr. Greig? I can fancy a purser on the *Seven Sisters* upon nae ither footin' and that made me dubious o' ye when I first learned o' this hell's caper for Jamieson o' the Grange. If ye hadna fought wi' the skipper I would hae coonted ye in wi' the rest."

"He has two pounds of my money," I answered; "at least I've saved the other two if we fail to reach Halifax."

At that he laughed softly again.

"It might be as well wi' Risk as wi' the conger," said he, meaningly. "I'm no' sae sure that you and me's meant to come oot o' this; that's what I might tak' frae their leaving only the twa o' us aft when they were puttin' the cargo aff there back at Blackness."

"The cargo!" I repeated.

"Of course," said Horn. "Ye fancied they were goin' to get rid o' ye there, did ye? I'll alloo I thought that but a pretence on your pairt, and no' very neatly done at that. Well, the smallest pairt but the maist valuable o' the cargo shipped at Borrowstouness is still in Scotland; and the underwriters 'll be to pay through the nose for what has never run sea risks."

At that a great light came to me. This was the reason for the masked cuddy skylights, the utter darkness of the *Seven Sisters* while her boats were plying to the shore; for this was I so closely kept at her ridiculous manifest; the lists of lace and plate I had been fatuously copying were lists of stuff no longer on the ship at all, but back in the possession of the owner of the brigantine.

"You are an experienced seaman—— ?"

"I have had a vessel of my own," broke in Horn, some vanity as well as shame upon his countenance.

"Well, you are the more likely to know the best way out of this trap we are in," I went on. "For a certain reason I am not at all keen on it to go back to Scotland, but I would sooner risk that than run in leash with a scoundrel like this who's sinking his command, not to speak of hazarding my unworthy life with a villainous gang. Is there any way out of it, Horn?"

The seaman pondered, a dark frown upon his tanned forehead, where the veins stood out in knots, betraying his perturbation. The wind whistled faintly in the tops, the *Seven Sisters* plainly went by the head ; she had a slow response to her helm, and moved sluggishly. Still the pump was clanking and we could hear the water streaming through the scupper holes. Risk had joined his mate and was casting anxious eyes over the waters.

"If we play the safty here, Mr. Greig," said Horn, "there's a chance o' a thwart for us when the *Seven Sisters* comes to her labour. That's oor only prospect. At least they daurna murder us."

"And what about the crew ?" I asked. "Do you tell me there is not enough honesty among them all to prevent a blackguardly scheme like this ? "

"We're the only twa on this ship this morning wi' oor necks ootside tow, for they're all men o' the free trade, and broken men at that," said Horn resolutely, and even in the midst of this looming disaster my private horror rose within me.

"Ah !" said I, helpless to check the revelation, "speak for yourself, Mr. Horn ; it's the hangman I'm here fleeing from."

He looked at me with quite a new countenance, clearly losing relish for his company.

"Anything by-ordinar dirty ? " he asked, and in my humility I did not have the spirit to resent what that tone and query implied.

"Dirty enough," said I, " the man's dead," and Horn's face cleared.

"Oh, faith ! is that all ? " quo' he, "I was thinkin' it might be coinin'—beggin' your pardon, Mr. Greig, or somethin' in the fancy way. But a gentleman's quarrel ower the cartes or a wench—that's a different tale. I hate homicide mysel', to tell the truth, but whiles I've had it in my heart, and in a way o' speakin' Dan Risk this meenute has my gully-knife in his ribs."

As he spoke the vessel, mishandled, or a traitor to her helm, now that she was all awash internally with water, yawed and staggered in the wind. The sails shivered, the yards swung violently, appalling noises came from the hold. At once the pumping ceased and Risk's voice roared in the confusion, ordering the launch of the Kirkcaldy boat.

CHAPTER XII

MAKES PLAIN THE DEEPEST VILLAINY OF RISK
AND SETS ME ON A FRENCHMAN

When I come to write these affairs down after the lapse of years, I find my memory but poorly retains the details of that terrific period between the cry of Risk and the moment when Horn and I, abandoned on the doomed vessel, watched the evening fall upon the long Kirkcaldy boat, her mast stepped, but her sails down, hovering near us for the guarantee of our eternal silence regarding the crime the men on her were there and then committing. There is a space—it must have been brief, but I lived a lifetime in it—whose impressions rest with me, blurred, but with the general hue of agony. I can see the sun again sailing overhead in the arching sky of blue; the enormous ocean, cruel, cold, spread out to the line of the horizon; the flapping sails and drumming reef-points, the streaming halliards and clew-garnets, the spray buffeting upon our hull and spitting in our faces like an enemy; I hear the tumult of the seamen hurrying vulgarly to save their wretched lives, the gluck of waters in the bowels of the ship, the thud of cargo loose and drifting under decks.

But I see and hear it all as in a dream or play, and myself someway standing only a spectator.

It seemed that Risk and his men put all their dependence on the long-boat out of Kirkcaldy. She was partly decked at the bows like a Ballantrae herring-skiff, beamy and commodious. They clustered round her like ants; swung her out, and over she went, and the whole hellish plot lay revealed in the fact that she was all found with equipment and provisions.

Horn and I made an effort to assist at her preparation; we were shoved aside with frantic curses; we were beaten back by her oars when we sought to enter her, and when she pushed off from the side of the *Seven Sisters*, Dan Risk was so much the monster that he could jeer at our perplexity. He sat at the tiller of her without a hat, his long hair, that was turning lyart, blown by the wind about his black and mocking eyes.

"Head her for Halifax, Horn," said he, "and ye'll get there by-and-by."

"Did I ever do ye any harm, skipper?" cried the poor seaman, standing on the gunwale, hanging to the shrouds, and his aspect hungry for life.

"Ye never got the chance, Port Glesca," cried back Risk, hugging the tiller of the Kirkcaldy boat under his arm. "I'll gie ye a guess—

Come-a-riddle, come-a-riddle, come-a-rote-tote-tote—

Oh to bleezes! I canna put a rhyme till't, but this is the sense o't—a darkie's never deaf and dumb till he's deid. Eh! Antonio, ye rascal!"

He looked forward as he spoke and exchanged a villainous laugh with the cook, his instrument, who had overheard us and betrayed.

"Ye would mak' me swing for it, would ye, John Horn, when ye get ashore? That's what I would expect frae a keelie oot o' Clyde."

It is hard to credit that man could be so vile as this, but of such stuff was Daniel Risk. He was a fiend in the glory of his revenge upon the seaman who had threatened him with the gallows; up-lifted like a madman's, his face, that was naturally sallow, burned lamp-red at his high cheek-bones, his hale eye gloated, his free hand flourished as in an exultation. His mate sat silent beside him on the stern-thwart, clearing the sheets: the crew, who had out the sweeps to keep the boat's bows in the wind, made an effort to laugh at his jocosities, but clearly longed to be away from this tragedy. And all the time, I think, I stood beside the weather bul-wark, surrendered to the certainty of a speedy death, with the lines of a ballad coming back again and again to my mind:

> An' he shall lie in fathoms deep,
> The star-fish ower his een shall creep,
> An' an auld grey wife shall sit an' weep
> In the hall o' Monaltrie.

I thrust that ungodly rhyme from me each time that it arose, but in spite of me at last it kept time to the lap of a wave of encroaching sea that beat about my feet.

My silence—my seeming indifference—would seem to have touched the heart that could not be affected by the entreaties of the seaman Horn. At least Risk ceased his taunts at last, and cast a more friendly eye on me.

"I'm saying, Greig," he cried, "noo that I think o't, your Uncle Andy was no bad hand at makin' a story. Ye've an ill tongue, but I'll thole that—astern, lads, and tak' the purser aboard."

The seamen set the boat about willingly enough, and she crept in to pick me off the doomed ship.

At that my senses cleared like hill-well water. It was for but a second—praise God! my instincts joyed in my reprieve; my hand never released the cleat by which I steadied myself. I looked at Horn still upon the lower shrouds and saw hope upon his countenance.

"Of course this man comes with me, Captain Risk?" said I.

"Not if he offered a thousand pounds," cried Risk, "in ye come!" and Murchison clawed at the shrouds with a boat-hook. Horn made to jump among them and, with an oath, the mate thrust at him with the hook as with a spear, striking him under the chin. He fell back upon the deck, bleeding profusely and half insensible.

"You are a foul dog!" I cried to his assailant. "And I'll settle with you for that!"

"Jump, ye fool, ye, jump!" cried Risk impatient.

"Let us look oot for oorselves, that's whit I say," cried Murchison angry at my threat, and prepared cheerfully to see me perish. "What for should we risk oor necks with either o' them?" and he pushed off slightly with his boat-hook.

The skipper turned, struck down the hook, and snarled upon him. "Shut up, Murchison!" he cried. "I'm still the captain, if ye please, and I ken as much aboot the clerk here as will keep his gab shut on any trifle we hae dune."

I looked upon the clean sea, and then at that huddle of scoundrels in the Kirkcaldy boat, and then upon the seaman Horn coming back again to the full consciousness of his impending fate. He gazed upon me with eyes alarmed and pitiful, and at that I formed my resolution.

"I stick by Horn," said I. "If he gets too, I'll go; if not I'll bide and be drowned with an honest man."

"Bide and be damned then! Ye've had your chance," shouted Risk, letting his boat fall off. "It's time we werena here." And the halliards of his main-sail were running in the blocks as soon as he said it. The boat swept away rapidly, but not before I gave him a final touch of my irony. From my pocket I took out my purse and threw it upon his lap.

"There's the ither twa, Risk," I cried; "it's no' like the thing at all to murder a harmless lad for less than what ye bargained for."

He bawled back some reply I could not hear, and I turned about, to see Horn making for the small boat on the starboard chocks. I followed with a hope again wakened, only to share his lamentation when he found that two of her planks had been wantonly sprung from their clinkers, rendering her utterly useless. The two other boats were in a similar condition; Risk and his confederates had been determined that no chance should be left of our escape from the *Seven Sisters*.

It was late in the afternoon. The wind had softened somewhat; in the west there were rising billowy clouds of silver and red, and half a mile away the Kirkcaldy boat, impatient doubtless for the end of us, that final assurance of safety, plied to windward with only her foresail set. We had gone below in a despairing mind on the chance that the leakage might be checked, but the holes were under water in the after peak, and in other parts we could not come near. An inch-and-a-half auger, and a large bung-borer, a gouge and chisel in the captain's private locker, told us how the crime had been committed whereof we were the victims.

We had come on deck again, the pair of us, without the vaguest notion of what was next to do, and—speaking for myself—convinced that nothing could avert our hurrying fate. Horn told me later that he proposed full half a score of plans for at least a prolongation of our time, but that I paid no heed to them. That may be, for I know the ballad stanza went in my head like a dirge, as I sat on a hatch with the last few days of my history rolling out before my eyes. The dusk began to fall like a veil, the wind declined still further. Horn feverishly hammered and caulked at the largest of the boats, now and then throwing the tools from him as in momentary realisations of the hopelessness of his toil that finally left him in despair.

"It's no use, Mr. Greig," he cried then, "they did the job ower weel," and he shook his fist at the Kirkcaldy boat. He checked the gesture suddenly and gave an astonished cry.

"They're gone, Greig," said he, now frantic. "They're gone. O God! they're gone! I was sure they couldna hae the heart to leave us at the last," and as he spoke I chanced to look astern, and behold! a ship with all her canvas full was swiftly bearing down the wind upon us. We had been so intent upon our fate that we had never seen her!

I clambered up the shrouds of the main-mast, and cried upon the coming vessel with some mad notion that she might fancy the *Seven Sisters* derelict. But indeed that was not necessary. In a little she went round into the wind, a long-boat filled with men came towards us, and twenty minutes later we were on the deck of the *Roi Rouge*.

CHAPTER XIII

WHEREIN APPEARS A GENTLEMANLY CORSAIR AND
A FRENCH-IRISH LORD

WHILE it may be that the actual crisis of my manhood came to me on the day I first put on my Uncle
Andrew's shoes, the sense of it was mine only when
I met with Captain Thurot. I had put the past for
ever behind me (as I fancied) when I tore the verses
of a moon-struck boy and cast them out upon the
washing-green at Hazel Den, but I was bound to
foregather with men like Thurot and his friends ere
the scope and fashion of a man's world were apparent
to me. Whether his influence on my destiny in
the long run was good or bad I would be the last to
say; he brought me into danger, but—in a manner—
he brought me good, though that perhaps was never
in his mind.

You must fancy this Thurot a great tall man,
nearly half a foot exceeding myself in stature, peak-
bearded, straight as a lance, with plum-black eyes
and hair, polished in dress and manner to the rarest
degree and with a good humour that never failed.
He sat under a swinging lamp in his cabin when
Horn and I were brought before him, and asked my

name first in an accent of English that was if anything somewhat better than my own.

"Greig," said I; "Paul Greig," and he started as
if I had pricked him with a knife.

A little table stood between us, on which there
lay a book he had been reading when we were
brought below, some hours after the *Seven Sisters*
had gone down, and the search for the Kirkcaldy
boat had been abandoned. He took the lamp off its
hook, came round the table and held the light so
that he could see my face the clearer. At any time
his aspect was manly and pleasant; most of all was
it so when he smiled, and I was singularly encouraged
when he smiled at me, with a rapid survey of my
person that included the Hazel Den mole and my
Uncle Andrew's shoes.

A seaman stood behind us; to him he spoke a
message I could not comprehend, as it was in French,
of which I had but little. The seaman retired; we
were offered a seat, and in a minute the seaman
came back with a gentleman—a landsman by his
dress.

"Pardon, my lord," said the captain to his visitor,
"but I thought that here was a case—speaking of
miracles—you would be interested in. Our friends
here"—he indicated myself particularly with a
gracious gesture—"are not, as you know, dropped
from heaven, but come from that unfortunate ship
we saw go under a while ago. May I ask your
lordship to tell us—you will see the joke in a
moment—whom we were talking of at the moment
our watch first announced the sight of that vessel?"

His lordship rubbed his chin and smilingly peered at the captain.

"Gad!" he said. "You are the deuce and all, Thurot. What are you in the mood for now ? Why, we talked of Greig—Andrew Greig, the best player of *passe-passe* and the cheerfullest loser that ever cut a pack."

Thurot turned to me, triumphant.

"Behold," said he, "how ridiculously small the world is. *Ma foi!* I wonder how I manage so well to elude my creditors, even when I sail the high seas. Lord Clancarty, permit me to have the distinguished honour to introduce another Greig, who I hope has many more of his charming uncle's qualities than his handsome eyes and red shoes. I assume it is a nephew, because poor Monsieur Andrew was not of the marrying kind. Anyhow, 'tis a Greig of the blood, or Antoine Thurot is a bat! And—Monsieur Greig, it is my felicity to bid you know one of your uncle's best friends and heartiest admirers—Lord Clancarty."

"Lord Clancarty!" I cried, incredulous. "Why he figured in my uncle's log-book a dozen years ago."

"A dozen, no less!" cried his lordship, with a grimace. "We need not be so particular about the period. I trust he set me down there a decently good companion; I could hardly hope to figure in a faithful scribe's tablets as an example otherwise," said his lordship, laughing and taking me cordially by the hand. "Gad! one has but to look at you to see Andrew Greig in every line. I loved your uncle, lad. He had a rugged, manly nature, and just sufficient folly, bravado, and sinfulness to keep a poor Irishman in countenance. Thurot, one must apologise for taking from your very lips the suggestion I see hesitating there, but sure 'tis an Occasion this; it must be a bottle—the best bottle on your adorable but somewhat ill-found vessel. Why 'tis Andy Greig come young again. Poor Andy! I heard of his death no later than a month ago, and have ordered a score of masses for him—which by the way are still unpaid for to good Father Hamilton. I could not sleep happily of an evening—of a forenoon rather—if I thought of our Andy suffering aught that a few candles and such-like could modify." And his lordship with great condescension tapped and passed me his jewelled box of maccabaw.

You can fancy a raw lad, untutored and untravelled, fresh from the plough-tail, as it were, was vastly tickled at this introduction to the genteel world. I was no longer the shivering outlaw, the victim of a Risk. I was honoured more or less for the sake of my uncle (whose esteem in this quarter my father surely would have been surprised at), and it seemed as though my new life in a new country were opening better than I had planned myself. I blessed my shoes—the Shoes of Sorrow—and for the time forgot the tragedy from which I was escaping.

They birled the bottle between them, Clancarty and Thurot, myself virtually avoiding it, but clinking now and then, and laughing with them at the numerous exploits they recalled of him that was the bond between us; Horn elsewhere found himself well treated also; and listening to these two gentlemen of the world, their allusions, off-hand, to the great, their indications of adventure, travel, intrigue, enterprise, gaiety, I saw my horizon expand until it was no longer a cabin on the sea I sat in, with the lamplight swinging over me, but a spacious world of castles, palaces, forests, streets, churches, casernes, harbours, masquerades, routs, operas, love, laughter, and song. Perhaps they saw my elation and fully understood, and smiled within them at my efforts to figure as a little man of the world too—as boys will —but they never showed me other than the finest sympathy and attention.

I found them fascinating at night; I found them much the same at morning, which is the test of the thing in youth, and straightway made a hero of the foreigner Thurot. Clancarty was well enough, but without any method in his life, beyond a principle of keeping his character ever trim and presentable like his cravat. Thurot carried on his strenuous career as soldier, sailor, spy, politician, with a plausible enough theory that thus he got the very juice and pang of life, that at the most, as he would aye be telling me, was brief to an absurdity.

"Your Scots," he would say to me, "as a rule, are too phlegmatic—is it not, Lord Clancarty?—but your uncle gave me, on my word, a regard for your whole nation. He had aplomb—Monsieur Andrew; he had luck too, and if he cracked a nut anywhere there was always a good kernel in it. And the shoes it is your felicity to have inherited, they got him, he used to say himself, out of a thousand perils. I used to wish I had half his opportunities ; my name as a corsair would sound around the world."

"A corsair ! ' I cried, astonished.

"*Certainement !* " said Thurot, laughing. "Is it that Monsieur Greig's nephew is afraid of the word? It is not a reputable word perhaps ; it is a cut-throat word, this 'corsair.' Bah ! you must find your pretty shoes tight in the toes for you, Monsieur Paul."

"Faith, I do not wonder at his surprise, Tony," said my lord. "To hear you talk of the humdrum career of a privateer he might well enough fancy you steadfastly flew the Jolly Roger and bade unhappy crews of English merchantmen walk the plank. I give you my word, Mr. Greig, our good friend has never cut a throat in his life, vicariously or otherwise. Good honest fighting he may be credited with—in that he was like your uncle, but——"

"What !" cried Thurot, at first surprised and then laughing. "Do you fancy me an ear-ringed pirate ? *Ma foi !* that were too brisk a profession for Antoine Thurot, who likes to keep the ports open to him, that he may go in when he wishes and eat a decent dinner. No, no ! A different corsair—a gentlemanly corsair, if you please."

"'Tis a distinction, Captain Thurot," said I, "we have not learned to make on the other side yet. My own notion of a corsair *in esse*, if not *in posse*——"

"Egad, that's Greek!" cried Clancarty. "I recognise it easily. What a thing it is to be a scholar!" and he winked at Thurot. I caught the sarcasm with the tail of my eye.

"In Scotland it's accounted Latin, my lord," I said, "but then we are poor provincials over yonder and may be mistaken."

At that he laughed heartily. "Greig! Greig! it is Greig for a hundred *louis;* you staggered me a little with what Thurot calls the tightness of your shoes, but the retort was made by your uncle's ghost."

"My own notion of a corsair," I went on, "in essence, is Dan Risk, the scoundrel who would have left me to drown last night."

"So!" cried Thurot, amused. "That may be the English corsair; for us we swear by types like Duguay-Trouin, Jean-Bart, and Jacques Cassard. Faith, anyway, 'tis a world of corsairs. If we do not plunder on the high seas, we harry in the haunts of commerce. In the one sense we risk our lives for the prize; in the other no more than our immortal souls, that can be saved at the pinch by a bland apology to *le bon Dieu.*"

"I give you fair warning, 'tis a preacher you have unloosed, Mr. Greig," said my lord, twiddling his thumbs.

Captain Thurot paid no heed to the interruption. "All corsairs!" he repeated. "All sharks. From your King George down to his poorest soldier fighting in America."

He looked at me out of the corner of his eyes to

see how I took the allusion to King George, and that gave me a flood of light upon my new position.

I remembered that in my uncle's log-book the greater part of the narrative of his adventures in France had to do with politics and the intrigues of the Jacobite party. He was not, himself, apparently, "out," as we call it, in the affair of the 'Forty-five, because he did not believe the occasion suitable, and thought the Prince precipitous, but before and after that untoward event for poor Scotland, he had been active with such men as Clancarty, Lord Clare, the Murrays, the Mareschal, and such-like, which was not to be wondered at, perhaps, for our family had consistently been Jacobite, a fact that helped to its latter undoing, though my father as nominal head of the house had taken no interest in politics; and my own sympathies had ever been with the Chevalier, whom I as a boy had seen ride through the city of Glasgow, wishing myself old enough to be his follower in such a glittering escapade as he was then embarked on.

But though I thought all this in a flash as it were, I betrayed nothing to Captain Thurot, who seemed somewhat dashed at my silence. There must have been something in my face, however, to show that I fully realised what he was feeling at, and was not too complacent, for Clancarty laughed.

"Sure, 'tis a good boy, Thurot," said he, "and loves his King George properly, like a true patriot."

"I won't believe it of a Greig," said Captain Thurot. "A pestilent, dull thing, loyalty in England; the other thing came much more readily, I

remember, to the genius of Andrew Greig. Come!
Monsieur Paul, to be quite frank about it, have you
no instincts of friendliness to the exiled house? M
Tête-de-fer has a great need at this particular
moment for English friends. Once he could count
on your uncle to the last ditch; can he count on the
nephew?"

"M. Tête-de-fer?" I repeated, somewhat bewildered.

"M. Tête-de-mouche, rather," cried my lord,
testily, and then hurried to correct himself. "He
alluded, Monsieur Greig, to Prince Charles Edward.
We are all, I may confess, his Royal Highness's
most humble servants; some of us, however—as
our good friend, Captain Thurot — more actively
than others. For myself I begin to weary of a
cause that has been dormant for eight years,
but no matter; sure one must have a recreation!"

I looked at his lordship to see if he was joking.
He was the relic of a handsome man, though still, I
daresay, less than fifty years of age, with a clever
face and gentle, just tinged by the tracery of small
surface veins to a redness that accused him of too
many late nights; his mouth and eyes, that at one
time must have been fascinating, had the ultimate
irresolution that comes to one who finds no finger-
posts at life's cross-roads and thinks one road just
as good's another. He was born at Atena, near
Hamburg (so much I had remembered from my
uncle's memoir), but he was, even in his accent, as
Irish as Kerry. Someway I liked and yet doubted

him, in spite of all the praise of him that I had read in a dead man's diurnal.

"*Fi donc! vous devriez avoir honte, milord,*" cried Thurot, somewhat disturbed, I saw, at this reckless levity.

"Ashamed!" said his lordship, laughing; "why, 'tis for his Royal Highness who has taken a diligence to the devil, and left us poor dependants to pay the bill at the inn. But no matter, Master Greig, I'll be cursed if I say a single word more to spoil a charming picture of royalty under a cloud." And so saying he lounged away from us, a strange exquisite for shipboard, laced up to the nines, as the saying goes, parading the deck as it had been the Rue St. Honoré, with merry words for every sailorman who tapped a forehead to him.

Captain Thurot looked at him, smiling, and shrugged his shoulders.

"*Tête-de-mouche!* There it is for you, M. Paul— the head of a butterfly. Now *you*—" he commanded my eyes most masterfully—"now *you* have a Scotsman's earnestness; I should like to see you on the right side. *Mon Dieu*, you owe us your life, no less; 'tis no more King George's, for one of his subjects has morally sent you to the bottom of the sea in a scuttled ship. I wish we had laid hands on your Risk and his augers."

But I was learning my world; I was cautious; I said neither yea nor nay.

CHAPTER XIV

IN DUNKERQUE—A LADY SPEAKS TO ME IN SCOTS AND A FAT PRIEST SEEMS TO HAVE SOMETHING ON HIS MIND

Two days after, the *Roi Rouge* came to Dunkerque; Horn the seaman went home to Scotland in a vessel out of Leith with a letter in his pocket for my people at Hazel Den, and I did my best for the next fortnight to forget by day the remorse that was my nightmare. To this Captain Thurot and Lord Clancarty, without guessing 'twas a homicide they favoured, zealously helped me.

And then Dunkerque at the moment was sparkling with attractions. Something was in its air to distract every waking hour, the pulse of drums, the sound of trumpets calling along the shores, troops manœuvring, elation apparent in every countenance. I was Thurot's guest in a lodging over a *boulangerie* upon the sea front, and at daybreak I would look out from the little window to see regiments of horse and foot go by on their way to an enormous camp beside the old fort of Risebank. Later in the morning I would see the soldiers toiling at the grand sluice for deepening the harbour or repairing the basin, or on the dunes near Graveline manœuvring under the command of the Prince de Soubise and Count St. Germain. All day the paving thundered with the roll of tumbrels, with the noise of plunging horse; all night the front of the *boulangerie* was clamorous with carriages bearing cannon, timber, fascines, gabions, and other military stores.

Thurot, with his ship in harbour, became a man of the town, with ruffled neck- and wristbands, the most extravagant of waistcoats, hats laced with point d'Espagne, and up and down Dunkerque he went with a restless foot as if the conduct of the world depended on him. He sent an old person, a reduced gentleman, to me to teach me French that I laboured with as if my life depended on it from a desire to be as soon as possible out of his reverence, for, to come to the point and be done with it, he was my benefactor to the depth of my purse.

Sometimes Lord Clancarty asked me out to a *déjeuner*. He moved in a society where I met many fellow countrymen—Captain Foley, of Rooth's regiment; Lord Roscommon and his brother young Dillon; Lochgarry, Lieutenant-Colonel of Ogilvie's Corps, among others, and by-and-by I became known favourably in what, if it was not actually the select society of Dunkerque, was so at least in the eyes of a very ignorant young gentleman from the moors of Mearns.

It was so strange a thing as to be almost incredible, but my Uncle Andy's shoes seemed to have some magic quality that brought them for ever on tracks they had taken before, and if my cast of countenance did not proclaim me a Greig wherever I went, the shoes did so. They were a passport to the favour of folks the most divergent in social state—to a poor Swiss who kept the door and attended on the table at Clancarty's (my uncle, it appeared, had once saved his life), and to Soubise himself, who counted my uncle the bravest man and the best mimic he had ever met, and on that consideration alone pledged his influence to find me a post.

You may be sure I did not wear such tell-tale shoes too often. I began to have a freit about them as he had to whom they first belonged, and to fancy them somehow bound up with my fortune.

I put them on only when curiosity prompted me to test what new acquaintances they might make me, and one day I remember I donned them for a party of blades at Lord Clancarty's, the very day indeed upon which the poor Swiss, weeping, told me what he owed to the old rogue with the scarred brow now lying dead in the divots of home.

There was a new addition to the company that afternoon—a priest who passed with the name of Father Hamilton, though, as I learned later, he was formerly Vliegh, a Fleming, born at Ostend, and had been educated partly at the College Major of Louvain and partly in London. He was or had been parish priest of Dixmunde near Ostend, and his most decent memory of my uncle, whom he, too, knew, was a challenge to a drinking-bout in which the thin man of Mearns had been several bottles more thirsty than the fat priest of Dixmunde.

He was corpulent beyond belief, with a dewlap like an ox; great limbs, a Gargantuan appetite, and a laugh like thunder that at its loudest created such convulsions of his being as compelled him to unbutton the neck of his *soutane*, else he had died of a seizure.

His friends at Lord Clancarty's played upon him a little joke wherein I took an unconscious part. It seemed they had told him Mr. Andrew Greig was not really dead, but back in France and possessed of an elixir of youth which could make the ancient and furrowed hills themselves look like yesterday's creations.

"What! M. Andrew!" he had cried. "An elixir of grease were more in the fellow's line; I have never seen a man's viands give so scurvy a return for the attention he paid them. 'Tis a pole—this M. Andrew—but what a head—what a head!"

"Oh! but 'tis true of the elixir," they protested; "and he looks thirty years younger; here he comes!"

It was then that I stepped in with the servant bawling my name, and the priest surged to his feet with his face all quivering.

"What! M. Andrew!" he cried; "fattened and five-and-twenty. Holy Mother! It is, then, that miracles are possible? I shall have a hogshead, master, of thine infernal essence and drink away this paunch, and skip anon like to the goats of— of——"

And then his friends burst into peals of laughter as much at my bewilderment as at his credulity, and he saw that it was all a pleasantry.

" *Mon Dieu !* " he said, sighing like a November forest. " There was never more pestilent gleek played upon a wretched man. Oh ! oh ! oh ! I had an angelic dream for that moment of your entrance, for I saw me again a stripling—a stripling—and the girl's name was—never mind. God rest her ! she is under grass in Louvain."

All the rest of the day—at Clancarty's, at the Café de la Poste, in our walk along the dunes where cannon were being fired at marks well out at sea, this obese cleric scarcely let his eyes off me. He seemed to envy and admire, and then again he would appear to muse upon my countenance, debating with himself as one who stands at a shop window pondering a purchase that may be on the verge of his means.

Captain Thurot observed his interest, and took an occasion to whisper to me.

" Have a care, M. Greig," said he playfully ; " this priest schemes something ; that's ever the worst of your Jesuits, and you may swear 'tis not your eternal salvation."

'Twas that afternoon we went all together to the curious lodging in the Rue de la Boucherie. I remember as it had been yesterday how sunny was the weather, and how odd it seemed to me that there should be a country-woman of my own there.

She was not, as it seems to me now, lovely, though where her features failed of perfection it would beat me to disclose, but there was something inexpressibly fascinating in her—in the mild, kind, melting eyes, and the faint sad innuendo of her smile. She sat at a spinet playing, and for the sake of this poor exile, sang some of the songs we are acquainted with at home. Upon my word, the performance touched me to the core! I felt sick for home: my mother's state, the girl at Kirkillstane, the dead lad on the moor, sounds of Earn Water, clouds and heather on the hill of Ballageich—those mingled matters swept through my thoughts as I sat with these blithe gentlemen, hearkening to a simple Doric tune, and my eyes filled irrestrainably with tears.

Miss Walkinshaw—for so her name was—saw what effect her music had produced; reddened, ceased her playing, took me to the window while the others discussed French poetry, and bade me tell her, as we looked out upon the street, all about myself and of my home. She was, perhaps, ten years my senior, and I ran on like a child.

"The Mearns!" said she. "Oh dear, oh dear! And you come frae the Mearns!" She dropped into her Scots that showed her heart was true, and told me she had often had her May milk in my native parish.

"And you maybe know," said she, flushing, "the toun of Glasgow, and the house of Walkinshaw, my —my father, there?"

I knew the house very well, but no more of it than that it existed.

It was in her eyes the tears were now, talking of her native place, but she quickly changed the topic ere I could learn much about her, and she guessed— with a smile coming through her tears, like a sun through mist—that I must have been in love and wandered in its fever, to be so far from home at my age.

"There was a girl," I said, my face hot, my heart rapping at the recollection, and someway she knew all about Isobel Fortune in five minutes, while the others in the room debated on so trivial a thing as the songs of the troubadours.

"Isobel Fortune!" she said (and I never thought the name so beautiful as it sounded on her lips, where it lingered like a sweet); "Isobel Fortune; why, it's an omen, Master Greig, and it must be a good fortune. I am wae for the poor lassie that her big foolish lad"—she smiled with bewitching sympathy at me under long lashes—"should be so far away frae her side. You must go back as quick as you can; but stay now, is it true you love her still?"

The woman would get the feeling and the truth from a heart of stone; I only sighed for answer.

"Then you'll go back," said she briskly, "and it will be Earn-side again and trysts at Ballageich— oh! the name is like a bagpipe air to me!—and you will be happy, and be married and settle down —and—and poor Clemie Walkinshaw will be friendless far away from her dear Scotland, but not forgetting you and your wife."

"I cannot go back there at all," I said, with a long face, bitter enough, you may be sure, at the knowledge I had thrown away all that she depicted, and her countenance fell.

"What for no'?" she asked softly

"Because I fought a duel with the man that Isobel preferred, and—and—killed him!"

She shuddered with a little sucking in of air at her teeth and drew up her shoulders as if chilled with cold.

"Ah, then," said she, "the best thing's to forget. Are you a Jacobite, Master Greig?"

She had set aside my love affair and taken to politics with no more than a sigh of sympathy, whether for the victim of my jealousy, or Isobel Fortune, or for me, I could not say.

"I'm neither one thing nor another," said I. "My father is a staunch enough royalist, and so, I daresay, I would be too if I had not got a gliff of bonnie Prince Charlie at the Tontine of Glasgow ten years ago."

"Ten years ago!" she repeated, staring abstracted out at the window. "Ten years ago! So it was; I thought it was a lifetime since. And what did you think of him?"

Whatever my answer might have been it never got the air, for here Clancarty, who had had a message come to the door for him, joined us at the window, and she turned to him with some phrase about the trampling of troops that passed along the streets.

"Yes," he said, "the affair marches quickly. Have you heard that England has declared war? And our counter declaration is already on its way across. *Pardieu!* there shall be matters toward in a month or two and the Fox will squeal. Braddock's affair in America has been the best thing that has happened us in many years."

Thus he went on with singular elation that did not
escape me, though my wits were also occupied by
some curious calculations as to what disturbed the
minds of Hamilton and of the lady. I felt that I
was in the presence of some machinating influences
probably at variance, for while Clancarty and Roscommon and Thurot were elate, the priest made
only a pretence at it, and was looking all abstracted
as if weightier matters occupied his mind, his large
fat hand, heavy-ringed, buttressing his dewlap,
and Miss Walkinshaw was stealing glances of
inquiry at him—glances of inquiry and also of
distrust. All this I saw in a mirror over the
mantelpiece of the room.

"Sure there's but one thing to regret in it,"
cried Clancarty suddenly, stopping and turning to
me, "it must mean that we lose Monsieur des
Souliers Rouges. *Peste !* There is always something to worry one about a war !"

"*Comment ?*" said Thurot.

"The deportment," answered his lordship. "Every
English subject has been ordered out of France.
We are going to lose not only your company, Fathei
Hamilton, because of your confounded hare-brained
scheme for covering all Europe in a glass coach,
but our M. Greig must put the Sleeve between him
and those best qualified to estimate and esteem his
thousand virtues of head and heart. For a *louis* or
two I'd take ship with him and fight on the other
side. Gad ! it would always be fighting anyway,
and one would be by one's friend."

The priest's jaw fell as if my going was a blow to

his inmost affections; he turned his face rapidly into shadow; Miss Walkinshaw lost no movement of his; she was watching him as he had been a snake.

"Oh! but it is not necessary that we lose my compatriot so fast as that," she said. "There are such things as permits, excepting English friends of ours from deportment,—and—and—I fancy I could get one for Mr. Greig."

In my heart I thanked her for her ready comprehension of my inability to go back to Britain with an easy mind; and I bowed my recognition of her goodness.

She was paying no heed to my politeness; she had again an eye on the priest, who was obviously cheered marvellously by the prospect.

And then we took a dish of tea with her, the lords and Thurot loudly cheerful, Hamilton ruminant and thundering alternately, Miss Walkinshaw showing a score of graces as hostess, myself stimulated to some unusual warmth of spirit as I sat beside her, well-nigh fairly loving her because she was my country-woman and felt so fond about my native Mearns.

CHAPTER ⅩⅤ

WHEREIN A SITUATION OFFERS AND I ENGAGE
TO GO TRAVELLING WITH THE PRIEST

A WEEK passed with no further incident particularly affecting this history. With my reduced and antique mentor I studied *la belle langue*, sedulous by day, at night pacing the front of the sea, giving words to its passion as it broke angry on the bar or thundered on the beach—the sea that still haunts me and invites, whose absence makes often lonely the moorland country where is my home, where are my people's graves. It called me then, in the dripping weather of those nights in France—it called me temptingly to try again my Shoes of Fortune (as now I named them to myself), and learn whereto they might lead.

But in truth I was now a prisoner to that inviting sea. The last English vessel had gone; the Channel was a moat about my native isle, and I was a tee'd ball with a passport that was no more and no less than a warder's warrant in my pouch. It had come to me under cover of Thurot two days after Miss Walkinshaw's promise; it commanded *tous les gouverneurs et tous les lieutenants-généraux de nos provinces et de nos armées, gouverneurs particuliers et commandants de nos villes, places et troupes* to permit and pass the Sieur Greig anywhere in the country, *sans lui donner aucun empêchement*, and was signed for the king by the Duc de Choiseuil.

I went round to make my devoirs to the lady to whom I owed the favour, and this time I was alone.

"Where's your shoon, laddie?" said she at the first go-off. "Losh! do ye no' ken that they're the very makin' o' ye? If it hadna been for them Clementina Walkinshaw wad maybe never hae lookit the gait ye were on. Ye'll be to put them on again!" She thrust forth a *bottine* like a doll's for size and trod upon my toes, laughing the while with her curious suggestion of unpractised merriment at my first solemn acceptance of her humour as earnest.

"Am I never to get quit o' thae shoes?" I cried; "the very deil maun be in them."

"It was the very deil," said she, "was in them when it was your Uncle Andrew." And she stopped and sighed. "O Andy Greig, Andy Greig! had I been a wise woman and ta'en a guid-hearted though throughither Mearns man's advice—toots! laddie, I micht be a rudas auld wife by my preachin'. Oh, gie's a sang, or I'll dee."

And then she flew to the spinet (a handsome instrument singularly out of keeping with the rest of the plenishing in that odd lodging in the Rue de la Boucherie of Dunkerque), and touched a prelude and broke into an air.

To-day they call that woman lost and wicked; I have seen it said in books: God's pity on her! she was not bad; she was the very football of fate, and a heart of the yellow gold. If I was warlock or otherwise had charms, I would put back the dial two score years and wrench her from her chains.

> O waly, waly up the bank,
> O waly, waly doon the brae.
> And waly, waly yon burn-side,
> Where I and my love wont to gae.
> I leaned my back unto an aik,
> I thocht it was a trusty tree,
> But first it bowed and syne it brak,
> Sae my true love did lichtly me.

They have their own sorrow even in script those ballad words of an exile like herself, but to hear Miss Walkinshaw sing them was one of the saddest things I can recall in a lifetime that has known many sorrows. And still, though sad, not wanting in a sort of brave defiance of calumny, a hope, and an unchanging affection. She had a voice as sweet as a bird in the thicket at home; she had an eye full and melting; her lips, at the sentiment, sometimes faintly broke.

I turned my head away that I might not spy upon her feeling, for here, it was plain, was a tragedy laid bare. She stopped her song mid-way with a laugh, dashed a hand across her eyes, and threw herself into a chair.

"Oh, fie! Mr. Greig, to be backing up a daft woman, old enough to know better, in her vapours. You must be fancying I am a begrutten bairn to be sneckin' my daidlie in this lamentable fashion, but it's just you and your Mearns, and your Ballageich, and your douce Scots face and tongue that have fair bewitched me. O Scotland! Scotland! Let us look oot at this France o' theirs, Mr. Greig." She came to the window (her movements were ever impetuous, like the flight of a butterfly), and "Do I no' wish that was the Gallowgate," said she, "and Glasgow merchants were in the shops and Christian signs abin the doors, like 'MacWhannal' and 'Mackay,' and 'Robin Oliphant'? If that was Bailie John Walkinshaw, wi' his rattan, and yon was the piazza o' Tontine, would no' his dochter be the happy woman? Look! look! ye Mearns man, look! look! at the bairn playing pal-al in the close. 'Tis my little sister Jeanie that's married on the great Doctor Doig—him wi' the mant i' the Tron kirk— and bairns o' her ain, I'm tell't, and they'll never hear their Aunt Clemie named but in a whisper. And yon auld body wi' the mob cap, that's the baxter's widow, and there's carvie in her scones that you'll can buy for a bawbee apiece."

The maddest thing!—but here was the woman smiling through her tears, and something tremulous in her as though her heart was leaping at her breast. Suddenly her manner changed, as if she saw a sobering sight, and I looked out again, and there was Father Hamilton heaving round the corner of a lane, his face as red as the moon in a fog of frost.

"Ah!" cried Miss Walkinshaw, "here's France, sure enough, Mr. Greig. We must put by our senti-ments, and be just witty or as witty as we can be.

if you're no' witty here, my poor Mr. Greig, you
might as well be dumb. A heart doesna maitter
much ; but, oh ! be witty."

The priest was making for the house. She dried
her tears before me, a frankness that flattered my
vanity ; "and let us noo to our English, Mr. Greig,"
said she as the knock came to the door. "It need
be nae honest Scots when France is chappin'.
Would you like to travel for a season ? "

The question took me by surprise ; it had so little
relevance to what had gone before.

"Travel ? " I repeated.

"Travel," said she again quickly. "In a glass
coach with a companion who has plenty of money—
wherever it comes from—and see all Europe, and
maybe—for you are Scots like myself—make money.
The fat priest wants a secretary ; that's the long
and the short of it, for there's his foot on the stairs,
and if you'll say yes, I fancy I can get you the
situation."

I did not hesitate a second.

"Why, then yes, to be sure," said I, "and thank
you kindly."

"Thank *you*, Paul Greig," said she softly, for now
the Swiss had opened the door, and she squeezed
my wrist.

"*Benedicite !*" cried his reverence and came in,
puffing hugely after his climb, his face now purple
almost to strangulation. "May the devil fly away
with turnpike stairs, Madame !—puff-puff—I curse
them whether they be wood or marble ;—puff-puff—
I curse them in Dunkerque ; in Ostend, Paris, all

Europe itself, ay even unto the two Americas. I curse their designers, artisans, owners, and defenders in their waking and sleeping! Madame, kindly consider your stairs anathema!"

"You need all your wind to cool your porridge, as we say in Scotland, Father Hamilton," cried Miss Walkinshaw, "and a bonny-like thing it is to have you coming here blackguarding my honest stairs."

He laughed enormously and fell into a chair, shaking the house as if the world itself had quaked. "Pardon, my dear Miss Walkinshaw," said he when his breath was restored, "but, by the Mass, you must confess 'tis the deuce and all for a man— a real man that loves his viands, and sleeps well o' nights, and has a contented mind and grows flesh accordingly, to trip up to Paradise—" here he bowed, his neck swelling in massive folds—"to trip up to Paradise, where the angels are, as easily as a ballet-dancer—bless her!—skips to the other place where, by my faith! I should like to pay a brief visit myself, if 'twere only to see old friends of the Opéra Comique. Madame, I give you goodday. Sir, Monsieur Greig—'shalt never be a man like thine Uncle Andrew for all thy confounded elixir. I favour not your virtuous early rising in the young. There! thine uncle would a-been abed at this hour an' he were alive and in Dunkerque; thou must be a confoundedly industrious and sober Greig to be dangling at a petticoat-tail—Pardon, Madame, 'tis the dearest tail, anyway!—before the hour meridian."

" And this is France," thought I. " Here's your papistical gospeller at home ! " I minded of the Rev. Scipio Walker in the kirk of Mearns, an image ever of austerity, waling his words as they had come from Solomon, groaning even-on for man's eternal doom.

The priest quickly comprehended my surprise at his humour, and laughed the more at that till a fit of coughing choked him. " *Mon Dieu !* " said he ; " our Andy reincarnate is an Andy most pestilent dull, or I'm a cockle, a convoluted cockle, and uncooked at that. Why, man ! cheer up, thou *croque mort,* thou lanthorn-jaw, thou veal-eye, thou melancholious eater of oaten-meal ! "

" It's a humblin' sicht ! " said I. The impertinence was no sooner uttered than I felt degraded that I should have given it voice, for here was a priest of God, however odd to my thinking, and, what was more, a man who might in years have been my father.

But luckily it could never then, or at any other time, be said of Father Hamilton that he was thin-skinned. He only laughed the more at me. " *Touche !* " he cried. " I knew I could prick the old Andy somewhere. Still, Master Paul, thine uncle was not so young as thou, my cockerel. Had seen his world and knew that Scotland and its—what do you call them ?—its manses, did not provide the universal ensample of true piety."

" I do not think, Father Hamilton," said I, " that piety troubled him very much, or his shoes had not been so well known in Dunkerque."

Miss Walkinshaw laughed.

"There you are, Father Hamilton!" said she. "You'll come little speed with a man from the Mearns moors unless you take him a little more seriously."

Father Hamilton pursed his lips and rubbed down his thighs, an image of the gross man that would have turned my father's stomach, who always liked his men lean, clean, and active. He was bantering me, this fat priest of Dixmunde, but all the time it was with a friendly eye. Thinks I, here's another legacy of goodwill from my extraordinary uncle !

"Hast got thy pass yet, Master Dull ?" said he.

"Not so dull, Master Minister, but what I resent the wrong word even in a joke," I replied, rising to go.

Thurot's voice was on the stair now, and Clancarty's. If they were not to find their *protégé* in an undignified war of words with the priest of Dixmunde, it was time I was taking my feet from there, as the saying went.

But Miss Walkinshaw would not hear of it. "No, no," she protested, "we have some business before you go to your ridiculous French—weary be on the language that ever I heard *Je t'aime* in it !—and how does the same march with you, Mr. Greig ? "

"I know enough of it to thank my good friends in," said I, "but that must be for another occasion."

"Father Hamilton," said she, "here's your secretary."

A curious flash came to those eyes pitted in rolls of flabby flesh. I thought of an eagle old and moulting, languid upon a mountain cliff in misty weather, catching the first glimpse of sun and turned thereby to ancient memories. He said nothing; there was at the moment no opportunity, for the visitors had entered, noisily polite and posturing as was their manner, somewhat touched by wine, I fancied, and for that reason scarcely welcomed by the mistress of the house.

There could be no more eloquent evidence of my innocence in these days than was in the fact that I never wondered at the footing upon which these noisy men of the world were with a countrywoman of mine. The cause they often spoke of covered many mysteries; between the Rue de Paris and the Rue de la Boucherie I could have picked out a score of Scots in exile for their political faiths, and why should not Miss Walkinshaw be one of the company? But sometimes there was just the faintest hint of over-much freedom in their manner to her, and that I liked as little as she seemed to do, for when her face flushed and her mouth firmed, and she became studiously deaf, I felt ashamed of my sex, and could have retorted had not prudence dictated silence as the wisest policy.

As for her, she was never but the minted metal, ringing true and decent, compelling order by a glance, gentle yet secure in her own strength, tolerant, but in bounds.

They were that day full of the project for invading England. It had gone so far that soldiers at Calais and Boulogne were being practised in embarkation. I supposed she must have a certain favour for a step

E

that was designed to benefit the cause wherefor I judged her an exile, but she laughed at the idea of Britain falling, as she said, to a parcel of *crapauds*.

" Treason !" treason !" cried Thurot laughingly. " Under the circumstances, Madame——"

" —Under the circumstances, Captain Thurot," she interrupted quickly, " I need not pretend at a lie. This is not in the Prince's interest, this invasion, and it is a blow at a land I love. Mr. Greig here has just put it into my mind how good are the hearts there, how pleasant the tongue, and how much I love the very name of Scotland. I would be sorry to think of its end come to pleasure the women in Versailles."

" Bravo ! bravo ! *vive la bagatelle !* " cried my Lord Clancarty. " Gad ! I sometimes feel the right old pathriot myself. Sure I have a good mind——"

" Then 'tis not your own, my lord," she cried quickly, displeasure in her expression, and Clancarty only bowed, not a whit abashed at the sarcasm.

Father Hamilton drew me aside from these cheerful contentions, and plunged into the matter that was manifestly occupying all his thoughts since Miss Walkinshaw had mooted me as his secretary.

" Monsieur Greig," he said, placing his great carcase between me and the others in the room, " I declare that women are the seven plagues, and yet here we come chasing them from *petit lever* till—till —well, till as late as the darlings will let us. By the Mass and Father Hamilton knows their value, and when a man talks to me about a woman and the love he bears her, I think 'tis a maniac shouting the praise of the snake that has crept to his breast to sting him. Women—chut!—now tell me what the mischief is a woman an' thou canst."

"I fancy, Father Hamilton," said I, "you could be convinced of the merits of woman if your heart was ever attacked by one—your heart, that does not believe anything in that matter that emanates from your head."

Again the eagle's gleam from the pitted eyes; and, upon my word, a sigh! It was a queer man this priest of Dixmunde.

"Ah, young cockerel," said he, "thou knowest nothing at all about it, and as for me—well, I dare not; but once—once—once there were dews in the woods, and now it is very dry weather, Master Greig. How about thine honour's secretaryship? Gripp'st at the opportunity, young fellow? Eh? Has the lady said sooth? Come now, I like the look of my old Andrew's—my old Merry Andrew's nephew, and could willingly tolerate his *croque-mort* countenance, his odour of the sanctuary, if he could weather it with a plethoric good liver that takes the world as he finds it."

He was positively eager to have me. It was obvious from his voice. He took me by the button of my lapel as if I were about to run away from his offer, but I was in no humour to run away. Here was the very office I should have chosen if a thousand offered. The man was a fatted sow to look on, and by no means engaging in his manner to myself, but what was I and what my state that I should be too particular? Here was a chance to see the world—and to forget. Seeing the world might have been of most importance some months ago in the mind of a clean-handed young lad in the parish of Mearns in Scotland, but now it was of vastly more importance that I should forget.

"We start in a week," said the priest, pressing me closely lest I should change my mind, and making the prospects as picturesque as he could. "Why should a man of flesh and blood vex his good stomach with all this babblement of king's wars? and a pox on their flat-bottomed boats! I have seen my last Mass in Dixmunde; say not a word on that to our friends nor to Madame; and I suffer from a very jaundice of gold. Is't a pact, friend Scotland?"

A pact it was; I went out from Miss Walkinshaw's lodging that afternoon travelling secretary to the fat priest.

CHAPTER XVI

RELATES HOW I INDULGED MY CURIOSITY
AND HOW LITTLE CAME OF IT

DUNKERQUE in these days (it may be so no longer) was a place for a man to go through with his nose in his fingers. Garbage stewed and festered in the gutters of the street so that the women were bound to walk high-kilted, and the sea-breeze at its briskest scarcely sufficed to stir the stagnant, stenching atmosphere of the town, now villainously over-populated by the soldiery with whom it was France's pleasant delusion she should whelm our isle.

"*Pardieu!*" cried Father Hamilton, as we emerged in this malodorous open, "'twere a fairy godfather's deed to clear thee out of this feculent cloaca. Think on't, boy; of you and me a week hence riding through the sweet woods of Somme or Oise, and after that Paris! Paris! my lad of tragedy; Paris, where the world moves and folk live. And then, perhaps, Tours, and Bordeaux, and Flanders, and Sweden, Seville, St. Petersburg itself, but at least the woods of Somme, where the roads are among gossamer and dew and enchantment in the early morning—if we cared to rise early enough to see them, which I promise thee we shall not."

His lips were thick and trembling: he gloated as he pictured me this mad itinerary, leaning heavily on my arm—Silenus on an ash sapling—half-trotting beside me, looking up every now and then to satisfy himself I appreciated the prospect. It was pleasant enough, though in a measure incredible, but at the moment I was thinking of Miss Walkinshaw, and wondering much to myself that this exposition of foreign travel should seem barely attractive because it meant a severance from her. Her sad smile, her brave demeanour, her kind heart, her beauty had touched me sensibly.

"Well, Master Scrivener!" cried the priest, panting at my side, "art dumb?"

"I fancy, sir, it is scarcely the weather for woods," said I. "I hope we are not to put off our journey till the first of April a twelvemonth." A suspicion unworthy of me had flashed into my mind that I might, after all, be no more than the butt of a practical joke. But that was merely for a moment; the priest was plainly too eager on his scheme to be play-acting it.

"I am very grateful to the lady," I hastened to add, "who gave me the chance of listing in your service. Had it not been for her you might have found a better secretary, and I might have remained long enough in the evil smells of Dunkerque that I'll like all the same in spite of that, because I have so good a friend as Miss Walkinshaw in it."

"La! la! la!" cried out Father Hamilton, squeezing my arm. "Here's our young cockerel trailing wing already! May I never eat fish again if 'tisn't a fever in this woman that she must infect every man under three score. For me I am within a month of the period immune, and only feel a malaise in her company. Boy, perpend! Have I not told thee every woman, except the ugliest, is an agent of the devil? I am the first to discover that his majesty is married and his wife keeps shop when he is travelling —among Jesuits and Jacobites and such busy fuel for the future fires. His wife keeps shop, lad, and does a little business among her own sex, using the handsomest for her purposes. Satan comes back to the *boutique*. 'What!' he cries, and counts the till, 'these have been busy days, good wife.' And she, Madame Dusky, chuckles with a 'Ha! Jack, old man, hast a good wife or not? Shalt never know how to herd in souls like sheep till thou hast a quicker eye for what's below a Capuchin hood.' This—this is a sweet woman, this Walkinshaw, Paul, but a dangerous. 'Ware hawk, lad, 'ware hawk!"

I suppose my face reddened at that; at least he looked at me again and pinched, and "Smitten to the marrow; may I drink water and grow thin else. *Sacré nom de nom!* 'tis time thou wert on the highways of Europe."

"How does it happen that a countrywoman of mine is here alone?" I asked.

"I'll be shot if thou art not the rascalliest young innocent in France. Aye! or out of Scotland," cried Father Hamilton, holding his sides for laughter.

"Is thy infernal climate of fogs and rains so pleasant that a woman of spirit should abide there for ever an' she have the notion to travel otherwheres ? La ! la ! la ! Master Scrivener, and thou must come to an honest pious priest for news of the world. But, boy, I'm deaf and dumb ; mine eyes on occasion are without vision. Let us say the lady has been an over-ardent Jacobite ; 'twill suffice in the meantime. And now has't ever set eyes on Charles Edward ? "

I told him I had never had any hand in the Jacobite affairs, if that was what he meant.

His countenance fell at that.

"What ! " he cried, losing his Roman manner, "do you tell me you have never seen him ? "

But once, I explained, when he marched into Glasgow city with his wild Highlanders and bullied the burgesses into providing shoes for his ragged army.

"Ah," said he with a clearing visage, "that will suffice. Must point him out to me. Dixmunde parish was a poor place for seeing the great ; 'tis why I go wandering now."

Father Hamilton's hint at politics confirmed my guess about Miss Walkinshaw, but I suppose I must have been in a craze to speak of her on any pretence, for later in the day I was at Thurot's lodging, and there must precognosce again.

Oh, mon Dieu, quelle espièglerie ! " cried out the captain. "And this a Greig too ! Well, I do not wonder that your poor uncle stayed so long away from home ; faith, he'd have died of an *ennui* else. Miss Walkinshaw is—Miss Walkinshaw ; a country-

man of her own should know better than I all that
is to be known about her. But 'tis not our affair,
Mr. Greig. For sure 'tis enough that we find her
smiling, gentle, tolerant, what you call the 'perfect
lady'—*n'est-ce pas?* And of all the virtues, upon
my word, kindness is the best and rarest, and that
she has to a miracle."

"I'm thinking that is not a corsair's creed, Captain
Thurot," said I, smiling at the gentleman's eagerness. He was standing over me like a lighthouse,
with his eyes on fire, gesturing with his arms as
they had been windmill sails.

"No, faith! but 'tis a man's, Master Greig, and I
have been happy with it. Touching our fair friend,
I may say that, much as I admire her, I agree with
some others that ours were a luckier cause without
her. Gad! the best thing you could do, Mr. Greig,
would be to marry her yourself and take her back
with you to Scotland."

"What! by way of Paris in Father Hamilton's
glass coach," I said, bantering to conceal my confusion at such a notion.

"H'm," said he. "Father Hamilton and the lady
are a pair." He walked a little up and down the
room as if he were in a quandary. "A pair," he
resumed. "I fancied I could see to the very centre
of the Sphinx itself, for all men are in ourselves if
we only knew it, till I came upon this Scotswoman
and this infernal Flemish-English priest of Dixmunde. Somehow, for them Antoine Thurot has
not the key in himself yet. Still, 'twill arrive, 'twill
arrive! I like the lady—and yet I wish she were a

thousand miles away; I like the man too, but a Jesuit is too many men at once to be sure of; and, Gad! I can scarcely sleep at nights for wondering what he may be plotting. This grand tour of his——"

"Stop, stop!" I cried, in a fear that he might compromise himself in an ignorance of my share in the tour in question; "I must tell you that I am going with Father Hamilton as his secretary, although it bothers me to know what scrivening is to be accomplished in a glass coach. Like enough I am to be no more, in truth, than the gentleman's companion or courier, and it is no matter so long as I am moving."

"Indeed, and is it so?" cried Captain Thurot, stopping as if he had been shot. "And how happens it that this priest is willing to take you, that are wholly a foreigner and a stranger to the country?"

"Miss Walkinshaw recommended me," said I.

"Oh!" he cried, "you have not been long of getting into your excellent countrywoman's kind favour. Is it that Tony Thurot has been doing the handsome by an ingrate? No, no, Monsieur, that were a monstrous innuendo, for the honour has been all mine. But that Miss Walkinshaw should be on such good terms with the priest as to trouble with the provision of his secretary is opposed to all I had expected of her. Why, she dislikes the man, or I'm a stuffed fish."

"Anyhow, she has done a handsome thing by me," said I. "It is no wonder that so good a heart as hers should smother its repugnances (and the

priest is a fat sow, there is no denying) for the sake
of a poor lad from its own country. You are but
making it the plainer that I owe her more than at
first I gave her credit for."

"Bless me, here's gratitude!" cried the captain,
laughing at my warmth. "Mademoiselle Walkinshaw has her own plans; till now, I fancied them
somewhat different from Hamilton's, but more fool I
to fancy they were what they seemed! All that, my
dear lad, need not prevent your enjoying your grand
tour with the priest, who has plenty of money and
the disposition to spend it like a gentleman."

Finally I went to my Lord Clancarty, for it will
be observed that I had still no hint as to the origin
of the lady who was so good a friend of mine.
Though the last thing in the world I should have
done was to pry into her affairs for the indulgence of
an idle curiosity, I would know the best of her before
the time came to say farewell, and leave of her with
me no more than a memory.

The earl was at the Café du Soleil d'Or, eating
mussels on the terrace and tossing the empty shells
into the gutter what time he ogled passing women
and exchanged levitous repartee with some other
frequenters of the place.

"Egad, Paul," he cried, meeting me with effusion,
"'tis said there is one pearl to be found for every
million mussels; but here's a pearl come to me in
the midst of a single score. An Occasion, lad; I
sat at the dice last night till a preposterous hour
this morning, and now I have a headache like the
deuce and a thirst to take the Baltic. I must have

the tiniest drop, and on an Occasion too. *Voilà! Gaspard, une autre bouteille.*"

He had his bottle, that I merely made pretence to help him empty, and I had my precognition.

But it came to little in the long run. Oh yes, he understood my interest in the lady (with rakish winking); 'twas a delicious creature for all its *hauteur* when one ventured a gallantry, but somehow no particular friend to the Earl of Clancarty, who, if she only knew it, was come of as noble a stock as any rotten Scot ever went unbreeched; not but what (this with a return of the naturally polite man) there were admirable and high-bred people of that race, as instance my Uncle Andrew and myself. But was there any reason why such a man as Charlie Stuart should be King of Ireland? "I say, Greig, blister the old Chevalier and his two sons! There is not a greater fumbler on earth than this sotted person, who has drunk the Cause to degradation and would not stir a hand to serve me and my likes, that are, begad! the fellow's betters."

"But all this," said I, "has little to do with Miss Walkinshaw. I have nothing to say of the Prince, who may be all you say, though that is not the repute he has in Scotland."

"Bravo, Mr. Greig!" cried his lordship. "That is the tone if you would keep in the lady's favour. Heaven knows she has little reason to listen to praise of such a creature, but, then, women are blind. She loves not Clancarty, as I have said; but, no matter, I forgive her that; 'tis well known 'tis because I cannot stomach her prince."

"And yet," said I, "you must interest yourself in these Jacobite affairs and mix with all that are here of that party."

"Faith and I do," he confessed heartily. "What! am I to be a mole and stay underground? A man must have his diversion, and though I detest the Prince I love his foolish followers. Do you know what, Mr. Greig? 'Tis the infernal irony of things in this absurd world that the good fellows, the bloods, the men of sensibilities must for ever be wrapped up in poor mad escapades and emprises. And a Clancarty is ever of such a heart that the more madcap the scheme the more will he dote on it."

A woman passing in a chair at this moment looked in his direction; fortunately, otherwise I was condemned to a treatise on life and pleasure.

"Egad!" he cried, "there's a face that's like a line of song," and he smiled at her with unpardonable boldness as it seemed to me, a pleasant pucker about his eyes, a hint of the good comrade in his mouth.

She flushed like wine and tried to keep from smiling, but could not resist, and smiling she was borne away.

"Do you know her, my lord?" I could not forbear asking.

"Is it know her?" said he. "Devil a know, but 'tis a woman anyhow, and a heart at that. Now who the deuce can she be?" And he proceeded, like a true buck, to fumble with the Mechlin of his fall and dust his stockings in an airy foppish manner so graceful that I swear no other could have done the same so well.

"Now this Miss Walkinshaw—" I went on, determined to have some satisfaction from my interview.

"Confound your Miss Walkinshaw, by your leave, Mr. Greig," he interrupted. "Can you speak of Miss Walkinshaw when the glory of the comet is still trailing in the heavens? And—hum!—I mind me of a certain engagement, Mr. Greig," he went on hurriedly, drawing a horologe from his fob and consulting it with a frowning brow. "In the charm of your conversation I had nigh forgot, so *adieu, adieu, mon ami!*"

He gave me the tips of his fingers, and a second later he was gone, stepping down the street with a touch of the minuet, tapping his legs with his cane, his sword skewering his coat-skirts, all the world giving him the cleanest portion of the thoroughfare and looking back after him with envy and admiration.

CHAPTER XVII

AND all this time it may well be wondered where was
my remorse for a shot fired on the moor of Mearns,
for two wretched homes created by my passion and
my folly. And where, in that shifting mind of mine,
was the place of Isobel Fortune, whose brief days of
favour for myself (if that, indeed, was not imagination on my part) had been the cause of these my
wanderings? There is one beside me as I write,
ready to make allowance for youth and ignorance,
the untutored affection, the distraught mind, if not
for the dubiety as to her feelings for myself when I
was outlawed for a deed of blood and had taken, as
the Highland phrase goes, the world for my pillow.

I did not forget the girl of Kirkillstane; many a
time in the inward visions of the night, and of the
day too, I saw her go about that far-off solitary
house in the hollow of the hills. Oddly enough,
'twas ever in sunshine I saw her, with her sun-bonnet
swinging from its ribbons and her hand above her
eyes, shading them that she might look across the
fields that lay about her home, or on a tryst of fancy
by the side of Earn, hearing the cushats mourn in a

magic harmony with her melancholy thoughts. As for the killing of young Borland, that I kept, waking at least, from my thoughts, or if the same intruded, I found it easier, as time passed, to excuse myself for a fatality that had been in the experience of nearly every man I now knew—of Clancarty and Thurot, of the very baker in whose house I lodged and who kneaded the dough for his little bread not a whit the less cheerily because his hands had been imbrued.

The late Earl of Clare, in France called the Maréchal Comte de Thomond, had come to Dunkerque in the quality of Inspector-General of the Armies of France, to review the troops in garrison and along that menacing coast. The day after my engagement with Father Hamilton I finished my French lesson early and went to see his lordship and his army on the dunes to the east of the town. Cannon thundered, practising at marks far out in the sea; there was infinite manœuvring of horse and foot; the noon was noisy with drums and the turf shook below the hoofs of galloping chargers. I fancy it was a holiday; at least, as I recall the thing, Dunkerque was all *en fête*, and a happy and gay populace gathered in the rear of the maréchal's flag. Who should be there among the rest, or rather a little apart from the crowd, but Miss Walkinshaw! She had come in a chair; her dainty hand beckoned me to her side almost as soon as I arrived.

"Now, that's what I must allow is very considerate," said she, eyeing my red shoes, which were put on that day from some notion of proper splendour.

"Well considered?" I repeated.

"Just well considered," said she. "You know how much it would please me to see you in your red shoes, and so you must put them on."

I was young in these days, and, like the ass I was, I quickly set about disabusing her mind of a misapprehension that injured her nor me.

"Indeed, Miss Walkinshaw," said I, "how could I do that when I did not know you were to be here? You are the last I should have expected to see here."

"What!" she exclaimed, growing very red. "Does Mr. Greig trouble himself so much about the *convenances*? And why should I not be here if I have the whim? Tell me that, my fastidious compatriot."

Here was an accountable flurry over a thoughtless phrase!

"No reason in the world that I know of," said I gawkily, as red as herself, wondering what it was my foot was in.

"That you know of," she repeated, as confused as ever. "It seems to me, Mr. Greig, that the old gentleman who is tutoring you in the French language would be doing a good turn to throw in a little of the manners of the same. Let me tell you that I am as much surprised as you can be to find myself here, and now that you are so good as to put me in mind of the—of the—of the *convenances*, I will go straight away home. It was not the priest, nor was it Captain Thurot that got your ear, for they are by the way of being gentlemen; it could only have been this Irishman Clancarty—the quality of that country have none of the scrupulosity that distinguishes our own. You can tell his lordship, next time you see him, that Miss Walkinshaw will see day about with him for this."

She ordered her chairmen to take her home, and then—burst into tears!

I followed at her side, in a stew at my indiscoverable blundering, my *chapeau-de-bras* in my hand, and myself like to greet too for sympathy and vexation.

"You must tell me what I have done, Miss Walkinshaw," I said. "Heaven knows I have few enough friends in this world without losing your good opinion through an offence of whose nature I am entirely ignorant."

"Go away!" she said, pushing my fingers from the side of her chair, that was now being borne towards the town.

"Indeed, and I shall not, Miss Walkinshaw, asking your pardon for the freedom," I said, "for here's some monstrous misconception, and I must clear myself, even at the cost of losing your favour for ever."

She hid her face in her handkerchief and paid no more heed to me. Feeling like a mixture of knave and fool, I continued to walk deliberately by her side all the way into the Rue de la Boucherie. She dismissed the chair and was for going into the house without letting an eye light on young persistency.

"One word, Miss Walkinshaw," I pleaded. "We

are a Scottish man and a Scottish woman, our lee-lones of all our race at this moment in this street, and it will be hard-hearted of the Scottish woman if she will not give her fellow countryman, that has for her a respect and an affection, a chance to know wherein he may have blundered."

"Respect and affection," she said, her profile turned to me, her foot on the steps, visibly hesitating.

"Respect and affection," I repeated, flushing at my own boldness.

"In spite of Clancarty's tales of me?" she said, biting her nether lip and still manifestly close on tears.

"How?" said I, bewildered. "His lordship gave me no tales that I know of."

"And why," said she, "be at such pains to tell me you wondered I should be there?"

I got very red at that.

"You see, you cannot be frank with me, Mr. Greig," she said bitterly.

"Well, then," I ventured boldly, "what I should have said was that I feared you would not be there, for it's there I was glad to see you. And I have only discovered that in my mind since you have been angry with me and would not let me explain myself."

"What!" she cried, quite radiant, "and, after all, the red shoon were not without a purpose? Oh, Mr. Greig, you're unco' blate! And, to tell you the truth, I was just play-acting yonder myself. I was only making believe to be angry wi' you, and now that we understand each ither you can see me to my parlour."

CHAPTER XVIII

I MAKE IT UP WITH MADAME AND MAKE A
FOOL OF MYSELF

"WELL, Bernard," she said to the Swiss as we entered, "any news?"

He informed her there was none.

"What! no one called?" said she with manifest disappointment.

"*Personne, Madame.*"

"No letters?"

Nor were there any letters, he replied.

She sighed, paused irresolute a moment with her foot on the stair, one hand at her heart, the other at the fastening of her coat, and looked at me with a face almost tragic in its trouble. I cannot but think she was on the brink of a confidence, but ere it came she changed her mind and dashed up the stair with a tra-la-la of a song meant to indicate her indifference, leaving me a while in her parlour while she changed her dress. She came back to me in a little, attired in a pale primrose-coloured paduasoy, the cuffs and throat embroidered in a pattern of roses and leaves, her hair unpowdered and glossy, wantoning in and out of a neck beyond description. The first thing she did on entrance was odd enough, for it was to stand over me where I lounged on her settee, staring down into my eyes until I felt a monstrous embarrassment.

"I am wonderin'," said she, "if ye are the man I tak' ye for."

Her eyes were moist; I saw she had been crying in her toilet room.

"I'm just the man you see," I said, "but for some unco' troubles that are inside me and are not for airing to my friends on a fine day in Dunkerque."

"Perhaps, like the lave of folks, ye dinna ken yoursel'," she went on, speaking with no sprightly humour though in the Scots she was given to fall to in her moments of fun. "All men, Mr. Greig, mean well, but most of them fall short of their own ideals; they're like the women in that, no doubt, but in the men the consequence is more disastrous."

"When I was a girl in a place you know," she went on even more soberly, "I fancied all men were on the model of honest John Walkinshaw—better within than without. He was stern to austerity, demanding the last particle of duty from his children, and to some he might seem hard, but I have never met the man yet with a kinder heart, a pleasanter mind, a more pious disposition than John Walkinshaw's. It has taken ten years, and acquaintance with some gentry not of Scotland, to make it plain that all men are not on his model."

"I could fancy not, to judge from his daughter," I said, blushing at my first compliment that was none the less bold because it was sincere.

At that she put on a little mouth and shrugged her shoulders with a shiver that made the snaps in her ears tremble.

"My good young man," said she, "there you go! If there's to be any friendship between you and Clementina Walkinshaw, understand there must be a different key from that. You are not only learning your French, but you are learning, it would seem, the manners of the nation. It was that made me wonder if you could be the man I took you for the first day you were in this room and I found I could make you greet with a Scots sang, and tell me honestly about a lass you had a notion of and her no' me. That last's the great stroke of honesty in any man, and let me tell you there are some women who would not relish it. But you are in a company here so ready with the tongue of flattery that I doubt each word they utter, and that's droll enough in me that loves my fellow creatures, and used to think the very best of every one of them. If I doubt them now I doubt them with a sore enough heart, I'll warrant you. Oh! am I not sorry that my man of Mearns should be put in the reverence of such creatures as Clancarty and Thurot, and all that gang of worldlings? I do not suppose I could make you understand it, Mr. Paul Greig, but I feel motherly to you, and to see my son—this great giant fellow who kens the town of Glasgow and dwelt in Mearns where I had May milk, and speaks wi' the fine Scots tongue like mysel' when his heart is true—to see him the boon comrade with folks perhaps good enough for Clementina Walkinshaw but lacking a particle of principle, is a sight to sorrow me."

"And is it for that you seek to get me away with the priest?" I asked, surprised at all this, and a little resenting the suggestion of youth implied in her feeling like a mother to me. Her face was lit, her movement free and beautiful; something in her fascinated me.

She dropped in a chair and pushed the hair from her ears with a hand like milk, and laughed.

"Now how could you guess?" said she. "Am I no' the careful mother of you to put you in the hands o' the clergy? I doubt this play-acting rhetorician of a man from Dixmunde is no great improvement on the rest of your company when all's said and done, but you'll be none the worse for seeing the world at his costs, and being in other company than Clancarty's and Thurot's and Roscommon's. He told me to-day you were going with him, and I was glad that I had been of that little service to you."

"Then it seems you think so little of my company as to be willing enough to be rid of me at the earliest opportunity," I said, honestly somewhat piqued at her readiness to clear me out of Dunkerque.

She looked at me oddly. "Havers, Mr. Greig!" said she, "just havers!"

I was thanking her for her offices, but she checked me. "You are well off," she said, "to be away from here while these foolish manœuvrings are on foot. Poor me! I must bide and see them plan the breaking down of my native country. It's a mercy I know in what a fiasco it will end, this planning. Hearken!

Do you hear the bugles? That's Soubise going back to the caserne. He and his little men are going back to eat another dinner destined to assist in the destruction of an island where you and I should be this day if we were wiser than we are. Fancy them destroying Britain, Mr. Greig!—Britain, where honest John Walkinshaw is, that never said an ill word in his life, nor owed any man a penny: where the folks are guid and true, and fear God and want nothing but to be left to their crofts and herds. If it was England—if it was the palace of Saint James —no, but it's Scotland, too, and the men you saw marching up and down to-day are to be marching over the moor o' Mearns when the heather's red. Can you think of it?" She stamped her foot. "Where the wee thack hooses are at the foot o' the braes, and the bairns playing under the rowan trees; where the peat is smelling, and the burns are singing in the glens, and the kirk-bells are ringing. Poor Mr. Greig! Are ye no' wae for Scotland? Do ye think Providence will let a man like Thomond ye saw to-day cursing on horseback—do ye think Providence will let him lead a French army among the roads you and I ken so well, affronting the people we ken too, who may be a thought dull in the matter of repartee, but are for ever decent, who may be hard-visaged, but are so brave?"

She laughed, herself, half bitterly, half contemptuously, at the picture she drew. Outside, in the sunny air of the afternoon, the bugles of Soubise filled the street with brazen cries, and nearer came the roar of pounding drums I thought I heard them menacing the sleep of evening valleys far away, shattering the calm of the hearth of Hazel Den.

"The cause for which—for which so many are exile here," I said, looking on this Jacobite so strangely inconsistent, "has no reason to regret that France should plan an attack on Georgius Rex."

She shook her head impatiently. "The cause has nothing to do with it, Mr. Greig," said she. "The cause will suffer from this madness more than ever it did, but in any case 'tis the most miserable of lost causes."

"Prince Charlie——"

"Once it was the cause with me, now I would sooner have it Scotland," she went on, heedless of my interruption. "Scotland! Scotland! Oh, how the name of her is like a dirge to me, and my heart is sore for her! Where is your heart, Mr. Greig, that it does not feel alarm at the prospect of these *crapauds* making a single night's sleep uneasy for the folks you know? Where is your heart, I'm asking?"

"I wish I knew," said I impulsively, staring at her, completely bewitched by her manner so variable and intense, and the straying tendrils of her hair.

"Do you not?" said she. "Then I will tell you. It is where it ought to be—with a girl of the name of Isobel Fortune. Oh, the dear name! oh, the sweet name! And when you are on your travels with this priest do not be forgetting her. Oh, yes!

I know you will tell me again that all is over between the pair of you, and that she loved another—but I am not believing a word of that, Mr. Greig, when I look at you—(and will ye say 'thank ye' for the compliment that's there?)—you will just go on thinking her the same, and you will be the better man for it. There's something tells me she is thinking of you though I never saw her, the dear! Let me see, this is what sort of girl she will be."

She drew her chair closer to the settee and leaned forward in front of me, and, fixing her eyes on mine, drew a picture of the girl of Kirkillstane as she imagined her.

" She will be about my own height, and with the same colour of hair——"

" How do you know that ? I never said a word of that to you," I cried, astonished at the nearness of her first guess.

" Oh, I'm a witch," she cried triumphantly, " a fair witch. Hoots ! do I no' ken ye wadna hae looked the side o' the street I was on if I hadna put ye in mind o' her ? Well, she's my height and colour— but, alack-a-day, no' my years. She 'll have a voice like the mavis for sweetness, and 'll sing to perfection. She'll be shy and forward in turns, accordin' as you are forward and shy ; she 'll can break your heart in ten minutes wi' a pout o' her lips or mak' ye fair dizzy with delight at a smile. And then "— here Miss Walkinshaw seemed carried away herself by her fancy portrait, for she bent her brows studiously as she thought, and seemed to speak in an abstraction—" and then she'll be a managing woman.

She'll be the sort of woman that the Bible tells of whose value is over rubies ; knowing your needs as you battle with the world, and cheerful when you come in to the hearthstone from the turmoil outside. A witty woman and a judge of things, calm but full of fire in your interests. A household where the wife's a doll is a cart with one wheel, and your Isobel will be the perfect woman. I think she must have travelled some, too, and seen how poor is the wide world compared with what is to be found at your own fire-end ; I think she must have had trials and learned to be brave."

She stopped suddenly, looked at me and got very red in the face.

"A fine picture, Miss Walkinshaw !" said I, with something drumming at my heart. "It is not just altogether like Isobel Fortune, who has long syne forgot but to detest me, but I fancy I know who it is like."

"And who might that be ? " she asked in a low voice and with a somewhat guilty look.

"Will I tell you ? " I asked, myself alarmed at my boldness.

"No ! no ! never mind," she cried. "I was just making a picture of a girl I once knew—poor lass ! and of what she might have been. But she's dead— dead and buried. I hope, after all, your Isobel is a nobler woman than the one I was thinking on and a happier destiny awaiting her."

"That cannot matter much to me now," I said, "for, as I told you, there is nothing any more between us—except—except a corp upon the heather."

She shuddered as she did the first time I told her of my tragedy, and sucked in the air again through her clenched teeth.

"Poor lad! poor lad!" said she. "And you have quite lost her. If so, and the thing must be, then this glass coach of Father Hamilton's must take you to the country of forgetfulness. I wish I could drive there myself this minute, but wae's me, there's no chariot at the *remise* that'll do that business for John Walkinshaw's girl."

Something inexpressively moving was in her mien, all her heart was in her face as it seemed; a flash of fancy came to me that she was alone in the world with nothing of affection to hap her round from its abrasions, and that her soul was crying out for love. Sweet beyond expression was this woman and I was young; up to my feet I rose, and turned on her a face that must have plainly revealed my boyish passion.

"Miss Walkinshaw," I said, "you may put me out of this door for ever, but I'm bound to say I'm going travelling in no glass coach; Dunkerque will be doing very well for me."

Her lips trembled; her cheek turned pale; she placed a hand upon her breast, and there was I contrite before her anger!

"Is this—is this your respect and your esteem, Mr. Greig?" she asked brokenly.

"They were never greater than at this moment," I replied.

"And how are they to be manifested by your waiting on in Dunkerque?" she asked, recovering her colour and some of her ordinary manner.

How indeed? She had no need to ask me the question, for it was already ringing through my being. That the Spoiled Horn from Mearns, an outlaw with blood on his hands and borrowed money in his pocket, should have the presumption to feel any ardour for this creature seemed preposterous to myself, and I flushed in an excess of shame and confusion.

This seemed completely to reassure her. "Oh, Mr. Greig—Mr. Greig, was I not right to ask if ye were the man ye seemed? Here's a nice display o' gallantry from my giant son! I believe you are just makin' fun o' this auld wife; and if no' I hae just one word for you, Paul Greig, and it's this that I said afore—jist havers!"

She went to her spinet and ran her fingers over the keys and broke into a song—

> Oh, what ails the laddie, new twined frae his mither?
> The laddie gallantin' roun' Tibbie and me?—

with glances coquettish yet repelling round her shoulder at me as I stood turning my *chapeau-de-bras* in my hand as a boy turns his bonnet in presence of laird or dominie. The street was shaking now with the sound of marching soldiers, whose platoons were passing in a momentary silence of trumpet or drum. All at once the trumpets blared forth just in front of the house, broke upon her song, and gave a heaven-sent diversion to our comedy or tragedy or whatever it was in the parlour.

We both stood looking out at the window for a while in silence, watching the passing troops, and when the last file had gone, she turned with a change of topic.

"If these men had been in England ten years ago," she said, "when brisk affairs were doing there with Highland claymores, your Uncle Andrew would have been there, too, and it would not perhaps be your father who was Laird of Hazel Den. But that's all by with now. And when do you set out with Father Hamilton?"

She had a face as serene as fate; my heart ached to tell her that I loved her, but her manner made me hold my tongue on that.

"In three days," I said, still turning my hat and wishing myself elsewhere, though her presence intoxicated.

"In three days!" she said, as one astonished. "I had thought it had been a week at the earliest. Will I tell you what you might do? You are my great blate bold son, you know, from the moors of Mearns, and I will be wae, wae, to think of you travelling all round Europe without a friend of your own country to exchange a word with. Write to me; will you?"

"Indeed and I will, and that gaily," I cried, delighted at the prospect.

"And you will tell me all your exploits and where you have been and what you have seen, and where you are going and what you are going to do, and be sure there will be one Scots heart thinking of you (besides Isobel, I daresay), and I declare to you this one will follow every league upon the map, saying 'the blate lad's there to-day,' 'the blate lad's to be here at noon to-morrow.' Is it a bargain? Because you know I will write to you—but oh! I forgot; what of the priest? Not for worlds would I have him know that I kept up a correspondence with his secretary. That is bad."

She gazed rather expectantly at me as if looking for a suggestion, but the problem was beyond me, and she sighed.

"Of course his reverence need not know anything about it," she said then.

"Certainly," I acquiesced, jumping at so obvious a solution. "I will never mention to him anything about it."

"But how will I get your letters and how will you get mine without his suspecting something?"

"Oh, but he cannot suspect."

"What, and he a priest, too! It's his trade, Mr. Greig, and this Father Hamilton would spoil all if he knew we were indulging ourselves so innocently. What you must do is to send your letters to me in a way that I shall think of before you leave and I shall answer in the same way. But never a word, remember, to his reverence; I depend on your honour for that."

As I was going down the stair a little later, she leaned over the bannister and cried after me:

"Mr. Greig," said she, "ye needna' be sae hainin' wi' your red shoes when ye're traivellin' in the coach. I would be greatly pleased to be thinkin' of you as traivellin' in them a' the time."

I looked up and saw her smiling saucily at me over the rail.

"Would you indeed?" said I. "Then I'll never put them aff till I see ye again, when I come back to Dunkerque."

"That is kind," she answered, laughing outright, "but fair reediculous. To wear them to bed would be against your character for sobriety."

CHAPTER XIX

IT was the last, for many months, I was to see of
my countrywoman. Before the crow of the cock next
morning I was on the unending roads, trundling in
a noisy vehicle through pitch darkness, my companion
snoring stertorous at my side, his huge head falling
every now and then upon my shoulder, myself peering to catch some revelation of what manner of
country-side we went through as the light from the
swinging lanthorn lit up briefly passing banks of
frosted hedge or sleeping hamlets on whose pave
the hoofs of our horses hammered as they had been
the very war-steeds of Bellona.

But how came I there ? How but by my master's
whim, that made him anticipate his departure by
three days and drag me from my bed incontinent to
set out upon his trip over Europe.

I had been sleeping soundly, dreaming I heard
the hopper of the mill of Driepps at home banging
to make Jock Alexander's fortune, when I awakened,
or rather half-wakened, to discover that 'twas no

F

hopper but a nieve at my door, rapping with a vigour to waken the dead.

"Come out! Sir Secretary, come out! or I shall pull thy domicile about thine ears," cried the voice of Father Hamilton.

He stood at the door when I opened, wrapped over the chin in a muffler of multitudinous folds, and covered by a roquelaure.

"*Pax!*" he cried, thrusting a purple face into the room, "and on with thy boots like a good lad. We must be off and over the dunes before the bell of St. Eloi knocks another nail in the coffin of time."

"What!" I said, dumbfoundered, "are we to start on our journey to-day?"

"Even so, my sluggardly Scot; faith! before the day even, for the day will be in a deuce of a hurry an' it catch up on us before we reach Pont-Opoise. Sop a crust in a jug of wine—I've had no better *petit déjeuner* myself—put a clean cravat and a pair of hose in thy sack, and in all emulate the judicious flea that wastes no time in idle rumination, but transacts its affairs in a succession of leaps."

"And no time to say good-bye to any one?" I asked, struggling into my toilet.

"La! la! la! the flea never takes a *congé* that I've heard on, Master Punctilio. Not so much as a kiss o' the hand for you; I have had news, and 'tis now or never."

Twenty minutes later, Thurot's landlord (for Thurot himself was from home) lit me to the court-yard, and the priest bundled me and my sack into the bowels of an enormous chariot waiting there.

The clocks began to strike the hour of five; before the last stroke had ceased to shiver the darkness we were thundering along the sea front and my master was already composed to sleep in his corner, without vouchsafing me a sentence of explanation for so hurried a departure. Be sure my heart was sore! I felt the blackest of ingrates to be thus speeding without a sign of farewell from a place where I had met with so much of friendship.

Out at the window of the coach I gazed, to see nothing but the cavernous night on one side, on the other, lit by the lanthorn, the flashing past of houses all shuttered and asleep.

It was dry and pleasant weather, with a sting of frost in the air, and the propinquity of the sea manifest not in its plangent voice alone but in the odour of it that at that hour dominated the natural smells of the faubourgs. Only one glimpse I had of fellow creatures; as we passed the fort, the flare of flambeaux showed an enormous body of soldiers working upon the walls of Risebank; it but added to the poignance of my melancholy to reflect that here were my country's enemies unsleeping, and I made a sharp mental contrast of this most dauntening spectacle with a picture of the house of Hazel Den dreaming among its trees, and only crying lambs perhaps upon the moor to indicate that any life was there. Melancholy! oh, it was eerie beyond expression for me that morning! Outside, the driver talked to his horses and to some one with him on the boot; it must have been cheerier for him than for me as I sat in that sombre and close interior, jolted

by my neighbour, and unable to refrain from re-
habilitating all the past. Especially did I think of
my dark home-coming with a silent father on the
day I left the college to go back to the Mearns. And
by a natural correlation, that was bound to lead to
all that followed—even to the event for which I was
now so miserably remote from my people.

Once or twice his reverence woke, to thrust his
head out at the window and ask where we were.
Wherever we were when he did so, 'twas certain
never to be far enough for his fancy, and he condemned the driver for a snail until the whip cracked
wickedly and the horses laboured more strenuously
than ever, so that our vehicle swung upon its springs
till it might well seem we were upon a ship at sea.

For me he had but the one comment—" I wonder
what's for *déjeuner*." He said it each time solemnly
as it were his matins, and then slid into his swinish
sleep again.

The night seemed interminable, but by-and-by the
day broke. I watched it with eagerness as it
gradually paled the east, and broke up the black
bulk of the surrounding land into fields, orchards,
gardens, woods. And the birds awoke—God bless
the little birds!—they woke, and started twittering
and singing in the haze, surely the sweetest, the
most sinless of created things, the tiny angels of the
woods, from whom, walking in summer fields in the
mornings of my age as of my youth, I have borrowed
hope and cheer.

Father Hamilton wakened too, and heard the
birds; indeed, they filled the ear of the dawn with

melodies. A smile singularly pleasant came upon
his countenance as he listened.

"*Pardieu!*" said he, "how they go on! Has't
the woodland soul, *Sieur Croque-mort?* Likely
enough not; I never knew another but myself and
thine uncle that had it, and 'tis the mischief that
words will not explain the same. 'Tis a gift of the
fairies"—here he crossed himself devoutly and
mumbled a Romish incantation—"that, having the
said woodland spirit—in its nature a Pagan thing
perchance, but *n'importe!*—thou hast in the song of
the tiny beings choiring there something to make the
inward tremor that others find in a fiddle and a glass
of wine. No! no! not that, 'tis a million times
more precious; 'tis—'tis the pang of the devotee, 'tis
the ultimate thrill of things. Myself, I could expire
upon the ecstasy of the thrush, or climb to heaven
upon the lark's May rapture. And there they go!
the loves! and they have the same ditty I heard
from them first in Louvain. There are but three
clean things in this world, my lad of Scotland—a
bird, a flower, and a child's laughter. I have been
confessor long enough to know all else is filth. But
what's the luck in waiting for us at Azincourt? and
what's the *pot-au-feu* to-day?"

He listened a little longer to the birds, and fell
asleep smiling, his fat face for once not amiss, and I
was left again alone as it were to receive the day.

We had long left the dunes and the side of the
sea, though sometimes on puffs of wind I heard its
distant rumour. Now the land was wooded with
the apple tree; we rose high on the side of a glen,

full of a rolling fog that streamed off as the day grew. A tolerable land enough; perhaps more lush than my own, with scarce a rood uncultivated, and dotted far and wide by the strangest farm steadings and pendicles, but such steadings and pendicles as these eyes never before beheld, with enormous eaves of thatch reaching almost to the ground, and ridiculous windows of no shape; with the yokings of the cattle, the boynes, stoups, carts, and ploughs about the places altogether different from our own. We passed troops marching, peasants slouching with baskets of poultry to market towns, now and then a horseman, now and then a caleche. And there were numerous hamlets, and at least two middling-sized towns, and finally we came, at the hour of eleven, upon the place appointed for our *déjeuner*. It was a small inn on the banks of the only rivulet I had seen in all the journey. I forget its name, but I remember there was a patch of heather on the side of it, and that I wished ardently the season had been autumn that I might have looked upon the purple bells.

"'Tis a long lane that has no tavern," said his reverence, and oozed out of his side of the coach with groanings. The innkeeper ran forth, louted, and kissed his hand.

"'*Jour, m'sieu, 'jour!*" said Father Hamilton hurriedly. "And now, what have you here that is worth while?"

The innkeeper respectfully intimated that the church of Saint-Jean-en-Grève was generally considered worth notice. Its vestments, relics, and windows were of merit, and the view from the tower——

"*Mort de ma vie!*" cried the priest angrily, "do I look like a traveller who trots up belfrys in strange villages at the hour of *déjeuner?* A plague on Saint-Jean-en-Grève! I said nothing at all of churches; I spoke of *déjeuner*, my good fellow. What's for *déjeuner?*"

The innkeeper recounted a series of dishes. Father Hamilton hummed and hawed, reflected, condemned, approved, all with an eagerness beyond description. And when the meal was being dished up, he went frantically to the kitchen and lifted pot-lids, and swung a salad for himself, and confounding the ordinary wine for the vilest *piquette* ordered a special variety from the cellar. It was a spectacle of gourmandise not without its humour; I was so vastly engaged in watching him that I scarce glanced at the men who had travelled on the outside of the coach since morning.

What was my amazement when I did so to see that the servant or valet (as he turned out to be) was no other than the Swiss, Bernard, who had been in the service of Miss Walkinshaw no later than yesterday morning!

I commented on the fact to Father Hamilton when we sat down to eat.

"Why, yes!" he said, gobbling at his vivers with a voracity I learned not to wonder at later when I knew him more. "The same man. A good man, too, or I'm a Turk. I've envied Miss Walkinshaw this lusty, trusty, secret rogue for a good twelvemonth, and just on the eve of my leaving Dunkerque, by a very providence, the fellow gets drunk and finds himself dismissed. He came to me with a flush and a hiccough last night to ask a recommendation, and overlooking the peccadillo that is not of a nature confined to servants, Master Greig, let me tell thee, I gave him a place in my *entourage*. Madame will not like it, but no matter! she'll have time to forget it ere I see her again."

I felt a mild satisfaction to have the Swiss with us just because I had heard him called "Bernard" so often by his late employer.

We rested for some hours after *déjeuner*, seated under a tree by the brink of the rivulet, and in the good humour of a man satisfied in nature the priest condescended to let me into some of his plans.

We were bound for Paris in the first place. "Zounds!" he cried, "I am all impatience to clap eyes again on Lutetia, the sweet rogue, and eat decent bread and behold a noble gown and hear a right cadenza. And though thou hast lost thy Lyrnessides—la! la! la! I have thee there!—thou canst console thyself with the Haemonian lyre. Paris! oh, lad, I'd give all to have thy years and a winter or two in it. Still, we shall make shift—oh, yes! I warrant thee we shall make shift. We shall be there, at my closest reckoning, on the second day of Holy Week, and my health being so poorly we shall not wait to commence *de faire les Pâques* an hour after. What's in a *soutane*, anyhow, that it should be permitted to mortify an honest priest's œsophagus?"

I sighed in spite of myself, for he had made me think of our throwing of Easter eggs on the green at Hazel Den.

"What!" he cried. "Does my frugal Scot fancy

we have not enough trinkgeld for enjoyment. Why, look here !—and here !—and here !"

He thrust his hand into his bosom and drew forth numerous rouleaux—so many that I thought his corpulence might well be a plethora of coin.

"There!" said he, squeezing a rouleau till it burst and spreading out the gold upon the table before him. "Am I a poor parish priest or a very Crœsus?"

Then he scooped in the coins with his fat hands and returned all to his bosom. "*Allons!*" he said shortly; we were on the road again!

That night we put up at the Bon Accueil in a town whose name escapes my recollection.

He had gone to bed; through the wall from his chamber came the noise of his sleep, while I was at the writing of my first letter to Miss Walkinshaw, making the same as free and almost affectionate as I had been her lover, for as I know it now, I was but seeking in her for the face of the love of the first woman and the last my heart was given to.

I had scarcely concluded when the Swiss came knocking softly to my door, and handed me a letter from the very woman whose name was still in wet ink upon my folded page. I tore it open eagerly, to find a score of pleasant remembrances. She had learned the night before that the priest was to set out in the morning: "I have kept my word," she went on. "Your best friend is Bernard, so I let you have him, and let us exchange our billets through him. It will be the most Discreet method. And I am, with every consideration, Ye Ken Wha."

F 2

CHAPTER XX

LEADS ME TO THE FRONT OF A COFFEE-HOUSE WHERE
I AM STARTLED TO SEE A FACE I KNOW

THE occasion for this precaution in our correspondence was beyond my comprehension; nevertheless
I was too proud to have the patronage of so fine a
woman to cavil at what system she should devise
for its discreet conduct, and the Swiss that night
got my first letter to frank and despatch. He got
one next evening also, and the evening after that;
in short, I made a diurnal of each stage in our
journey and Bernard was my postman—so to name
it—on every occasion that I forwarded the same to
Miss Walkinshaw. He assured me that he was in
circumstances to secure the more prompt forwarda-
tion of my epistles than if I trusted in the common
runner, and it was a proof of this that when we got,
after some days, into Versailles, he should bring to
me a letter from the lady herself informing me how
much of pleasure she had got from the receipt of
the first communication I had sent her.

Perhaps it is a sign of the injudicious mind that I
should not be very mightily pleased with this same
Versailles. We had come into it of a sunny after-

noon and quartered at the Cerf d'Or Inn, and went out in the evening for the air. Somehow the place gave me an antagonism; its clipt trees all in rows upon the wayside like a guard of soldiers; its trim gardens and bits of plots; its fountains crying, as it seemed, for attention—these things hurt me as a liberty taken with nature. Here, thought I, is the fitting place for the raff in ruffles and the scented wanton; it should be the artificial man and the insincere woman should be condemned to walk for ever in these alleys and drink in these *bosquets;* I would not give a fir planting black against the evening sky at home for all this pompous play-acting at landscape, nor a yard of the brown heather of the hills for all these well-drilled flower parterres.

"Eh! M. Croque-mort," said the priest, delighted visibly with all he saw about him; "what think'st thou of Le Notre's gardening?"

"A good deal, sir," I said, "that need never be mentioned. I feel a pity for the poor trees as I did for yon clipt poodle dog at Griepon."

"La! la! la! *sois raissonable*, Monsieur," cried the priest. "We cannot have the tastes of our Dubarrys and Pompadours and Maintenons so called in question by an untravelled Scot that knows but the rude mountain and stunted oaks dying in a murrain of climate. 'Art too ingenuous, youth. And yet—and yet"—here he paused and tapped his temple and smiled whimsically—"between ourselves, I prefer the woods of Somme where the birds sang together so jocund t'other day. But there now—ah, *quelle gloire!*"

We had come upon the front of the palace, and its huge far-reaching masonry, that I learned later to regard as cold, formal, and wanting in a soul, vastly discomposed me. I do not know why it should be so, but as I gazed at this—the greatest palace I had ever beheld—I felt tears rush irrestrainably to my eyes. Maybe it was the poor little poet in MacGibbon's law chamber in Lanark town that used to tenant every ancient dwelling with spirits of the past, cropped up for the moment in Father Hamilton's secretary, and made me, in a flash, people the place with kings—and realise something of the wrench it must have been and still would be to each and all of them to say adieu at the long last to this place of noisy grandeur where they had had their time of gaiety and splendour. Anyhow, I well-nigh wept, and the priest was quick to see it.

"'Fore God!" he cried, "here's Andrew Greig again! 'Twas the wickedest rogue ever threw dice, and yet the man must rain at the eyes like a very woman."

And yet he was pleased, I thought, to see me touched. A band was playing somewhere in a garden unseen; he tapped time to its music with his finger tips against each other and smiled beatifically and hummed. He seemed at peace with the world and himself at that moment, yet a second later he was the picture of distress and apprehension.

We were going towards the Place d'Armes; he had, as was customary, his arm through mine, leaning on me more than was comfortable, for he was the poorest judge imaginable of his own corpulence. Of a sudden I felt him jolt as if he had been startled, and then he gripped my arm with a nervous grasp. All that was to account for his perturbation was that among the few pedestrians passing us on the road was one in a uniform who cast a rapid glance at us. It was not wonderful that he should do so, for indeed we were a singularly ill-assorted pair, but there was a recognition of the priest in the glance the man in the uniform threw at him in passing. Nothing was said; the man went on his way and we on ours, but looking at Father Hamilton I saw his face had lost its colour and grown blotched in patches. His hand trembled; for the rest of the walk he was silent, and he could not too soon hurry us back to the Cerf d'Or.

Next day was Sunday, and Father Hamilton went to Mass leaving me to my own affairs, that were not of that complexion perhaps most becoming on that day to a lad from Scotland. He came back anon and dressed most scrupulously in a suit of lay clothing.

"Come out, Master Greig," said he, "and use thine eyes for a poor priest that has ruined his own in studying the Fathers and seeking for honesty."

"It is not in the nature of a compliment to myself, that," I said, a little tired of his sour sentiments regarding humanity, and not afraid in the least to tell him so.

"Eh!" said he. "I spoke not of thee, thou savage. A plague on thy curt temper; 'twas ever the weakness of the Greigs. Come, and I shall show thee a house where thy uncle and I had many a game of dominoes."

We went to a coffee-house and watched the fashionable world go by. It was a sight monstrously fine. Because it was the Easter Sunday the women had on their gayest apparel, the men their most belaced *jabots*.

"Now look you well, Friend Scotland," said Father Hamilton, as we sat at a little table and watched the stream of quality pass, "look you well and watch particularly every gentleman that passes to the right, and when you see one you know tell me quickly."

He had dropped his Roman manner as if in too sober a mood to act.

"Is it a game?" I asked. "Who can I ken in the town of Versailles that never saw me here before?"

"Never mind," said he, "do as I tell you. A sharp eye, and——"

"Why," I cried, "there's a man I have seen before!"

"Where? where?" said Father Hamilton, with the utmost interest lighting his countenance.

"Yonder, to the left of the man with the velvet breeches. He will pass us in a minute or two."

The person I meant would have been kenspeckle in any company by the splendour of his clothing, but beyond his clothing there was a haughtiness in his carriage that singled him out even among the fashionables of Versailles, who were themselves obviously interested in his personality, to judge by

the looks that they gave him as closely as breeding
permitted. He came sauntering along the pavement
swinging a cane by its tassel, his chin in the air, his
eyes anywhere but on the crowds that parted to give
him room. As he came closer I saw it was a handsome face enough that thus was cocked in haughtiness to the heavens, not unlike Clancarty's in that
it showed the same signs of dissipation, yet with
more of native nobility in it than was in the good
enough countenance of the French-Irish nobleman.
Where had I seen that face before?

It must have been in Scotland; it must have been
when I was a boy; it was never in the Mearns.
This was a hat with a Dettingen cock; when I saw
that forehead last it was under a Highland bonnet.

A Highland bonnet—why! yes, and five thousand
Highland bonnets were in its company—whom had
I here but Prince Charles Edward!

The recognition set my heart dirling in my breast,
for there was enough of the rebel in me to feel a
romantic glow at seeing him who set Scotland in a
blaze, and was now the stuff of songs our women
sang in milking folds among the hills; that heads
had fallen for, and the Hebrides had been searched
for in vain for weary seasons. The man was never
a hero of mine so long as I had the cooling influence
of my father to tell me how lamentable for Scotland
had been his success had God permitted the same,
yet I was proud to-day to see him.

"Is it he?" asked the priest, dividing his attention between me and the approaching nobleman.

"It's no other," said I. "I would know Prince

Charles in ten thousand, though I saw him but the once in a rabble of caterans coming up the Gallow-gate of Glasgow."

"Ah," said the priest, with a curious sighing sound. "They said he passed here at the hour. And that's our gentleman, is it? I expected he would have been—would have been different."

When the Prince was opposite the café where we sat he let his glance come to earth, and it fell upon myself. His aspect changed; there was something of recognition in it; though he never slackened his pace and was gazing the next moment down the vista of the street, I knew that his glance had taken me in from head to heel, and that I was still the object of his thoughts.

"You see! you see!" cried the priest, "I was right, and he knew the Greig. Why, lad, shalt have an Easter egg for this—the best horologe in Versailles upon Monday morning."

"Why, how could he know me?" I asked. "It is an impossibility, for when he and I were in the same street last he rode a horse high above an army and I was only a raw laddie standing at a close-mouth in Duff's Land in the Gallowgate."

But all the same I felt the priest was right, and that there was some sort of recognition in the Prince's glance at me in passing.

Father Hamilton poured himself a generous glass and drank thirstily.

"La! la! la!" said he, resuming his customary manner of address. "I daresay his Royal Highness has never clapt eyes on thy *croque-mort* countenance before, but he has seen its like—ay, and had a regard for it, too! Thine Uncle Andrew has done the thing for thee again; the mole, the hair, the face, the shoes—sure they advertise the Greig as by a drum tuck! and Charles Edward knew thy uncle pretty well so I supposed he would know thee. And this is my gentleman, is it? Well, well! No, not at all well; mighty ill indeed. Not the sort of fellow I had looked for at all. Seems a harmless man enough, and has tossed many a goblet in the way of company. If he had been a sour whey-face now——"

Father Hamilton applied himself most industriously to the bottle that afternoon, and it was not long till the last of my respect for him was gone. Something troubled him. He was moody and hilarious by turns, but neither very long, and completed my distrust of him when he intimated that there was some possibility of our trip across Europe never coming into effect. But all the same, I was to be assured of his patronage, I was to continue in his service as secretary, if, as was possible, he should take up his residence for a time in Paris. And money—why, look again! he had a ship's load of it, and 'twould never be said of Father Hamilton that he could not share with a friend. And there he thrust some rouleaux upon me and clapped my shoulder and was so affected at his own love for Andrew Greig's nephew that he must even weep.

Weeping indeed was the priest's odd foible for the week we remained at Versailles. He that had been so jocular before was now filled with morose moods, and would ruminate over his bottle by the hour at a time.

He was none the better for the company he met during our stay at the Cerf d'Or—all priests, and to the number of half a dozen, one of them an abbé with a most noble and reverent countenance. They used to come to him late at night, confer with him secretly in his room, and when they were gone I found him each time drenched in a perspiration and feverishly gulping spirits.

Every day we went to the café where we had seen the Prince first, and every day at the same hour we saw his Royal Highness, who, it appeared, was not known to the world as such, though known to me. The sight of him seemed to trouble Father Hamilton amazingly, and yet 'twas the grand object of the day—its only diversion; when we had seen the Prince we went back straight to the inn every afternoon.

The Cerf d'Or had a courtyard, cobbled with rough stones, in which there was a great and noisy traffic. In the midst of the court there was a little clump of evergreen trees and bushes in tubs, round which were gathered a few tables and chairs whereat —now that the weather was mild—the world sat in the afternoon. The walls about were covered with dusty ivy where sparrows had begun to busy themselves with love and housekeeping; lilacs sprouted into green, and the porter of the house was for ever scratching at the hard earth about the plants, and tying up twigs and watering the pots. It was here

I used to write my letters to Miss Walkinshaw at a little table separate from the rest, and I think it was on Friday I was at this pleasant occupation when I looked up to see the man with the uniform gazing at me from the other side of the bushes as if he were waiting to have the letter when I was done with it.

I went in and asked Father Hamilton who this man was.

"What!" he cried in a great disturbance, "the same as we met near the Trianon! O Lord! Paul, there is something wrong, for that was Buhot."

"And this Buhot?" I asked.

"A police inspector. There is no time to lose. Monsieur Greig, I want you to do an office for me. Here is a letter that must find its way into the hands of the Prince. You will give it to him. You have seen that he passes the café at the same hour every day. Well, it is the easiest thing in the world for you to go up to him and hand him this. No more's to be done by you."

"But why should I particularly give him the letter? Why not send it by the Swiss?"

"That is my affair," cried the priest testily. "The Prince knows you—that is important. He knows the Swiss too, and that is why I have the Swiss with me as a second string to my bow, but I prefer that he should have this letter from the hand of M. Andrew Greig's nephew. 'Tis a letter from his Royal Highness's most intimate friend."

I took the letter into my hand, and was amazed to see that the address was in a writing exactly corresponding to that of a billet now in the bosom of my coat!

What could Miss Walkinshaw and the Prince have of correspondence to be conducted on such roundabout lines? Still, if the letter was hers I must carry it!

"Very well," I agreed, and went out to meet the Prince.

The sun was blazing; the street was full of the quality in their summer clothing. His Royal Highness came stepping along at the customary hour more gay than ever. I made bold to call myself to his attention with my hat in my hand.

"I beg your Royal Highness's pardon," I said in English, "but I have been instructed to convey this letter to you."

He swept his glance over me; pausing longest of all on my red shoes, and took the letter from my hand. He gave a glance at the direction, reddened, and bit his lip.

"Let me see now, what is the name of the gentleman who does me the honour?"

"Greig," I answered. "Paul Greig."

"Ah!" he cried, "of course: I have had friends in Monsieur's family. *Charmé, Monsieur, de faire votre connaissance.* M. Andrew Greig——"

"Was my uncle, your Royal Highness?"

"So! a dear fellow, but, if I remember rightly, with a fatal gift of irony. 'Tis a quality to be used with tact. I hope you have tact, M. Greig. Your good uncle once did me the honour to call me a— what was it now?—a gomeral."

"It was very like my uncle, that, your Royal Highness," I said. "But I know that he loved you and your cause."

"I daresay he did, Monsieur; I daresay he did," said the Prince, flushing, and with a show of pleasure at my speech. "I have learned of late that the fair tongue is not always the friendliest. In spite of it all I liked M. Andrew Greig. I hope I shall have the pleasure of seeing Monsieur Greig's nephew soon again. *Au plaisir de vous revoir !*"

And off he went, putting the letter, unread, into his pocket.

When I went back to the Cerf d'Or and told Hamilton all that had passed, he was straightway plunged into the most unaccountable melancholy.

CHAPTER XXI

THE ATTEMPT ON THE PRINCE

AND now I come to an affair of which there have
been many accounts written, some of them within a
mile or two of the truth, the most but sheer
romantics. I have in my mind notably the account
of the officer Buhot printed two years after the
events in question, in which he makes the most
fabulous statement as to the valiancy of Father
Hamilton's stand in the private house in the Rue
des Reservoirs, and maintains that myself—*le fier
Eccossais*, as he is flattering enough to designate
me—drew my sword upon himself and threatened
to run him through for his proposition that I should
confess to a complicity in the attempt upon his
Royal Highness. I have seen his statement re-
produced with some extra ornament in the *Edinburgh Courant*, and the result of all this is that till
this day my neighbours give me credit, of which I
am loth to advantage myself, for having felled two
or three of the French officers before I was overcome at the hinder-end.

The matter is, in truth, more prosaic as it happened, and if these memorials of mine leave the

shadow of a doubt in the minds of any interested in an old story that created some stir in its time, I pray them see the archives of M. Bertin, the late Lieut.-General of the police. Bertin was no particular friend of mine, that had been the unconscious cause of great trouble and annoyance to him, but he has the truth in the deposition I made and signed prior to my appointment to a company of the d'Auvergne regiment.

Well, to take matters in their right order, it was the evening of the day I had given the letter to the Prince that Father Hamilton expressed his intention of passing that night in the house of a friend.

I looked at him with manifest surprise, for he had been at the bottle most of the afternoon, and was by now more in a state for his bed than for going among friends.

"Well," he cried peevishly, observing my dubiety. "Do you think me too drunk for the society of a parcel of priests? *Ma foi!* it is a pretty thing that I cannot budge from my ordinary habitude of things without a stuck owl setting up a silent protest."

To a speech so wanting in dignity I felt it better there should be no reply, and instead I helped him into his great-coat. As I did so, he made an awkward lurching movement due to his corpulence, and what jumped out of an inner pocket but a pistol? Which of us was the more confused at that it would be hard to say. For my part, the weapon—that I had never seen in his possession before—was a fillip to my sleeping conscience; I picked it up with a distaste, and he took it from me with trembling fingers and an averted look.

"A dangerous place, Versailles, after dark," he explained feebly. "One never knows, one never knows," and into his pocket hurriedly with it.

"I shall be back for breakfast," he went on. "Unless—unless—oh, I certainly shall be back." And off he set.

The incident of the pistol disturbed me for a while. I made a score of speculations as to why a fat priest should burden himself with such an article, and finally concluded that it was as he suggested, to defend himself from night birds if danger offered; though that at the time had been the last thing I myself would have looked for in the well-ordered town of Versailles. I sat in the common-room or *salle* of the inn for a while after he had gone, and thereafter retired to my own bedchamber, meaning to read or write for an hour or two before going to bed. In the priest's room— which was on the same landing and next to my own — I heard the whistle of Bernard the Swiss, but I had no letters for him that evening, and we did not meet each other. I was at first uncommon dull, feeling more than usually the hame-wae that must have been greatly wanting in the experience of my Uncle Andrew to make him for so long a wanderer on the face of the earth. But there is no condition of life so miserable but what one finds in it remissions, diversions, nay, and delights also, and soon I was—of all things in the world to be doing when what followed came to pass !—inditing a song to a lady, my quill scratching across the paper in spurts and dashes, and baffled pauses where the matter would not attend close enough on the mood, stopping altogether at a stanza's end to hum the stuff over to myself with great satisfaction. I was, as I say, in the midst of this; the Swiss had gone downstairs; all in my part of the house was still, though vehicles moved about in the courtyard, when unusually noisy footsteps sounded on the stair, with what seemed like the tap of scabbards on the treads.

It was a sound so strange that my hand flew by instinct to the small sword I was now in the habit of wearing and had learned some of the use of from Thurot.

There was no knock for entrance; the door was boldly opened and four officers with Buhot at their head were immediately in the room.

Buhot intimated in French that I was to consider myself under arrest, and repeated the same in indifferent English that there might be no mistake about a fact as patent as that the sword was in his hand.

For a moment I thought the consequence of my crime had followed me abroad, and that this squat, dark officer, watching me with the scrutiny of a forest animal, partly in a dread that my superior bulk should endanger himself, was in league with the law of my own country. That I should after all be dragged back in chains to a Scots gallows was a prospect unendurable; I put up the ridiculous small sword and dared him to lay a hand on me. But I had no sooner done so than its folly was apparent, and I laid the weapon down.

"*Tant mieux!*" said he, much relieved, and then an assurance that he knew I was a gentleman of discretion and would not make unnecessary trouble. "Indeed," he went on, "*Voyez!* I take these men away; I have the infinite trust in Monsieur; Monsieur and I shall settle this little affair between us."

And he sent his friends to the foot of the stair.

"Monsieur may compose himself," he assured me with a profound inclination.

"I am very much obliged to you," I said, seating myself on the corner of the table and crushing my poor verses into my pocket as I did so, "I am very much obliged to you, but I'm at a loss to understand to what I owe the honour."

"Indeed!" he said, also seating himself on the table to show, I supposed, that he was on terms of confidence with his prisoner. "Monsieur is Father Hamilton's secretary?"

"So I believe," I said; "at least I engaged for the office that's something of a sinecure, to tell the truth."

And then Buhot told me a strange story.

He told me that Father Hamilton was now a prisoner, and on his way to the prison of Bicêtre. He was—this Buhot—something of the artist and loved to make his effects most telling (which accounts, no doubt, for the romantical nature of the accounts aforesaid), and sitting upon the table-edge he embarked upon a narrative of the most crowded two hours that had perhaps been in Father Hamilton's lifetime.

It seemed that when the priest had left the Cerf d'Or, he had gone to a place till recently called the Bureau des Carrosses pour la Rochelle, and now unoccupied save by a concierge, and the property of some person or persons unknown. There he had ensconced himself in the only habitable room and waited for a visitor regarding whom the concierge had his instructions.

"You must imagine him," said the officer, always with the fastidiousness of an artist for his effects, "you must imagine him, Monsieur, sitting in this room, all alone, breathing hard, with a pistol before him on the table, and——"

"What! a pistol!" I cried, astounded and alarmed.

"*Certainement*," said Buhot, charmed with the effect his dramatic narrative was creating. "Your friend, *mon ami*, would be little good, I fancy, with a rapier. Anyway, 'twas a pistol. A carriage drives up to the door; the priest rises to his feet with the pistol in his hand; there is the rap at the door. '*Entrez!*' cries the priest, cocking the pistol, and no sooner was his visitor within than he pulled the trigger; the explosion rang through the dwelling; the chamber was full of smoke."

"Good heavens!" I cried in horror, "and who was the unhappy wretch?"

Buhot shrugged his shoulders, made a French gesture with his hands, and pursed his mouth.

"Whom did you invite to the room at the hour of ten, M. Greig?" he asked.

"Invite!" I cried. "It's your humour to deal in parables. I declare to you I invited no one."

"And yet, my good sir, you are Hamilton's secretary and you are Hamilton's envoy. 'Twas you handed to the Prince the *poulet* that was designed to bring him to his fate."

My instinct grasped the situation in a second; I had been the ignorant tool of a madman; the whole events of the past week made the fact plain, and I was for the moment stunned.

Buhot watched me closely, and not unkindly, I can well believe, from what I can recall of our interview and all that followed after it.

"And you tell me he killed the Prince?" I cried at last.

"No, Monsieur," said Buhot; "I am happy to say he did not. The Prince was better advised than to accept the invitation you sent to him."

"Still," I cried with remorse, "there's a man dead, and 'tis as much as happens when princes themselves are clay."

"*Parfaitement*, Monsieur, though it is indiscreet to shout it here. Luckily there is no one at all dead in this case, otherwise it had been myself, for I was the man who entered to the priest and received his pistol fire. It was not the merriest of duties either," he went on, always determined I should lose no iota of the drama, "for the priest might have discovered before I got there that the balls of his pistol had been abstracted."

"Then Father Hamilton has been under watch?"

"Since ever you set foot in Versailles last

Friday," said Buhot complacently. "The Damiens affair has sharpened our wits, I warrant you."

"Well, sir," I said, "let me protest that I have been till this moment in utter darkness about Hamilton's character or plans. I took him for what he seemed—a genial buffoon of a kind with more gear than guidance."

"We cannot, with infinite regret, assume that, Monsieur, but personally I would venture a suggestion," said Buhot, coming closer on the table and assuming an affable air. "In this business, Hamilton is a tool—no more; and a poor one at that, badly wanting the grindstone. To break him—phew!—'twere as easy as to break a glass, but he is one of a great movement and the man we seek is his master—one Father Fleuriau of the Jesuits. Hamilton's travels were but part of a great scheme that has sent half a dozen of his kind chasing the Prince in the past year or two from Paris to Amsterdam, from Amsterdam to Orleans, from Orleans to Hamburg, Seville, Lisbon, Rome, Brussels, Potsdam, Nuremburg, Berlin. The same hand that extracted his bullets tapped the priest's portfolio and found the wretch was in promise of a bishopric and a great sum of money. You see, M. Greig, I am curiously frank with my prisoner."

"And no doubt you have your reasons," said I, but beat, myself, to imagine what they could be save that he might have proofs of my innocence.

"Very well," said M. Buhot. "To come to the point, it is this, that we desire to have the scheme of the Jesuits for the Prince's assassination, and other atrocities shocking to all that revere the divinity of princes, crumbled up. Father Hamilton is at the very roots of the secret; if, say, a gentleman so much in his confidence as yourself—now, if such a one were, say, to share a cell with this regicide for a night or two, and pursue judicious inquiries——"

"Stop! stop!" I cried, my blood hammering in my head, and the words like to choke me. "Am I to understand that you would make me your spy and informer upon this miserable old madman that has led me such a gowk's errand?"

Buhot slid back off the table edge and on to his feet.

"Oh," said he, "the terms are not happily chosen: 'spy'—'informer'—come, Monsieur Greig; this man is in all but the actual accomplishment of his purpose an assassin. 'Tis the duty of every honest man to help in discovering the band of murderers whose tool he has been."

"Then I'm no honest man, M. Buhot," said I bitterly, "for I've no stomach for a duty so dirty."

"Think of it for a moment," he pressed, with evident surprise at my decision. "Bicêtre is an unwholesome hostelry, I give you my word. Consider that your choice is between a night or two there and—who knows?—a lifetime of Galbanon that is infinitely worse."

"Then let it be Galbanon!" I said, and lifted my sword and slapped it furiously, sheathed as it was, like a switch upon the table.

Buhot leaped back in a fear that I was to attack him, and cried his men from the stair foot.

"This force is not needed at all," I said. "I am innocent enough to be prepared to go quietly."

CHAPTER XXII

OF A NIGHT JOURNEY AND BLACK BICÊTRE
AT THE END OF IT

'Twas a long journey to the prison of Bicêtre, which
is two miles to the south of the city of Paris, a great
building that had once (they say) been a palace, but
now in the time of my experience was little better
than a vestibule of hell.   I was driven to it through
a black loud night of rain, a plunging troop of horse
on either hand the coach as if I were a traveller of
state, and Buhot in front of me as silent as the
priest had been the day we left Dunkerque, though
wakeful, and the tip of his scabbard leaning on my
boot to make sure that in the darkness no movement of mine should go unobserved.

The trees swung and roared in the wind; the
glass lozens of the carriage pattered to the pelting
showers; sometimes we lurched horribly in the ruts
of the highway, and were released but after monstrous efforts on the part of the cavaliers.   Once,
as we came close upon a loop of a brawling river,
I wished with all fervency that we might fall in,
and so end for ever this pitiful coil of trials whereto
fate had obviously condemned poor Paul Greig.   To
die among strangers (as is widely known) is counted

the saddest of deaths by our country people, and so, nowadays, it would seem to myself, but there and then it appeared an enviable conclusion to the Spoiled Horn that had blundered from folly to folly. To die there and then would be to leave no more than a regret and an everlasting wonder in the folks at home; to die otherwise, as seemed my weird, upon a block or gallows, would be to foul the name of my family for generations, and I realised in my own person the agony of my father when he got the news, and I bowed my shoulders in the coach below the shame that he would feel as in solemn blacks he walked through the Sabbath kirkyard in summers to come in Mearns, with the knowledge that though neighbours looked not at him but with kindness, their inmost thoughts were on the crimson chapter of his son.

Well, we came at the long last to Bicêtre, and I was bade alight in the flare of torches. A strange, a memorable scene; it will never leave me. Often I remit me there in dreams. When I came out of the conveyance the lights dazzled me, and Buhot put his hands upon my shoulders and turned me without a word in the direction he wished me to take. It was through a vast and frowning doorway that led into a courtyard so great that the windows on the other side seemed to be the distance of a field. The windows were innumerable, and though the hour was late they were lit in stretching corridors. Fires flamed in corners of the yard—great leaping fires round which warders (as I guessed them) gathered to dry themselves or get warmth against the chill of the early April morning. Their scabbards or their muskets glittered now and then in the light of the flames; their voices—restrained by the presence of Buhot—sounded deep and dreadful to me that knew not the sum of his iniquity yet could shudder at the sense of what portended.

It were vain for me to try and give expression to my feeling as I went past these fires across the stony yard, and entered between a guard or two at the other side. At the root of my horror was the sentiment that all was foreign, that I was no more to these midnight monsters round their torturing flames than a creature of the wood, less, perhaps, for were they not at sworn war with my country-men, and had not I a share at least of the repute of regicide? And when, still led by the silent officer, I entered the building itself and walked through an unending corridor broken at intervals by black doors and little barred borrowed lights, and heard sometimes a moan within, or a shriek far off in another part of the building, I experienced some-thing of that long swound that is insanity. Then I was doomed for the rest of my brief days to be among these unhappy wretches—the victims of the law or political vengeance, the *forçat* who had thieved, or poisoned, perjured himself, or taken human blood!

At last we came to a door, where Buhot stopped me and spoke, for the first time, almost, since we had left Versailles. He put his hand out to check a warder who was going to open the cell for my entrance.

"I am not a hard man, M. Greig," said he, in a

G

stumbling English, "and though this is far beyond my duties, and, indeed, contrary to the same, I would give you another chance. We shall have, look you, our friend the priest in any case, and to get the others is but a matter of time. 'Tis a good citizen helps the law always; you must have that respect for the law that you should feel bound to circumvent those who would go counter to it with your cognisance."

"My good man," I said, as quietly as I could, and yet internally with feelings like to break me, "I have already said my say. If the tow was round my thrapple I would say no more than that I am innocent of any plot against a man by whose family mine have lost, and that I myself, for all my loyalty to my country, would do much to serve as a private individual."

"Consider," he pleaded. "After all, this Hamilton may be a madman with nothing at all to tell that will help us."

"But the bargain is to be that I must pry and I must listen," said I, "and be the tale-pyat whose work may lead to this poor old buffoon's and many another's slaughtering. Not I, M. Buhot, and thank ye kindly! It's no' work for one of the Greigs of Hazel Den."

"I fear you do not consider all," he said patiently—so patiently indeed that I wondered at him. "I will show you to what you are condemned even before your trial, before you make up your mind irrevocably to refuse this very reasonable request of ours," and he made a gesture that caused the warder to open the door so that I could see within.

There was no light of its own in the cell, but it borrowed wanly a little of the radiance of the corridor, and I could see that it was bare to the penury of a mausoleum, with a stone floor, a wooden palliasse, and no window other than a barred hole above the door. There was not even a stool to sit on. But I did not quail.

"I have been in more comfortable quarters, M. Buhot," I said, "but in none that I could occupy with a better conscience." Assuming with that a sort of bravado, I stepped in before he asked me.

"Very good," he cried; "but I cannot make you my felicitations on your decision, M. Greig," and without more ado he had the door shut on me.

I sat on the woollen palliasse for a while, with my head on my hands, surrendered all to melancholy; and then, though the thing may seem beyond belief, I stretched myself and slept till morning. It was not the most refreshing of sleep, but still 'twas wonderful that I should sleep at all in such circumstances, and I take it that a moorland life had been a proper preparation for just such trials.

When I wakened in the morning the prison seemed full of eerie noises—of distant shrieks as in a bedlam, and commanding voices, and of ringing metals, the clank of fetters, or the thud of musket-butts upon the stones. A great beating of feet was in the yard, as if soldiers were manœuvring, and it mastered me to guess what all this might mean, until a warder opened my door and ordered me out for an airing.

I mind always of a parrot at a window.

This window was one that looked into the yard from some official's dwelling in that dreadful place, and the bird occupied a great cage that was suspended from a nail outside.

The bird, high above the rabble of rogues in livery, seemed to have a devilish joy in the spectacle of the misery tramping round and round beneath, for it clung upon the bars and thrust out its head to whistle, as if in irony, or taunt us with a foul song. There was one air it had, expressed so clearly that I picked up air and words with little difficulty, and the latter ran something like this :

> *Ah ! ah ! Pierrot, Pierrot !*
> *Fais ta toilette,*
> *Voila le barbier, oh ! oh !*
> *Et sa charrette—*

all in the most lugubrious key.

And who were we that heard that reference to the axe ? We were the scum, the *sordes*, the rot of France. There was, doubtless, no crime before the law of the land, no outrage against God and man, that had not here its representative. We were not men, but beasts, cut off from every pleasant—every clean and decent association, the visions of sin always behind the peering eyes, the dreams of vice and crime for ever fermenting in the low brows. I felt 'twas the forests we should be frequenting—the forests of old, the club our weapon, the cave our habitation ; no song ours, nor poem, no children to

infect with fondness, no women to smile at in the
light of evening lamps. The forest—the cave—
the animal! What were we but children of the
outer dark, condemned from the start of time, our
faces ground hard against the flints, our feet bogged
in hag and mire?

There must have been several hundreds of the
convicts in the yard, and yet I was told later that it
was not a fourth of the misery that Bicêtre held,
and that scores were leaving weekly for the *bagnes*
—the hulks at Toulon and at Brest—while others
took their places.

Every man wore a uniform—a coarse brown
jacket, vast wide breeches of the same hue, a high
sugar-loaf cap and wooden shoes—all except some
privileged, whereof I was one—and we were divided
into gangs, each gang with its warders—tall grenadiers with their muskets ready.

Round and round and across and across we
marched in the great quadrangle, every man tread-
ing the rogues' measure with leg-weary reluctance,
many cursing their warders under breath, most
scowling, all hopeless and all lost.

'Twas the exercise of the day.

As we slouched through that mad ceremony in
the mud of the yard, with rain still drizzling on us,
the parrot in its cage had a voice loud and shrill
above the commands of the grenadiers and officers;
sang its taunting song, or whistled like a street boy,
a beast so free, so careless and remote, that I had a
fancy it had the only soul in the place.

As I say, we were divided into gangs, each gang

taking its own course back and forward in the yard as its commander ordered. The gang I was with marched a little apart from the rest. We were none of us in this gang in the ugly livery of the prison, but in our own clothing, and we were, it appeared, allowed that privilege because we were yet to try. I knew no reason for the distinction at the time, nor did I prize it very much, for looking all about the yard—at the officers, the grenadiers, and other functionaries of the prison, I failed to see a single face I knew. What could I conclude but that Buhot was gone and that I was doomed to be forgotten here?

It would have been a comfort even to have got a glimpse of Father Hamilton, the man whose machinations were the cause of my imprisonment, but Father Hamilton, if he had been taken here as Buhot had suggested, was not, at all events, in view.

After the morning's exercise we that were the privileged were taken to what was called the *salle d'épreuve*, and with three or four to each *gamelle* or mess-tub, ate a scurvy meal of a thin soup and black bread and onions. To a man who had been living for a month at heck and manger, as we say, this might naturally seem unpalatable fare, but truth to tell I ate it with a relish that had been all the greater had it been permitted me to speak to any of my fellow sufferers. But speech was strictly interdict and so our meal was supped in silence.

When it was over I was to be fated for the pleasantest of surprises!

There came to me a sous-officer of the grenadiers.

In French he asked if I was Monsieur Greig. I said as best I could in the same tongue that I was that unhappy person at his service. Then, said he, "Come with me." He led me into a hall about a hundred feet long that had beds or mattresses for about three hundred people. The room was empty, as those who occupied it were, he said, at Mass. Its open windows in front looked into another court-yard from that in which we had been exercising, while the windows at the rear looked into a garden where already lilac was in bloom and daffodillies endowed the soil of a few mounds with the colour of the gold. On the other side of the court first named there was a huge building. "Galbanon," said my guide, pointing to it, and then made me understand that the same was worse by far than the Bastille, and at the moment full of Marquises, Counts, Jesuits, and other clergymen, many of them in irons for abusing or writing against the Marchioness de Pompadour.

I listened respectfully and waited Monsieur's explanation. It was manifest I had not been brought into this hall for the good of my education, and naturally I concluded the name of Galbanon, that I had heard already from Buhot, with its villainous reputation, was meant to terrify me into a submission to what had been proposed. The moment after a hearty meal—even of *soup maigre*—was not, however, the happiest of times to work upon a Greig's feelings of fear or apprehension, and so I waited, very dour within upon my resolution though outwardly in the most complacent spirit.

The hall was empty when we entered as I have said, but we had not been many minutes in it when the tramp of men returning to it might be heard, and this hurried my friend the officer to his real business.

He whipped a letter from his pocket and put it in my hand with a sign to compel secrecy on my part. It may be readily believed I was quick enough to conceal the missive. He had no cause to complain of the face I turned upon another officer who came up to us, for 'twas a visage of clownish vacuity.

The duty of the second officer, it appeared, was to take me to a new cell that had been in preparation for me, and when I got there it was with satisfaction I discovered it more than tolerable, with a sufficiency of air and space, a good light from the quadrangle, a few books, paper, and a writing standish.

When the door had been shut upon me, I turned to open my letter and found there was in fact a couple of them—a few lines from her ladyship in Dunkerque expressing her continued interest in my welfare and adventures, and another from the Swiss through whom the first had come. He was still— said the honest Bernard—at my service, having eluded the vigilance of Buhot, who doubtless thought a lackey scarce worth his hunting, and he was still in a position to post my letters, thanks to the good-will of the sous-officer who was a relative. Further-more, he was in hopes that Miss Walkinshaw, who was on terms of intimacy with the great world and something of an *intriguante*, would speedily take steps to secure my freedom. " Be tranquil, dear Monsieur ! " concluded the brave fellow, and I was so exceedingly comforted and inspired by these matters that I straightway sat down to the continuation of my journal for Miss Walkinshaw's behoof. I had scarce dipped the pen, when my cell door opened and gave entrance to the man who was the cause of my incarceration.

The door shut and locked behind him; it was Father Hamilton !

CHAPTER XXIII

FATHER HAMILTON MANIFESTS A STRANGE SATISFACTION IN THE ODDEST CIRCUMSTANCES

IT was indeed Father Hamilton, by all appearance none the worse in body for his violent escapade, so weighty with the most fatal possibilities for himself, for he advanced to me almost gaily, his hand extended and his face red and smiling.

"Scotland! to my heart!" cries he in the French, and throws his arms about me before I could resist, and kisses me on the cheeks after the amusing fashion of his nation. "La! la! la! Paul," he cried, "I'd have wanted three breakfasts sooner than miss this meeting with my good secretary lad that is the lovablest rogue never dipped a pen in his master's service. Might have been dead for all I knew, and run through by a brutal rapier, victim of thine own innocence. But here's my Paul, *pardieu!* I would as soon have my *croque-mort* now as that jolly dog his uncle, that never waked till midnight or slept till the dull, uninteresting noon in the years when we went roving. What! Paul! Paul Greig! my *croque-mort!* my Don Dolorous!—oh, Lord, my child, I am the most miserable of wretches!"

And there he let me go, and threw himself upon a chair, and gave his vast body to a convulsion of arid sobs. The man was in hysterics, compounding smiles and sobs a score to the minute, but at the end 'twas the natural man won the bout, else he had taken a stroke. I stood by him in perplexity of opinions whether to laugh or storm, whether to give myself to the righteous horror a good man ought to feel in the presence of a murtherer, or shrug my shoulders tolerantly at the imbecile.

"There!" said he, recovering his natural manner, "I have made a mortal enemy of Andrew Greig's nephew. Yes, yes, master, glower at Misery, fat Misery—and the devil take it!—old Misery, without a penny in 'ts pocket, and its next trip upon wheels a trip to the block to nuzzle at the dirty end in damp sawdust a nose that has appreciated the bouquet of the rarest wines. Paul, my boy, has't a pinch of snuff? A brutal bird out there sings a stave of the *Chanson de la Veuve* so like the confounded thing that I heard my own foolish old head drop into the basket, and there! I swear to you the smell of the sawdust is in my nostrils now."

I handed him my box; 'twas a mull my Uncle Andy gave me before he died, made of the horn of a young bullock, with a blazon of the house on the silver lid. He took it eagerly and drenched himself with the contents.

"Oh, la! la!" he cried; "I give thanks. My head was like yeast. I wish it were Christmas last, and a man called Hamilton was back in Dixmunde parish. But there! that is enough, I have made my bed and I must lie on't, with a blight on all militant jesuitry! When last I had this box in my fingers they were as steady as Mont St. Michel, now look—they are trembling like aspen, *n'est-ce pas?* And all that's different is that I have eaten one or two better dinners and cracked a few pipkins of better wine, and—and—well-nigh killed a police officer. Did'st ever hear of one Hamilton, M. Greig? 'Twas a cheery old fellow in Dixmunde whose name was the same as mine, and had a garden and bee-hives, and I am on the rack for my sins."

He might be on the rack—and, indeed, I daresay the man was in a passion of feelings so that he knew not what he was havering about, but what impressed me most of all about him was that he seemed to have some momentary gleams of satisfaction in his situation.

"I have every ground of complaint against you, sir," I said.

"What!" he interrupted. "Would'st plague an old man with complaints when M. de Paris is tapping him on the shoulder to come away and smell the sawdust of his own coffin? Oh, 'tis not in this wise thy uncle had done, but no matter!"

"I have no wish, Father Hamilton, to revile you for what you have brought me," I hastened to tell him. "That is far from my thoughts, though now that you put me in mind of it, there is some ground for my blaming you if blaming was in my intention. But I shall blame you for this, that you are a priest of the Church and a Frenchman, and yet did draw a murderous hand upon a prince of your own country."

This took him somewhat aback. He helped himself to another voluminous pinch of my snuff to give him time for a rejoinder and then—"Regicide, M. Greig, is sometimes to be defended when——"

"Regicide!" I cried, losing all patience, "give us the plain English of it, Father Hamilton, and call it murder. To call it by a Latin name makes it none the more respectable a crime against the courts of heaven where the curse of Babel has an end. But for an accident, or the cunning of others, you had a corpse upon your conscience this day, and your name had been abhorred throughout the whole of Europe."

He put his shoulders up till his dew-laps fell in massive folds.

"'Fore God!" said he, "here's a treatise in black letter from Andrew Greig's nephew. It comes indifferently well, I assure thee, from Andrew's nephew. Those who live in glass houses, *cher ami*, —those who live in glass houses——"

He tapped me upon the breast with his fat finger and paused, with a significant look upon his countenance.

"Oh, ye can out with it, Father Hamilton!" I cried, certain I knew his meaning.

"Those who live in glass houses," said he, "should have some pity for a poor old devil out in the weather without a shelter of any sort."

"You were about to taunt me with my own unhappy affair," I said, little relishing his consideration.

"Was I, M. Greig?" he said softly. "Faith! a glass residence seems to breed an ungenerous disposition! If thou can'st credit me I know nothing of thine affair beyond what I may have suspected from a Greig travelling hurriedly and in red shoes. I make you my compliments, Monsieur, of your morality that must be horror-struck at my foolish play with a pistol, yet thinks me capable of a retort so vile as that you indicate. My dear lad, I but spoke of what we have spoken of together before in our happy chariot in the woods of Somme—thine uncle's fate, and all I expected was, that remembering the same, thou his nephew would'st have enough tolerance for an old fool to leave his punishment in the hands of the constitute authority. *Voilà!* I wish to heaven they had given me another cell, after all, that I might have imagined thy pity for one that did thee no harm, or at least meant to do none, which is the main thing with all our acts else Purgatory's more crowded than I fancy."

He went wearily over to the fire and spread his trembling hands to the blaze; I looked after him perplexed in my mind, but not without an overpowering pity.

"I have come, like thyself, doubtless," he said after a little, "over vile roads in a common cart, and lay awake last night in a dungeon—a pretty conclusion to my excursion! And yet I am vastly more happy to-day than I was this time yesterday morning."

"But then you were free," I said, "you had all you need wish for—money, a conveyance, servants, leisure——"

"And M. Croque-mort's company," he added with

a poor smile. "True, true! But the thing was then to do," and he shuddered. "Now my part is done, 'twas by God's grace a failure, and I could sing for content like one of the little birds we heard the other day in Somme."

He could not but see my bewilderment in my face.

"You wonder at that," said he, relinquishing the Roman manner as he always did when most in earnest. "Does Monsieur fancy a poor old priest can take to the ancient art of assassination with an easy mind? *Nom de nom!* I could skip to the block like a ballet-dancer if 'twere either that or live the past two days over again and fifty years after. I have none of the right stomach for murder; that's flat! 'tis a business that keeps you awake too much at night, and disturbs the gastric essence; calls, too, for a confounded agility that must be lacking in a person of my handsome and plenteous bulk. I had rather go fishing any day in the week than imbrue. When Buhot entered the room where I waited for a less worthy man and I fired honestly for my money and missed, I could have died of sheer rapture. Instead I threw myself upon his breast and embraced him."

"He said none of that to me."

"Like enough not, but 'tis true none the less, though he may keep so favourable a fact out of his records. A good soul enough, Buhot! We knew him, your uncle and I, in the old days when I was thinner and played a good game of chess at three in the morning. Fancy Ned Hamilton cutting short the glorious career of old Buhot! I'd sooner pick a pocket."

"Or kill a prince!"

"Felicitations on your wit, M. Greig! Heaven help the elderly when the new wit is toward! *N'importe!* Perhaps 'twere better to kill some princes than to pick a pocket. Is it not better, or less wicked, let us say, to take the life of a man villainously abusing it than the purse of a poor wretch making the most of his scanty *livres?*"

And then the priest set out upon his defence. It is too long here to reproduce in his own words, even if I recalled them, and too specious in its terms for the patience of the honest world of our time. With his hands behind his back he marched up and down the room for the space of a half-hour at the least, recounting all that led to his crime. The tale was like a wild romance, but yet, as we know now, true in every particular. He was of the Society of Jesus, had lived a stormy youth, and fallen in later years into a disrepute in his own parish, and there the heads of his Society discovered him a very likely tool for their purposes. They had only half convinced him that the death of Charles Edward was for the glory of God and the good of the Church when they sent him marching with a pistol and £500 in bills of exchange and letters of credit upon a chase that covered a great part of three or four countries, and ended at Lisbon, when a German Jesuit in the secret gave him ten crusadoes to bring him home with his task unaccomplished.

"I have what amounts almost to a genius for

losing the opportunities of which I do not desire to avail myself," said Father Hamilton with a whimsical smile.

And then he had lain in disgrace with the Jesuits for a number of years until it became manifest (as he confessed with shame) that his experience of leisure, wealth, and travel had enough corrupted him to make the prospect of a second adventure of a similar kind pleasing. At that time Charles, lost to the sight of Europe, and only discovered at brief and tantalising intervals by the Jesuit agents, scarce slept two nights in the same town, but went from country to country *incognito*, so that 'twas no trivial task Father Hamilton undertook to run him to earth.

"The difficulty of it—indeed the small likelihood there was of my ever seeing him," he said, "was what mainly induced me to accept the office, though in truth it was compelled. I was doing very well at Dunkerque," he went on, "and very happy if I had never heard more of prince or priesthood, when Father Fleuriau sent me a hurried intimation that my victim was due at Versailles on Easter and ordered my instant departure there."

The name of Fleuriau recalled me to my senses. "Stop, stop, Father Hamilton!" I cried, "I must hear no more."

"What!" said he, bitterly, "is't too good a young gentleman to listen to the confession of a happy murderer that has failed at his trade?"

"I have no feeling left but pity," said I, almost like to weep at this, "but you have been put into this cell along with me for a purpose."

"And what might that be, M. Greig?" he asked, looking round about him, and seeing for the first time, I swear, the sort of place he was in. "Faith! it is comfort, at any rate; I scarce noticed that, in my pleasure at seeing Paul Greig again."

"You must not tell me any more of your Jesuit plot, nor name any of those involved in the same, for Buhot has been at me to cock an ear to everything you may say in that direction, and betray you and your friends. It is for that he has put us together into this cell."

"*Pardieu!* am not I betrayed enough already?" cried the priest, throwing up his hands. "I'll never deny my guilt."

"Yes," I said, "but they want the names of your fellow conspirators, and Buhot says they never expect them directly from you."

"He does, does he?" said the priest, smiling. "Faith, M. Buhot has a good memory for his friend's characteristics. No, M. Greig, if they put this comfortable carcase to the rack itself. And was that all thy concern? Well, as I was saying—let us speak low lest some one be listening—this Father Fleuriau——"

Again I stopped him.

"You put me into a hard position, Father Hamilton," I said. "My freedom—my life, perhaps—depends on whether I can tell them your secret or not, and here you throw it in my face."

"And why not?" he asked, simply. "I merely wish to show myself largely the creature of circumstances, and so secure a decent Scot's most favourable opinion of me before the end."

"But I might be tempted to betray you."

The old eagle looked again out at his eyes. He gently slapped my cheek with a curious touch of fondness almost womanly, and gave a low, contented laugh.

"*Farceur!*" he said. "As if I did not know my Don Dolorous, my merry Andrew's nephew!"

His confidence hugely moved me, and, lest he should think I feared to trust myself with his secrets, I listened to the remainder of his story, which I shall not here set down, as it bears but slightly on my own narrative, and may even yet be revealed only at cost of great distress among good families, not only on the Continent but in London itself.

When he had done, he thanked me for listening so attentively to a matter that was so much on his mind that it gave him relief to share it with some one. "And not only for that, M. Greig," said he, "are my thanks due, for you saved the life that might have been the prince's instead of my old gossip, Buhot's. To take the bullet out of my pistol was the device your uncle himself would have followed in the like circumstances."

"But I did not do that!" I protested.

He looked incredulous.

"Buhot said as much," said he; "he let it out unwittingly that I had had my claws clipped by my own household."

"Then assuredly not by me, Father Hamilton."

"So!" said he, half incredulous, and a look of speculation came upon his countenance.

CHAPTER XXIV

PHILOSOPHY IN A FELON'S CELL

IT seemed for a while as if we were fated to lie for-gotten in Bicêtre till the crack of doom; not that we were many days there when all was done, but that in our natural hourly expectation at first of being called forth for trial the hours passed so sluggishly that Time seemed finally to sleep, and a week, to our fancy—to mine at all events—seemed a month at the most modest computation.

I should have lost my reason but for the com-pany of the priest, who, for considerations best known to others and to me monstrously inadequate, was permitted all the time to share my cell. In his singular society there was a recreation that kept me from too feverishly brooding on my wrongs, and his character every day presented fresh features of interest and admiration. He had become quite cheerful again, and as content in the confine of his cell as he had been when the glass coach was jolting over the early stages of what had been intended for a gay procession round the courts of Europe. Once more he affected the Roman manner 'hat was due to his devotion to Shakespeare and

L'Estrange's Seneca, and "Clarissa Harlowe," a knowledge of which, next to the Scriptures, he counted the first essentials for a polite education. I protest he grew fatter every day, and for ease his corpulence was at last saved the restraint of buttons, which was an indolent indulgence so much to his liking that of itself it would have reconciled him to spend the remainder of his time in prison.

" *Tiens !* Paul," he would say, " here's an old fool has blundered through the greater part of his life without guessing till now how easy a thing content is to come by. Why, 'tis no more than a loose waistcoat and a chemise unbuttoned at the neck. I dared not be happy thus in Dixmunde, where the folks were plaguily particular that their priest should be point-devise, as if mortal man had time to tend his soul and keep a constant eye on the lace of his fall."

And he would stretch himself—a very mountain of sloth—in his chair.

With me 'twas different. Even in a gaol I felt sure a day begun untidily was a day ill-done by. If I had no engagements with the fastidious fashionable world I had engagements with myself; moreover, I shared my father's sentiment, that a good day's darg of work with any thinking in it was never done in a pair of slippers down at the heel. Thus I was as perjink (as we say) in Bicêtre as I would have been at large in the genteel world.

"Not," he would admit, " but that I love to see thee in a decent habit, and so constant plucking at thy hose, for I have been young myself, and had some right foppish follies, too. But now, my good man Dandiprat, my *petit-maître*, I am old—oh, so old!—and know so much of wisdom, and have seen such a confusion of matters, that I count comfort the greatest of blessings. The devil fly away with buttons and laces! say I, that have been parish priest of Dixmunde—and happily have not killed a man nor harmed a flea, though like enough to get killed myself."

The weather was genial, yet he sat constantly hugging the fire, and I at the window, which happily gave a prospect of the yard between our building and that of Galbanon. I would be looking out there, and perhaps pining for freedom, while he went prating on upon the scurviest philosophy surely ever man gave air to.

"Behold, my scrivener, how little man wants for happiness! My constant fear in Dixmunde was that I would become so useless for all but eating and sleeping, when I was old, that no one would guarantee me either; poverty took that place at my table the skull took among the Romans—the thought on't kept me in a perpetual apprehension. *Nom de chien!* and this was what I feared—this, a hard lodging, coarse viands, and sour wine! What was the fellow's name?—Demetrius, upon the taking of Megara, asked Monsieur Un-tel the Philosopher what he had lost. 'Nothing at all,' said he, 'for I have all that I could call my own about me,' and yet 'twas no more than the skin he stood in. A cell in Bicêtre would have been paradise to such a gallant fellow. Oh, Paul, I fear thou may'st be ungrateful

to this good Buhot, who has given us such a fine
lodging, and saved us the care of providing for ourselves."

"'Tis all very well, father," I said, leaning on the
sill of the window, and looking at a gang of prisoners
being removed from one part of Galbanon to another
—"'tis all very well, but I mind a priest that thought
jaunting round the country in a chariot the pinnacle
of bliss. And that was no further gone than a fortnight ago."

"Bah!" said he, and stretched his fat fingers to
the fire; "he that cannot live happily anywhere
will live happily nowhere at all. What avails travel,
if Care waits like a hostler to unyoke the horses at
every stage? I tell thee, my boy, I never know
what a fine fellow is Father Hamilton till I have
him by himself at a fireside; 'tis by firesides all the
wisest notions come to one."

"I wish there came a better dinner than to-day's,"
said I, for we had agreed an hour ago that smoked
soup was not very palatable.

"La! la! la! there goes Sir Gourmet!" cried
his reverence. "Have I infected this poor Scot
that ate naught but oats ere he saw France, with
mine own fever for fine feeding from which, praise
le bon Dieu! I have recovered? 'Tis a brutal
entertainment, and unworthy of man, to place his
felicity in the service of his senses. I maintain
that even smoked soup is pleasant enough on the
palate of a man with an easy conscience, and a mind
purged of vulgar cares."

"And you can be happy here, Father Hamilton?"

I asked, astonished at such sentiments from a man before so ill to please.

He heaved like a mountain in travail, and brought forth a peal of laughter out of all keeping with our melancholy situation.

"Happy!" said he, "I have never been happy for twenty years till Buhot clapped claw upon my wrist. Thou may'st have seen a sort of mask of happiness, a false face of jollity in Dunkerque parlours, and heard a well-simulated laughter now and then as we drank by wayside inns, but may I be called coxcomb if the miserable wretch who play-acted then was half so light of heart as this that sits here at ease, and has only one regret—that he should have dragged Andrew Greig's nephew into trouble with him. What man can be perfectly happy that runs the risk of disappointment—which is the case of every man that fears or hopes for anything? Here am I, too old for the flame of love or the ardour of ambition; all that knew me and understood me best and liked me most are dead long since. I have a state palace prepared for me free; a domestic in livery to serve my meals; parishioners do not vex me with their trifling little hackneyed sins, and my conclusion seems like to come some morning after an omelet and a glass of wine."

I could not withhold a shudder.

"But to die that way, Father!" I said.

"C'est ègal!" said he, and crossed himself. "We must all die somehow, and I had ever a dread of a stone. Come, come, M. Croque-mort, enough

of thy confounded dolours! I'll be hanged if thou
did'st not steal these shoes, and art after all but an
impersonator of a Greig. The lusty spirit thou
call'st thine uncle would have used his teeth ere
now to gnaw his way through the walls of Bicêtre,
and here thou must stop to converse cursedly on
death to the fatted ox that smells the blood of the
abattoir—oh lad, give's thy snuff-box, sawdust
again!"

Thus by the hour went on the poor wretch,
resigned most obviously to whatever was in store
for him, not so much from a native courage, I fear,
as from a plethora of flesh that smothered every
instinct of self-preservation. As for me I kept up
hope for three days that Buhot would surely come
to test my constancy again, and when that seemed
unlikely, when day after day brought the same
routine, the same cell with Hamilton, the same brief
exercise in the yard, the same vulgar struggle at the
gamelle in the *salle d'épreuve*—I could have welcomed Galbanon itself as a change, even if it meant
all the horror that had been associated with it by
Buhot and my friend the sous-officer.

Galbanon! I hope it has long been levelled with
the dust, and even then I know the ghosts of those
there tortured in their lives will habitate the same
in whirling eddies, for a constant cry for generations
has gone up to heaven from that foul spot. It must
have been a devilish ingenuity, an invention of all
the impish courts below, that placed me at a window
where Galbanon faced me every hour of the day or
night, its horror all revealed. I have seen in the

pool of Earn in autumn weather, when the river was in spate, dead leaves and broken branches borne down dizzily upon the water to toss madly in the linn at the foot of the fall; no less helpless, no less seared by sin and sorrow, or broken by the storms of circumstance, were the wretches that came in droves to Galbanon. The stream of crime or tyranny bore them down (some from very high places), cast them into this boiling pool, and there they eddied in a circle of degraded tasks from which it seemed the fate of many of them never to escape, though their luckier fellows went in twos or threes every other day in a cart to their doom appointed.

Be sure it was not pleasant each day for me to hear the hiss of the lash and the moans of the bastinadoed wretch, to see the blood spurt, and witness the anguish of the men who dragged enormous bilboes on their galled ankles.

At last I felt I could stand it no longer, and one day intimated to Father Hamilton that I was determined on an escape.

"Good lad!" he cried, his eye brightening. "The most sensible thing thou hast said in twenty-four hours. 'Twill be a recreation for myself to help," and he buttoned his waistcoat.

"We can surely devise some means of breaking out if——"

"We!" he repeated, shaking his head. "No, no, Paul, thou hast too risky a task before thee to burden thyself with behemoth. Shalt escape by thyself and a blessing with thee, but as for Father Hamilton he knows when he is well-off, and he shall not stir a step out of Buhot's charming and commodious inn until the bill is presented."

In vain I protested that I should not dream of leaving him there while I took flight; he would listen to none of my reasoning, and for that day at least I abandoned the project.

Next day Buhot helped me to a different conclusion, for I was summoned before him.

"Well, Monsieur," he said, "is it that we have here a more discerning young gentleman than I had the honour to meet last time?"

"Just the very same, M. Buhot," said I bluntly.

He chewed the stump of his pen and shrugged his shoulders.

"Come, come, M. Greig," he went on, "this is a *bêtise* of the most ridiculous. We have given you every opportunity of convincing yourself whether this Hamilton is a good man or a bad one, whether he is the tool of others or himself a genius of mischief."

"The tool of others, certainly, that much I am prepared to tell you, but that you know already. And certainly no genius of mischief himself; man! he has not got the energy to kick a dog."

"And—and—" said Buhot softly, fancying he had me in the key of revelation.

"And that's all, M. Buhot," said I, with a carriage he could not mistake.

He shrugged his shoulders again, wrote something in a book on the desk before him with great deliberation and then asked me how I liked my quarters in Bicêtre.

"Tolerably well," I said. "I've been in better, but I might be in waur."

He laughed a little at the Scotticism that seemed to recall something—perhaps a pleasantry of my uncle's—to him, and then said he, "I'm sorry they cannot be yours very much longer, M. Greig. We calculated that a week or two of this priest's company would have been enough to inspire a distaste and secure his confession, but apparently we were mistaken. You shall be taken to other quarters on Saturday."

"I hope, M. Buhot," said I, "they are to be no worse than those I occupy now."

His face reddened a little at this—I felt always there was some vein of special kindness to me in this man's nature—and he said hesitatingly, "Well, the truth is, 'tis Galbanon."

"Before a trial?" I asked, incredulous.

"The trial will come in good time," he said, rising to conclude the parley, and he turned his back on me as I was conducted out of the room and back to the cell, where Father Hamilton waited with unwonted agitation for my tidings.

"Well, lad," he cried, whenever we were alone, "what stirs? I warrant they have not a jot of evidence against thee," but in a second he saw from my face the news was not so happy, and his own face fell.

"We are to be separated on Saturday," I told him.

Tears came to his eyes at that—a most feeling old rogue!

"And where is't for thee, Paul?" he asked.

"Where is't for yourself ought to be of more importance to you, Father Hamilton."

"No, no," he cried, "it matters little about me, but surely for you it cannot be Galbanon?"

"Indeed, and it is no less."

"Then, Paul," he said firmly, "we must break out, and that without loss of time."

"Is it in the plural this time?" I asked him.

He affected an indifference, but at the last consented to share the whole of the enterprise.

CHAPTER XXV

WE ATTEMPT AN ESCAPE

FATHER HAMILTON was not aware of the extent of it, but he knew I was in a correspondence with the sous-officer. More than once he had seen us in the *salle d'épreuve* in a manifest understanding of each other, though he had no suspicion that the gentleman was a Mercury for Miss Walkinshaw, whose name seldom, if ever, entered into our conversation in the cell. From her I had got but one other letter—a brief acknowledgment of some of my fullest budgets, but 'twas enough to keep me at my diurnal on every occasion almost on which the priest slept. I sent her (with the strictest injunction to secrecy upon so important a matter) a great deal of the tale the priest had told me—not so much for her entertainment as for the purpose of moving in the poor man's interests. Especially was I anxious that she should use her influence to have some one communicate to Father Fleuriau, who was at the time in Bruges, how hazardous was the position of his unhappy cat's-paw, whose state I pictured in the most moving colours I could command. There was, it must be allowed, a risk in entrusting a document so damnatory to any one in Bicêtre, but that the packet was duly forwarded to its destination I had every satisfaction of from the sous-officer, who brought me an acknowledgment to that effect from Bernard the Swiss.

The priest knew, then, as I say, that I was on certain terms with this sous-officer, and so it was with no hesitation I informed him that, through the favour of the latter, I had a very fair conception of the character and plan of this building of Bicêtre in which we were interned. What I had learned of most importance to us was that the block of which our cell was a part had a face to the main road of Paris, from which thoroughfare it was separated by a spacious court and a long range of iron palisades. If ever we were to make our way out of the place it must be in this direction, for on two sides of our building we were overlooked by buildings vastly more throng than our own, and bordered by yards in which were constant sentinels. Our block jutted out at an angle from one very much longer, but lower by two storeys, and the disposition of both made it clear that to enter into this larger edifice, and towards the gable end of it that overlooked the palisades of the Paris road, was our most feasible method of essay.

I drew a plan of the prison and grounds on paper, estimating as best I might all the possible checks we were like to meet with, and leaving a balance of chances in our favour that we could effect our purpose in a night.

The priest leaned his chin upon his arms as he

lolled over the table on which I eagerly explained my diagram, and sighed at one or two of the feats of agility it assumed. There was, for example, a roof to walk upon—the roof of the building we occupied—though how we were to get there in the first place was still to be decided. Also there was a descent from that roof on to the lower building at right angles, though where the ladder or rope for this was to come from I must meanwhile airily leave to fortune. Finally, there was—assuming we got into the larger building, and in some unforeseeable way along its roof and clear to the gable end—a part of the yard to cross, and the palisade to escalade.

"Oh, lad! thou takest me for a bird," cried his reverence, aghast at all this. "Is thy poor fellow prisoner a sparrow? A little after this I might do't with my own wings—the saints guide me!—but figure you that at present I am not Philetas, the dwarf, who had to wear leaden shoes lest the wind should blow him away. 'Twould take a wind indeed to stir this amplitude of good humours, this sepulchre of twenty thousand good dinners and incomputible tuns of liquid merriment. Pray, Paul, make an account of my physical infirmities, and mitigate thy transport of vaultings and soarings and leapings and divings, unless, indeed, thou meditatest sewing me up in a sheet, and dragging me through the realms of space."

"We shall manage! we shall manage!" I insisted, now quite uplifted in a fanciful occupation that was all to my tastes, even if nothing came of it, and I plunged more boldly into my plans. They were favoured by several circumstances—the first, namely, that we were not in the uniform of the prison, and, once outside the prison, could mingle with the world without attracting attention. Furthermore, by postponing the attempt till the morrow night I could communicate with the Swiss, and secure his co-operation outside in the matter of a horse or a vehicle, if the same were called for. I did not, however, say so much as that to his reverence, whom I did not wish as yet to know of my correspondence with Bernard. Finally, we had an auspicious fact at the outset of our attempt, inasmuch as the cell we were in was in the corridor next to that of which the sous-officer had some surveillance, and I knew his mind well enough now to feel sure he would help in anything that did not directly involve his own position and duties. In other words, he was to procure a copy of the key of our cell, and find a means of leaving it unlocked when the occasion arose.

"A copy of the key, Paul!" said Father Hamilton; "sure there are no bounds to thy cheerful mad expectancy! But go on! go on! art sure he could not be prevailed on—this fairy godfather—to give us an escort of cavalry and trumpeters?"

"This is not much of a backing-up, Father Hamilton," I said, annoyed at his skeptic comments upon an affair that involved so much and agitated myself so profoundly.

"Pardon! Paul," he said hastily, confused and vexed himself at the reproof. "Art quite right, I'm

H

no more than a croaker, and for penance I shall compel myself to do the wildest feat thou proposest."

We determined to put off the attempt at escape till I had communicated with the sous-officer (in truth, though Father Hamilton did not know it, till I had communicated with Bernard the Swiss), and it was the following afternoon I had not only an assurance of the unlocked door, but in my hand a more trustworthy plan of the prison than my own, and the promise that the Swiss would be waiting with a carriage outside the palisades when we broke through, any time between midnight and five in the morning.

Next day, then, we were in a considerable agitation ; to that extent indeed that I clean forgot that we had no aid to our descent of twenty or thirty feet (as the sous-sergeant's diagram made it) from the roof of our block on to that of the one adjoining. We had had our minds so much on bolted doors and armed sentinels that this detail had quite escaped us until almost on the eve of setting out at midnight, the priest began again to sigh about his bulk and swear no rope short of a ship's cable would serve to bear him.

"Rope!" I cried, in a tremendous chagrin at my stupidity. "Lord! if I have not quite forgot it. We have none."

"Ah!" he said, "perhaps it is not necessary. Perhaps my heart is so light at parting with my *croque-mort* that I can drop upon the tiles like a pigeon."

"Parting," I repeated, eyeing him suspiciously,

for I thought perhaps he had changed his mind again.   " Who thinks of parting ?"

"Not I indeed," says he, "unless the rope do when thou hast got it."

There was no rope, however, and I cursed my own folly that I had not asked one from the sous-officer whose complaisance might have gone the length of a fathom or two, though it did not, as the priest suggested, go so far as an armed convoy and a brace of trumpeters. It was too late now to repair the overlook, and to the making of rope the two of us had there and then to apply ourselves, finding the sheets and blankets of our beds scanty enough for our purpose, and by no means of an assuring elegance or strength when finished. But we had thirty feet of some sort of cord at the last, and whether it was elegant or not it had to do for our purpose.

Luckily the night was dark as pitch and a high wind roared in the chimneys, and in the numerous corners of the prison. There was a sting in the air that drew many of the sentinels round the braziers flaming in the larger yard between the main entrance and the buildings, and that further helped our prospects ; so that it was with some hope, in spite of a heart that beat like a flail in my breast, I unlocked the door and crept out into the dimly-lighted corridor with the priest close behind me.

Midway down this gallery there was a stair of which our plan apprised us, leading to another gallery—the highest of the block—from which a few steps led to a cock-loft where the sous-officer told us there was one chance in a score of finding a blind window leading to the roof.

No one, luckily, appeared as we hurried down the long gallery. I darted like a fawn up the stair to the next flat, Father Hamilton grievously puffing behind me, and we had just got into the shadow of the steps leading to the cock-loft when a warder's step and the clank of his chained keys came sounding down the corridor. He passed within three feet of us and I felt the blood of all my body chill with fear!

"I told thee, lad," whispered the priest, mopping the sweat from his face, "I told thee 'twas an error to burden thyself with such a useless carcase. Another moment or two—a gasp for the wind that seems so cursed ill to come by at my years, and I had brought thee into trouble."

I paid no heed to him, but crept up the steps and into the cock-loft that smelt villainously of bats.

The window was unfastened! I stuck out my head upon the tiles and sniffed the fine fresh air of freedom as it had been a rare perfume.

Luckily the window was scarcely any height, and it proved easy to aid his reverence into the open air. Luckily, further, it was too dark for him to realise the jeopardies of his situation for whether his precarious gropings along the tiles were ten feet or thirty from the yard below was indiscoverable in the darkness. He slid his weighty body along with an honest effort that was wholly due to his regard for my interests, because 'twas done with groans and whispered protestations that 'twas the maddest thing for a man to leave a place where he was happy and risk his neck in an effort to discover misery. A rime of frost was on the tiles, and they were bitter cold to the touch. One fell, too, below me as I slid along, and rattled loudly over its fellows and plunged into the yard.

Naturally we stopped dead and listened breathless, a foolish action for one reason because in any case we had been moving silently at a great height above the place where the tile should fall so that there was no risk of our being heard or seen, but our listening discovered so great an interval between the loosening of the tile and its dull shattering on the stones below that the height on which we were perched in the darkness was made more plain—more dreadful to the instincts than if we could actually measure it with the eye. I confess I felt a touch of nausea, but nothing compared with the priest, whose teeth began to chitter in an ague of horror.

" Good Lord, Paul ! " he whispered to me, clutching my leg as I moved in front of him, " it is the bottomless pit."

" Not unless we drop," said I. And to cheer him up I made some foolish joke.

If the falling tile attracted any attention in the yard it was not apparent to us, and five minutes later we had to brace ourselves to a matter that sent the tile out of our minds.

For we were come to the end of the high building, and twenty feet below us, at right angles, we could plainly see the glow of several skylights in the long prison to which it was attached. It was now the moment for our descent on the extemporised rope.

CHAPTER XXVI

A RIMEY NIGHT ON ROOF-TOPS, AND A NEW USE FOR AN OLD KIRK BELL

I FASTENED the rope about a chimney-head with some misgivings that by the width and breadth of the same I was reducing our chance of ever getting down to the lower building, as the knotted sheets from the outset had been dubious measure for the thirty feet of which my sous-officer had given the estimate. But I said never a word to the priest of my fears on that score, and determined for once to let what was left of honesty go before well-fattened age and test the matter first myself. If the cord was too brief for its purpose, or (what was just as likely) on the frail side, I could pull myself back in the one case as the priest was certainly unfit to do, and in the other my weight would put less strain upon it than that of Father Hamilton.

I can hear him yet in my imagination after forty years, as he clung to the ridge of the roof like a seal on a rock, chittering in the cold night wind, enviously eyeing some fires that blazed in another yard and groaning melancholiously.

"A garden," said he, "and six beehives—no, i'

faith! 'twas seven last summer, and a roomful of books. Oh, Paul, Paul! Now I know how God cast out Satan. He took him from his warm fire-side, and his books before they were all read, and his pantoufles, and set him straddling upon a frozen house-top to ponder through eternal night upon the happy past. Alas, poor being! How could he know what joys were in the simplicity of a room of books half-read and a pair of warm old slippers?"

He was fair rambling in his fears, my poor priest, and I declare scarcely knew the half of what he uttered, indeed he spoke out so loudly that I had to check him lest he should attract attention from below.

"Father Hamilton," said I, when my cord was fastened, "with your permission I'll try it first. I want to make it sure that my seamanship on the sloop *Sarah*, of Ayr, has not deserted me to the extent that I cannot come down a rope without a ratline or tie a bowling knot."

"Certainly, Paul, certainly," said he, quite eagerly, so that I was tempted for a second to think he gladly postponed his own descent from sheer terror.

I threw over the free end of the cord and crouched upon the beak of the gable to lower myself.

"Well, Paul," said his reverence in a broken voice. "Let us say 'good-bye' in case aught should happen ere we are on the same level again."

"Oh!" said I, impatient, "that's the true *croque-mort* spirit indeed! Why, Father, it isn't—it isn't—" I was going to say it was not a gallows I was venturing on, but the word stuck in my throat, for a certain thought that sprung to me of how nearly in my own case it had been to the very gallows, and his reverence doubtless saw some delicacy, for he came promptly to my help.

"Not a priest's promise—made to be broken, you would say, good Paul," said he. "I promised the merriest of jaunts over Europe in a coach, and here my scrivener is hanging in the reins! Pardon, dear Scotland, *milles pardons*, and good-bye and good luck." And at that he made to embrace me.

"Here's a French ceremony just about nothing at all," I thought, and began my descent. The priest lay on his stomach upon the ridge. As I sank, with my eyes turned upwards, I could see his hair blown by the wind against a little patch of stars, that was the only break in the Ethiopia of the sky. He seemed to follow my progress breathlessly, and when I gained the other roof and shook the cord to tell him so he responded by a faint clapping of his hands.

"Art all right, lad?" he whispered down to me, and I bade him follow.

"Good-night, Paul, good-bye, and God bless you!" he whispered. "Get out of this as quick as you can; 'tis more than behemoth could do in a month of dark nights, and so I cut my share of the adventure. One will do't when two (and one of them a hogshead) will die in trying to do't."

Here was a pretty pickle! The man's ridiculous regard for my safety outweighed his natural inclinations, though his prospects in the prison of Bicêtre were blacker than my own, having nothing less dreadful than an execution at the end of them. He had been merely humouring me so far—and such a brave humouring in one whose flesh was in a quaking of alarms all the time he slid along the roof!

"Are you not coming?" I whispered.

"On the contrary, I'm going, dear Paul," said he with a pretence at levity. "Going back to my comfortable cell and my uniformed servant and M. Buhot, the charmingest of hostellers, and I declare my feet are like ice."

"Then," said I firmly, "I go back too. I'll be eternally cursed if I give up my situation as scrivener at this point. I must e'en climb up again." And with that I prepared to start the ascent.

"Stop! stop!" said he without a second's pause, "stop where you are and I'll go down. Though 'tis the most stupendous folly," he added with a sigh, and in a moment later I saw his vast bulk laboriously heaving over the side of the roof. Fortunately the knots in the cord where the fragments of sheet and blanket were joined made his task not so difficult as it had otherwise been, and almost as speedily as I had done it myself he reached the roof of the lower building, though in such a state he quivered like a jelly, and was dumb with fear or with exertion when the thing was done.

"Ah!" he said at last, when he had recovered himself. "Art a fool to be so particular about an old carcase accursed of easy humours and accused of regicide. Take another thought on't, Paul. What have you to do with this wretch of a priest that brought about the whole trouble in your ignorance? And think of Galbanon!"

"Think of the devil! Father Hamilton," I snapped at him, "every minute we waste havering away here adds to the chances against any of us getting free, and I am sure that is not your desire. The long and the short of it is that I'll not stir a step out of Bicêtre—no, not if the doors themselves were open—unless you consent to come with me."

"*Ventre Dieu!*" said he, "'tis just such a mulish folly as I might have looked for from the nephew of Andrew Greig. But lead on, good imbecile, lead on, and blame not poor Father Hamilton if the thing ends in a fiasco!"

We now crawled along a roof no whit more easily traversed than that we had already commanded. Again and again I had to stop to permit my companion to come up on me, for the pitch of the tiles was steep, and he in a peril from his own lubricity, and it was necessary even to put a hand under his arm at times when he suffered a vertigo through seeing the lights in the yard deep down as points of flame.

"Egad! boy," he said, and his perspiring hand clutching mine at one of our pauses, "I thrill at the very entrails. I'd liefer have my nose in the sawdust any day than thrash through thin air on to a paving-stone."

"A minute or two more and we are there," I answered him.

"Where?" said he, starting; "in purgatory?"

"Look up, man!" I told him. "There's a window beaming ten yards off." And again I pushed on.

In very truth there was no window, though I prayed as fervently for one as it had been a glimpse of paradise, but I was bound to cozen the old man into effort for his own life and for mine. What I had from the higher building taken for the glow of skylights had been really the light of windows on the top flat of the other prison block, and its roof was wholly unbroken. At least I had made up my mind to that with a despair benumbing when I touched wood. My fingers went over it in the dark with frantic eagerness. It was a trap such as we had come out of at the other block, but it was shut. Before the priest could come up to me and suffer the fresh horror of disappointment I put my weight upon it, and had the good fortune to throw it in. The flap fell with a shriek of hinges and showed gaping darkness. We stretched upon the tiles as close as limpets and as silent. Nothing stirred within.

"A garden," said he in a little, "as sweet as ever bean grew in, with the rarest plum-tree; and now I am so cold."

"I could be doing with some of your complaint," said I; "as for me, I'm on fire. Please heaven, you'll be back in the garden again."

I lowered myself within, followed by the priest, and found we were upon the rafters. A good bit off there was a beam of light that led us, groping, and in an imminent danger of going through the plaster, to an air-hole over a little gallery whose floor was within stretch as I lowered myself again.

Father Hamilton squeezed after me; we both looked over the edge of the gallery, and found it was a chapel we were in!

"*Sacré nom!*" said the priest and crossed himself, with a genuflexion to the side of the altar. "Oh, Lord! Paul," he said, whispering, "if 'twere the Middle Ages, and this were indeed a sanctuary, how happy was a poor undeserving son of Mother Church! Even Dagobert's hounds drew back from the stag in St. Denys."

It was a mean interior, as befitted the worship of the *misérables* who at times would meet there. A solemn quiet held the place, that seemed wholly deserted; the dim light that had shown through the air-hole and guided us came from some candles dripping before a shrine.

"Heaven help us!" said the priest. "I know just such another."

There was nobody in the church so far as we could observe from the little gallery in which we found ourselves, but when we had gone down a flight of steps into the body of the same, and made to cross towards the door, we were suddenly confronted by a priest in a white cope. My heart jumped to my mouth; I felt a prinkling in the roots of my hair, and stopped dumb, with all my faculties basely deserted from me. Luckily Father Hamilton kept his presence of mind. As he told me later, he remembered of a sudden the Latin proverb that in battles the eye is first overcome, and he fixed the man in the stole with a glance that was bold and disconcerting. As it happened, however, the other priest was almost as blind as a bat, and saw but two civil worshippers in his chapel. He did not even notice that it was a *soutane;* he passed peeringly, with a bow to our inclinations, and it was almost incredulous of our good fortune I darted out of the chapel into the darkness of a courtyard of equal extent with that I had crossed on the night of my first arrival at Bicêtre. At its distant end there were the same flaming braziers with figures around them, and the same glitter of arms.

Now this Bicêtre is set upon a hill and commands a prospect of the city of Paris, of the Seine and its environs. For that reason we could see to our right the innumerable lights of a great plain twinkling in the darkness, and it seemed as if we had only to proceed in that direction to secure freedom by the mere effort of walking. As we stood in the shadow of the chapel, Father Hamilton eyed the distant prospect of the lighted town with a singular rapture.

"Paris!" said he. "*Oh, Dieu!* and I thought never to clap an eye on't again. Paris, my Paul! Behold the lights of it—*la ville lumière* that is so fine I could spend eternity in it. Hearts are there, lad, kind and jocund——"

"And meditating a descent on unhappy Britain," said I.

"Good neighbourly hearts, or I'm a gourd else," he went on, unheeding my interruption. "The stars in heaven are not so good, are no more notably the expression of a glowing and fraternal spirit. There is laughter in the streets of her."

"Not at this hour, Father Hamilton," said I, and the both of us always whispering. "I've never seen the place by day nor put a foot in it, but it will be droll indeed if there is laughter in its streets at two o'clock in the morning."

"Ah, Paul, shall we ever get there?" said he longingly.

"We can but try, anyway. I certainly did not come all this way, Father Hamilton, just to look on the lowe of Paris."

What had kept us shrinking in the shadow of the chapel wall had been the sound of footsteps between us and the palisades that were to be distinguished a great deal higher than I had expected, on our right. On the other side of the rails was freedom, as well as Paris that so greatly interested my companion, but the getting clear of them seemed like to be a more difficult task than any we had yet overcome, and all the more hazardous because the footsteps obviously suggested a sentinel. Whether it was the rawness of the night that tempted him to a relaxation, or whether he was not strictly on duty, I know not, but, while we stood in the most wretched of quandaries, the man who was in our path very soon ceased his perambulation along the palisades, and went over to one of the distant fires, passing within a few yards of us as we crouched in the darkness. When he had gone sufficiently out of the way we ran for it. So plain were the lights of the valley, so flimsy a thing had seemed to part us from the high-road there, that never a doubt intruded on my mind that now we were as good as free, and when I came to the rails I beat my head with my hands when the nature of our folly dawned upon me.

"We may just go back," I said to the priest in a stricken voice.

"*Comment?*" said he, wiping his brow and gloating on the spectacle of the lighted town.

"Look," I said, indicating the railings that were nearly three times my own height, "there are no convenient trap-doors here"

"But the cord——" said he simply.

"Exactly," I said; "the cord's where we left it snugly tied with a bowling knot to the chimney of our block, and I'm an ass."

"Oh, poor Paul!" said the priest in a prostration at this divulgence of our error. "I'm the millstone on your neck, for had I not parleyed at the other end of the cord when you had descended, the necessity for it would never have escaped your mind. I gave you fair warning, lad, 'twas a quixotic imbecility to burden yourself with me. And are we really at a stand? God! look at Paris. Had I not seen these lights I had not cared for myself a straw, but, oh lord! lad, they are so pleasant and so close! Why will the world sleep when two unhappy wretches die for want of a little bit of hemp?"

"You are not to blame," said I, "one rope was little use to us in any case. But anyhow I do not desire to die of a little bit of hemp if I can arrange it better." And I began hurriedly to scour up and down the palisade like a trapped mouse. It extended for about a hundred yards, ending at one side against the walls of a gate-house or lodge ; on the other side it concluded at the wall of the chapel. It had no break in all its expanse, and so there was nothing left for us to do but to go back the way we had come, obliterate the signs of our attempt and find our cells again. We went, be sure, with heavy hearts, again ventured into the chapel, climbed the stairs, went through the ceiling, and stopped a little among the rafters to rest his reverence who was finding these manœuvres too much for his weighty body. While he sat regaining sufficient strength to resume his crawling on rimey tiles I made a search of the loft we were in and found it extended to the gable end of the chapel, but nothing more for my trouble beyond part of a hanging chain that came through the roof and passed through the ceiling. I had almost missed it in the darkness, and even when I touched it my first thought was to leave it alone. But I took a second thought and tried the lower end, which came up as I hauled, yard upon yard, until I had the end of it, finished with a bell-ringer's hempen grip, in my hands. Here was a discovery if bell-pulls had been made of rope throughout in Bicêtre prison ! But a chain with an end to a bell was not a thing to be easily borrowed.

I went back to where Father Hamilton was seated on the rafters, and told him my discovery.

"A bell," said he. "Faith ! I never liked them. Pestilent inventions of the enemy, that suggested duties to be done and the fleeting hours. But a bell-rope implies a belfry on the roof and a bell in it, and the chain that may reach the ground within the building may reach the same desirable place without the same."

"That's very true," said I, struck with the thing. And straight got through the trap and out upon the roof again. Father Hamilton puffed after me and in a little we came upon a structure like a dovecot at the very gable-end.

"The right time to harry a nest is at night," said I, "for then you get all that's in it." And I started to pull up the chain that was fastened to the bell.

I lowered behemoth with infinite exertion till he reached the ground outside the prison grounds in safety, wrapped the clapper of the bell in my waist-coat, and descended hand over hand after him.

We were on the side of a broad road that dipped down the hill into a little village. Between us and the village street, across which hung a swinging lamp, there mounted slowly a carriage with a pair of horses.

"Bernard!" I cried, running up to it, and found it was the Swiss in the very article of waiting for us, and he speedily drove us into Paris.

CHAPTER XXVII

OF the town of Paris that is so lamentably notable in these days I have but the recollection that one takes away from a new scene witnessed under stress of mind due to matters more immediately affecting him than the colour, shape, and properties of things seen, and the thought I had in certain parts of it is more clear to me to-day than the vision of the place itself. It is, in my mind, like a fog that the bridges thundered as our coach drove over them with our wretched fortunes on that early morning of our escape from Bicêtre, but as clear as when it sprung to me from the uproar of the wheels comes back the dread that the whole of this community would be at their windows looking out to see what folks untimeously disturbed their rest. We were delayed briefly at a gate upon the walls; I can scarcely mind what manner of men they were that stopped us and thrust a lantern in our faces, and what they asked eludes me altogether, but I mind distinctly how I gasped relief when we were permitted to roll on. Blurred, too—no better than the surplusage of dreams, is my first picture of the river and its isles in the dawn, but, like a favourite song, I mind the gluck of waters on the quays and that they made me think of Earn and Cart and Clyde.

We stopped in the place of the Notre Dame at the corner of a street; the coach drove off to a *remise* whence it had come, and we went to an hospital called the Hôtel Dieu, in the neighbourhood, where Hamilton had a Jesuit friend in one of the heads, and where we were accommodated in a room that was generally set aside for clergymen. It was a place of the most wonderful surroundings, this Hôtel Dieu, choked, as it were, among towers, the greatest of them those of Our Lady itself that were in the Gothic taste, regarding which Father Hamilton used to say, " *Dire gothique, c'est dire mauvais gout,*" though, to tell the truth, I thought the building pretty braw myself. Alleys and wynds were round about us, and so narrow that the sky one saw between them was but a ribbon by day, while at night they seemed no better than ravines.

'Twas at night I saw most of the city, for only in the darkness did I dare to venture out of the Hôtel Dieu. Daundering my lone along the cobbles, I took a pleasure in the exercise of tenanting these towering lands with people having histories little different from the histories of the folks far off in my Scottish home—their daughters marrying, their sons going throughither (as we say), their bairns wakening and crying in their naked beds, and grannies sitting by the ingle-neuk cheerfully cracking upon ancient days. Many a time in the by-going I looked up their pend closes seeking the eternal lovers of our own burgh towns and never finding them, for I take it that in love the foreign character is coyer than our own. But no matter how eagerly I went forth upon my nightly airing in a *roquelaure* borrowed from Father Hamilton's friend, the adventure always ended, for me, in a sort of eerie terror of those close-hemming walls, those tangled lanes where slouched the outcast and the ne'er-do-weel, and not even the glitter of the moon upon the river between its laden isles would comfort me.

"La! la! la!" would Father Hamilton cry at me when I got home with a face like a fiddle. "Art the most ridiculous rustic ever ate a cabbage or set foot in Arcady. Why, man! the woman must be wooed—this Mademoiselle Lutetia. Must take her front and rear, walk round her, ogling bravely. Call her dull! call her dreadful! *Ciel!* Has the child never an eye in his mutton head? I avow she is the queen of the earth this Paris. If I were young and wealthy I'd buy the glittering stars in constellations and turn them into necklets for her. With thy plaguey gift of the sonnet I'd deave her with ecstasies and spill oceans of ink upon leagues of paper to tell her about her eyes. Go to! Scotland, go to! Ghosts! ghosts! devil the thing else but ghosts in thy rustic skull, for to take a fear of Lutetia when her black hair is down of an evening and thou canst not get a glimpse of that beautiful neck that is rounded like the same in the Psyche of Praxiteles. Could I pare off a portion of this rotundity and go out in a masque as Apollo I'd show thee things."

And all he saw of Paris himself was from the windows of the hospital, where he and I would stand by the hour looking out into the square. For the air itself he had to take it in a little garden at the back, surrounded by a high wall, and affording a seclusion that even the priest could avail himself of without the hazard of discovery. He used to sit in an arbour there in the warmth of the day, and it was there I saw another trait of his character that helped me much to forget his shortcomings.

Over his head, within the doorway of the bower, he hung a box and placed therein the beginnings of a bird's nest. The thing was not many hours done when a pair of birds came boldly into his presence as he sat silent and motionless in the bower, and began to avail themselves of so excellent a start in householding. In a few days there were eggs in the nest, and 'twas the most marvellous of spectacles to witness the hen sit content upon them over the head of the fat man underneath, and the cock, without concern, fly in and out attentive on his mate.

But, indeed, the man was the friend of all helpless things, and few of the same came his way without an instinct that told them it was so. Not the birds in the nest alone were at ease in his society; he had but to walk along the garden paths whistling and chirping, and there came flights of birds about his head and shoulders, and some would even perch upon his hand. I have never seen him more like his office than when he talked with the creatures of the air, unless it was on another occasion when two bairns, the offspring of an inmate in the hospital, ventured into the garden, finding there another child, though monstrous, who had not lost the key to the fields where blossom the flowers of infancy, and frolic is a prayer.

But he dare not set a foot outside the walls of our retreat, for it was as useless to hide Ballageich under a Kilmarnock bonnet as to seek a disguise for his reverence in any suit of clothes. Bernard would come to us rarely under cover of night, but alas! there were no letters for me now, and mine that were sent through him were fewer than before. And there was once an odd thing happened that put an end to these intromissions; a thing that baffled me to understand at the time, and indeed for many a day thereafter, but was made plain to me later on in a manner that proved how contrary in his character was this mad priest, that was at once assassin and the noblest friend.

Father Hamilton was not without money, though all had been taken from him at Bicêtre. It was an evidence of the width and power of the Jesuit movement that even in the Hôtel Dieu he could command what sums he needed, and Bernard was habituated to come to him for moneys that might pay for himself and the coachman and the horses at the *remise*. On the last of these occasions I took the chance to slip a letter for Miss Walkinshaw into his hand. Instead of putting it in his pocket he laid it down a moment on a table, and he and I were busy packing linen for the wash when a curious cry from Father Hamilton made us turn to see him with the letter in his hand.

He was gazing with astonishment on the direction.

"Ah!" said he, "and so my Achilles is not consoling himself exclusively with the Haemonian lyre, but has taken to that far more dangerous instrument the pen. The pen, my child, is the curse of youth. When we are young we use it for our undoing, and for the facture of regrets for after years—even if it be no more than the reading of our wives' letters that I'm told are a bitter revelation to the married man. And so—and so, Monsieur Croque-mort keeps up a correspondence with the lady. H'm!"

He looked so curiously and inquiringly at me that I felt compelled to make an explanation.

"It is quite true, Father Hamilton," said I. "After all, you gave me so little clerkly work that I was bound to employ my pen somehow, and how better than with my countrywoman?"

"'Tis none of my affair—perhaps," he said, laying down the letter. "And yet I have a curiosity. Have we here the essential Mercury?" and he indicated Bernard who seemed to me to have a greater confusion than the discovery gave a cause for.

"Bernard has been good enough," said I. "You discover two Scots, Father Hamilton, in a somewhat sentimental situation. The lady did me the honour to be interested in my little travels, and I did my best to keep her informed."

He turned away as he had been shot, hiding his face, but I saw from his neck that he had grown as white as parchment.

"What in the world have I done?" thinks I, and

concluded that he was angry for my taking the
liberty to use the dismissed servant as a go-between.
In a moment or two he turned about again, eying
me closely, and at last he put his hand upon my
shoulder as a schoolmaster might do upon a boy's.

"My good Paul," said he, "how old are you?"

"Twenty-one come Martinmas," I said.

"Expiscate! elucidate! 'Come Martinmas,'"
says he, "and what does that mean? But no matter
—twenty-one says my barbarian; sure 'tis a right
young age, a very baby of an age, an age in frocks
if one that has it has lived the best of his life with
sheep and bullocks."

"Sir," I said, indignant, "I was in very honest
company among the same sheep and bullocks."

"Hush!" said he, and put up his hand, eying
me with compassion and kindness. "If thou only
knew it, lad, thou art due me a civil attention at the
very least. Sure there is no harm in my mentioning
that thou art mighty ingenuous for thy years. 'Tis
the quality I would be the last to find fault with,
but sometimes it has its inconveniences. And Bernard"—he turned to the Swiss who was still greatly
disturbed—"Bernard is a somewhat older gentleman. Perhaps he will say—our good Bernard—if
he was the person I have to thank for taking the
sting out of the wasp, for extracting the bullet from
my pistol? Ah! I see he is the veritable person.
Adorable Bernard, let that stand to his credit!"

Then Bernard fell trembling like a saugh tree,
and protested he did but what he was told.

"And a good thing, too," said the priest, still
very pale but with no displeasure. "And a good

thing too, else poor Buhot, that I have seen an infinity of headachy dawns with, had been beyond any interest in cards or prisoners. For that I shall forgive you the rest that I can guess at. Take Monsieur Greig's letter where you have taken the rest, and be gone."

The Swiss went out much crestfallen from an interview that was beyond my comprehension.

When he was gone Father Hamilton fell into a profound meditation, walking up and down his room muttering to himself.

"Faith, I never had such a problem presented to me before," said he, stopping his walk; "I know not whether to laugh or swear. I feel that I have been made a fool of, and yet nothing better could have happened. And so my Croque-mort, my good Monsieur Propriety, has been writing the lady? I should not wonder if he thought she loved him."

"Nothing so bold," I cried. "You might without impropriety have seen every one of my letters, and seen in them no more than a seaman's log."

"A seaman's log!" said he, smiling faintly and rubbing his massive chin; "nothing would give the lady more delight, I am sure. A seaman's log! And I might have seen them without impropriety, might I? That I'll swear was what her ladyship took very good care to obviate. Come now, did she not caution thee against telling me of this correspondence?"

I confessed it was so; that the lady naturally feared she might be made the subject of light talk, and I had promised that in that respect she should suffer nothing for her kindly interest in a countryman.

The priest laughed consumedly at this.

"Interest in her countryman!" said he. "Oh, lad, wilt be the death of me for thy unexpected spots of innocence."

"And as to that," I said, "you must have had a sort of correspondence with her yourself."

"I!" said he. "*Comment!*"

"To be quite frank with you," said I, "it has been the cause of some vexatious thoughts to me that the letter I carried to the Prince was directed in Miss Walkinshaw's hand of write, and as Buhot informed me, it was the same letter that was to wile his Royal Highness to his fate in the Rue des Reservoirs."

Father Hamilton groaned, as he did at any time the terrible affair was mentioned.

"It is true, Paul, quite true," said he, "but the letter was a forgery. I'll give the lady the credit to say she never had a hand in it."

"I am glad to hear that, for it removes some perplexities that have troubled me for a while back."

"Ah," said he, "and your perplexities and mine are not over even now, poor Paul. This Bernard is like to be the ruin of me yet. For you, however, I have no fear, but it is another matter with the poor old fool from Dixmunde."

His voice broke, he displayed thus and otherwise so troubled a mind and so great a reluctance to let me know the cause of it that I thought it well to leave him for a while and let him recover his old manner.

To that end I put on my coat and hat and went out rather earlier than usual for my evening walk.

CHAPTER XXVIII

THE MAN WITH THE TARTAN WAISTCOAT

IT was the first of May. But for Father Hamilton's
birds, and some scanty signs of it in the small garden,
the lengthened day and the kindlier air of the evenings, I might never have known what season it was out
of the almanac, for all seasons were much the same,
no doubt, in the Isle of the City where the priest and I
sequestered. 'Twas ever the shade of the tenements
there; the towers of the churches never greened
nor budded; I would have waited long, in truth, for
the scent of the lilac and the chatter of the rook
among these melancholy temples.

Till that night I had never ventured farther from
the gloomy vicinity of the hospital than I thought I
could safely retrace without the necessity of asking
any one the way; but this night, more courageous,
or perhaps more careless than usual, I crossed the
bridge of Notre Dame and found myself in something like the Paris of the priest's rhapsodies and
the same all thrilling with the passion of the summer.
It was not flower nor tree, though these were not
wanting, but the spirit in the air—young girls laughing in the by-going with merriest eyes, windows

wide open letting out the sounds of songs, the pave-
ments like a river with zesty life of Highland hills
when the frosts above are broken and the over-
hanging boughs have been flattering it all the way
in the valleys.

I was fair infected. My step, that had been
unco' dull and heavy, I fear, and going to the time
of dirges on the Isle, went to a different tune; my
being rhymed and sang. I had got the length of
the Rue de Richelieu and humming to myself in the
friendliest key, with the good-natured people pressing about me, when of a sudden it began to rain.
There was no close in the neighbourhood where I
could shelter from the elements, but in front of me
was the door of a tavern called the Tête du Duc de
Burgoyne shining with invitation, and in I went.

A fat wife sat at a counter; a pot-boy, with a cry
of "V'là!" that was like a sheep's complaining,
served two ancient citizens in skull-caps that played
the game of dominoes, and he came to me with my
humble order of a litre of ordinary and a piece of
bread for the good of the house.

Outside the rain pelted, and the folks upon the
pavement ran, and by-and-by the tavern-room filled
up with shelterers like myself and kept the pot-boy
busy. Among the last to enter was a group of five
that took a seat at another corner of the room than
that where I sat my lone at a little table. At first I
scarcely noticed them until I heard a word of Scots.
I think the man that used it spoke of "gully-knives,"
but at least the phrase was the broadest lallands,
and went about my heart.

I put down my piece of bread and looked across the room in wonder to see that three of the men were gazing intently at myself. The fourth was hid by those in front of him; the fifth that had spoken had a tartan waistcoat and eyes that were like a gled's, though they were not on me. In spite of that, 'twas plain that of me he spoke, and that I was the object of some speculation among them.

No one that has not been lonely in a foreign town, and hungered for communion with those that know his native tongue, can guess how much I longed for speech with this compatriot that in dress and eye and accent brought back the place of my nativity in one wild surge of memory. Every bawbee in my pocket would not have been too much to pay for such a privilege, but it might not be unless the overtures came from the persons in the corner.

Very deliberately, though all in a commotion within, I ate my piece and drank my wine before the stare of the three men, and at last, on the whisper of one of them, another produced a box of dice.

" No, no ! " said the man with the tartan waistcoat hurriedly, with a glance from the tail of his eye at me, but they persisted in their purpose and began to throw. My countryman in tartan got the last chance, of which he seemed reluctant to avail himself till the one unseen said : " *Vous avez le dé,* Kilbride."

Kilbride ! the name was the call of whaups at home upon the moors !

He laughed, shook, and tossed carelessly, and

then the laugh was all with them, for whatever they had played for he had seemingly lost and the dice were now put by.

He rose somewhat confused, looked dubiously across at me with a reddening face, and then came over with his hat in his hand.

" Pardon, Monsieur," he began ; then checked the French, and said : " Have I a countryman here ? "

" It is like enough," said I, with a bow and looking at his tartan. " I am from Scotland myself."

He smiled at that with a look of some relief and took a vacant chair on the other side of my small table.

" I have come better speed with my impudence," said he in the Hielan' accent, "than I expected or deserved. My name's Kilbride—MacKellar of Kilbride—and I am here with another Highland gentleman of the name of Grant and two or three French friends we picked up at the door of the play-house. Are you come off the Highlands, if I make take the liberty ? "

" My name is lowland," said I, "and I hail from the shire of Renfrew."

" Ah," said he, with a vanity that was laughable. " What a pity ! I wish you had been Gaelic, but of course you cannot help it being otherwise, and indeed there are many estimable persons in the lowlands."

" And a great wheen of Highland gentlemen very glad to join them there too," said I, resenting the implication.

"Of course, of course," said he heartily. "There is no occasion for offence."

"Confound the offence, Mr. MacKellar!" said I. "Do you not think I am just too glad at this minute to hear a Scottish tongue and see a tartan waistcoat? Heilan' or Lowlan', we are all the same" when our feet are off the heather.

"Not exactly," he corrected, "but still and on we understand each other. You must be thinking it gey droll, sir, that a band of strangers in a common tavern would have the boldness to stare at you like my friends there, and toss a dice about you in front of your face, but that is the difference between us. If I had been in your place I would have thrown the jug across at them, but here I am not better nor the rest, because the dice fell to me, and I was one that must decide the wadger."

"Oh, and was I the object of a wadger?" said I, wondering what we were coming to.

"Indeed, and that you were," said he shame-facedly, "and I'm affronted to tell it. But when Grant saw you first he swore you were a countryman, and there was some difference of opinion."

"And what, may I ask, did Kilbride side with?"

"Oh," said he promptly, "I had never a doubt about that. I knew you were Scots, but what beat me was to say whether you were Hielan' or Lowlan'."

"And how, if it's a fair question, did you come to the conclusion that I was a countryman of any sort?" said I.

He laughed softly, and "Man," said he, "I could

never make any mistake about that, whatever of it. There's many a bird that's like the woodcock, but the woodcock will aye be kennin' which is which, as the other man said. Thae bones were never built on bread and wine. It's a French coat you have there, and a cockit hat (by your leave), but to my view you were as plainly from Scotland as if you had a blue bonnet on your head and a sprig of heather in your lapels. And here am I giving you the strange cow's welcome (as the other man said), and that is all inquiry and no information. You must just be excusing our bit foolish wadger, and if the proposal would come favourably from myself, that is of a notable family, though at present under a sort of cloud, as the other fellow said, I would be proud to have you share in the bottle of wine that was dependent upon Grant's impudent wadger. I can pass my word for my friends there that they are all gentry like ourselves—of the very best, in troth, though not over-nice in putting this task on myself."

I would have liked brawly to spend an hour out any company than my own, but the indulgence was manifestly one involving the danger of discovery; it was, as I told myself, the greatest folly to be sitting in a tavern at all, so MacKellar's manner immediately grew cold when he saw a swithering in my countenance.

"Of course," said he, reddening and rising, "of course, every gentleman has his own affairs, and I would be the last to make a song of it if you have any dubiety about my friends and me. I'll allow the thing looks very like a gambler's contrivance."

"No, no, Mr. MacKellar," said I hurriedly, unwilling to let us part like that, "I'm swithering here just because I'm like yoursel' of it and under a cloud of my own."

"Dod! Is that so?" said he quite cheerfully again, and clapping down, "then I'm all the better pleased that the thing that made the roebuck swim the loch—and that's necessity—as the other man said, should have driven me over here to precognosce you. But when you say you are under a cloud, that is to make another way of it altogether, and I will not be asking you over, for there is a gentleman there among the five of us who might be making trouble of it."

"Have you a brother in Glasgow College?" says I suddenly, putting a question that had been in my mind ever since he had mentioned his name.

"Indeed, and I have that," said he quickly, "but now he is following the law in Edinburgh, where I am in the hopes it will be paying him better than ever it paid me that has lost two fine old castles and the best part of a parish by the same. You'll not be sitting there and telling me surely that you know my young brother Alasdair?"

"Man! him and me lodged together in Lucky Grant's, in Crombie's Land in the High Street, for two Sessions," said I.

"What!" said MacKellar. "And you'll be the lad that snow-balled the bylie, and your name will be Greig?"

As he said it he bent to look under the table, then

I

drew up suddenly with a startled face and a whisper
of a whistle on his lips.

"My goodness!" said he, in a cautious tone,
"and that beats all. You'll be the lad that broke
jyle with the priest that shot at Buhot, and there
you are, you *amadain*, like a gull with your red
brogues on you, crying 'come and catch me' in two
languages. I'm telling you to keep thae feet of
yours under this table till we're out of here, if it
should be the morn's morning. No — that's too
long, for by the morn's morning Buhot's men will be at
the Hôtel Dieu, and the end of the story will be little
talk and the sound of blows, as the other man said."

Every now and then as he spoke he would look
over his shoulder with a quick glance at his friends
—a very anxious man, but no more anxious than
Paul Greig.

"Mercy on us!" said I, "do you tell me you ken
all that?"

"I ken a lot more than that," said he, "but that's
the latest of my budget, and I'm giving it to you for
the sake of the shoes and my brother Alasdair, that
is a writer in Edinburgh. There's not two Scotch-
men drinking a bowl in Paris town this night that
does not ken your description, and it's kent by them
at the other table there—where better?—but because
you have that coat on you that was surely made for
you when you were in better health, as the other
man said, and because your long trams of legs and
red shoes are under the table there's none of them
suspects you. And now that I'm thinking of it, I
would not go near the hospital place again."

"Oh! but the priest's there," said I, "and it would never do for me to be leaving him there without a warning."

"A warning!" said MacKellar with contempt. "I'm astonished to hear you, Mr. Greig. The filthy brock that he is!"

"If you're one of the Prince's party," said I, "and it has every look of it, or, indeed, whether you are or not, I'll allow you have some cause to blame Father Hamilton, but as for me, I'm bound to him because we have been in some troubles together."

"What's all this about 'bound to him'?" said MacKellar with a kind of sneer. "The dog that's tethered with a black pudding needs no pity, as the other man said, and I would leave this fellow to shift for himself."

"Thank you," said I, "but I'll not be doing that."

"Well, well," said he, "it's your business, and let me tell you that you're nothing but a fool to be tangled up with the creature. That's Kilbride's advice to you. Let me tell you this more of it, that they're not troubling themselves much about you at all now that you have given them the information."

"Information!" I said with a start. "What do you mean by that?"

He prepared to join his friends, with a smile of some slyness, and gave me no satisfaction on the point.

"You'll maybe ken best yourself," said he, "and I'm thinking your name will have to be Robertson and yourself a decent Englishman for my friends on

the other side of the room there.   Between here
and yonder I'll have to be making up a bonny lie or
two that will put them off the scent of you."

A bonny lie or two seemed to serve the purpose,
for their interest in me appeared to go no further,
and by-and-by, when it was obvious that there would
be no remission of the rain, they rose to go.

The last that went out of the door turned on the
threshold and looked at me with a smile of recognition and amusement.

It was Buhot !

CHAPTER XXIX

WHEREIN THE PRIEST LEAVES ME, AND I MAKE
AN INLAND VOYAGE

WHAT this marvel betokened was altogether beyond
my comprehension, but the five men were no sooner
gone than I clapped on my hat and drew up the
collar of my coat and ran like fury through the
plashing streets for the place that was our tempor-
ary home. It must have been an intuition of the
raised that guided me; my way was made without
reflection on it, at pure hazard, and yet I landed
through a multitude of winding and bewildering
streets upon the Isle of the City and in front of the
Hôtel Dieu in a much shorter time than it had taken me
to get from there to the Duke of Burgundy's Head.

I banged past the doorkeeper, jumped upstairs to
the clergyman's quarters, threw open the door and
—found Father Hamilton was gone!

About the matter there could be no manner of
dubiety, for he had left a letter directed to myself
upon the drawers-head.

"MY GOOD PAUL (said the epistle, that I have
kept till now as a memorial of my adventure):
When you return you will discover from this that I

have taken leave *à l'anglaise*, and I fancy I can see my secretary looking like the arms of Bourges (though that is an unkind imputation). 'Tis fated, seemingly, that there shall be no rest for the sole of the foot of poor Father Hamilton. I had no sooner got to like a loose collar, and an unbuttoned vest, and the seclusion of a cell, than I must be plucked out ; and now when my birds—the darlings !—are on the very point of hatching I must make adieux. *Oh ! la belle équipée !* M. Buhot knows where I am —that's certain, so I must remove myself, and this time I do not propose to burden M. Paul Greig with my company, for it will be a miracle if they fail to find me. As for my dear Croque-mort, he can have the glass coach and Jacques and Bernard, and doubtless the best he can do with them is to take all to Dunkerque and leave them there. I myself, I go *sans trompette*, and no inquiries will discover to him where I go."

As a postscript he added, " And 'twas only a sailor's log, dear lad ! My poor young Paul !"

When I read the letter I was puzzled tremendously, and at first I felt inclined to blame the priest for a scurvy flitting to rid himself of my society, but a little deliberation convinced me that no such ignoble consideration was at the bottom of his flight. If I read his epistle aright the step he took was in my own interest, though how it could be so there was no surmising. In any case he was gone ; his friend in the hospital told me he had set out behind myself, and taken a candle with him and given a farewell visit to his birds, and almost cried about

them and about myself, and then departed for good
to conceal himself, in some other part of the city,
probably, but exactly where his friend had no way
of guessing. And it was a further evidence of the
priest's good feeling to myself (if such were needed)
that he had left a sum of a hundred livres for me
towards the costs of my future movements.

I left the Hôtel Dieu at midnight to wander very
melancholy about the streets for a time, and finally
came out upon the river's bank, where some small
vessels hung at a wooden quay. I saw them in
moonlight (for now the rain was gone), and there
rose in me such a feeling as I had often experienced
as a lad in another parish than the Mearns, to see
the road that led from strangeness past my mother's
door. The river seemed a pathway out of mystery
and discontent to the open sea, and the open sea
was the same that beat about the shores of Britain,
and my thought took flight there and then to Britain,
but stopped for a space, like a wearied bird, upon
the town Dunkerque. There is one who reads this
who will judge kindly, and pardon when I say that
I felt a sort of tenderness for the lady there, who
was not only my one friend in France, so far as I
could guess, but, next to my mother, the only
woman who knew my shame and still retained regard for me. And thinking about Scotland and about
Dunkerque, and seeing that watery highway to them
both, I was seized with a great repugnance for the
city I stood in, and felt that I must take my feet
from there at once. Father Hamilton was lost to
me : that was certain. I could no more have found

him in this tanglement of streets and strange faces than I could have found a needle in a haystack, and I felt disinclined to make the trial. Nor was I prepared to avail myself of his offer of the coach and horses, for to go travelling again in them would be to court Bicêtre anew.

There was a group of busses or barges at the quay, as I have said, all huddled together as it were animals seeking warmth, with their bows nuzzling each other, and on one of them there were preparations being made for her departure. A cargo of empty casks was piled up in her, lights were being hung up at her bow and stern, and one of her crew was ashore in the very act of casting off her ropes. At a flash it occurred to me that I had here the safest and the speediest means of flight.

I ran at once to the edge of the quay and clumsily propounded a question as to where the barge was bound for.

" Rouen or thereabouts," said the master.

I asked if I could have a passage, and chinked my money in my pocket.

My French might have been but middling, but Lewis d'Or talks in a language all can understand.

Ten minutes later we were in the fairway of the river running down through the city which, in that last look I was ever fated to have of it, seemed to brood on either hand of us like bordering hills, and at morning we were at a place by name Triel.

Of all the rivers I have seen I must think the Seine the finest. It runs in loops like my native Forth, sometimes in great, wide stretches that have the semblance of moorland lochs. In that fine weather, with a sun that was most genial, the country round about us basked and smiled. We moved upon the fairest waters, by magic gardens, and the borders of enchanted little towns. Now it would be a meadow sloping backward from the bank, where reeds were nodding, to the horizon; now an orchard standing upon grass that was the rarest green, then a village with rusty roofs and spires and the continual chime of bells, with women washing upon stones or men silent upon wherries fishing. Every link of the river opened up a fresher wonder; if not some poplared isle that had the invitation to a childish escapade, 'twould be another town, or the garden of a château, maybe, with ladies walking stately on the lawns, perhaps alone, perhaps with cavaliers about them as if they moved in some odd woodland minuet. I can mind of songs that came from open windows, sung in women's voices; of girls that stood drawing water and smiled on us as we passed, at home in our craft of fortune, and still the lucky roamers seeing the world so pleasantly without the trouble of moving a step from our galley fire.

Sometimes in the middle of the days we would stop at a red-faced, ancient inn, with bowers whose tables almost had their feet dipped in the river, and there would eat a meal and linger on a pot of wine while our barge fell asleep at her tether and dreamt of the open sea. About us in these inns came the kind country-people and talked of trivial things for the mere sake of talking, because the weather was sweet and God so gracious; homely sounds would waft from the byres and from the barns—the laugh of bairns, the whistle of boys, the low of cattle.

At night we moored wherever we might be, and once I mind of a place called Andelys, selvedged with chalky cliffs and lorded over by a castle called Gaillard, that had in every aspect of it something of the clash of weapons and of trumpet-cry. The sky shone blue through its gaping gables and its crumbling windows like so many eyes; the birds that wheeled all round it seemed to taunt it for its inability. The old wars over, the deep fosse silent, the strong men gone—and there at its foot the thriving town so loud with sounds of peaceful trade! Whoever has been young, and has the eye for what is beautiful and great and stately, must have felt in such a scene that craving for companionship that tickles like a laugh within the heart—that longing for some one to feel with him, and understand, and look upon with silence. In my case 'twas two women I would have there with me just to look upon this Gaillard and the town below it.

Then the bending, gliding river again, the willow and the aspen edges, the hazy orchards and the emerald swards; hamlets, towns, farm-steadings, châteaux, kirks, and mills; the flying mallard, the leaping perch, the silver dawns, the starry nights, the ripple of the water in my dreams, and at last the city of Rouen. My ship of fortune went no further on.

I slept a night in an inn upon the quay, and early the next morning, having bought a pair of boots to save my red shoes, I took the road over a hill that left Rouen and all its steeples, reeking at the bottom of a bowl. I walked all day, through woods and meadows and trim small towns and orchards, and late in the gloaming came upon the port of Havre de Grace.

The sea was sounding there, and the smell of it was like a salutation. I went out at night from my inn, and fairly joyed in its propinquity, and was so keen on it that I was at the quay before it was well daylight. The harbour was full of vessels. It was not long ere I got word of one that was in trim for Dunkerque, to which I took a passage, and by favour of congenial weather came upon the afternoon of the second day.

Dunkerque was more busy with soldiers than ever, all the arms of France seemed to be collected there, and ships of war and flat-bottomed boats innumerable were in the harbour.

At the first go-off I made for the lodgings I had parted from so unceremoniously on the morning of that noisy glass coach.

The house, as I have said before, was over a baker's shop, and was reached by a common outer stair that rose from a court-yard behind. Though internally the domicile was well enough, indeed had a sort of old-fashioned gentility, and was kept by a woman whose man had been a colonel of dragoons, but now was a tippling pensioner upon the king, and his own wife's labours, it was, externally, somewhat mean, the place a solid merchant of our own country might inhabit, but scarce the place wherein to look for royal blood.   What was my astonishment, then, when, as I climbed the stair, I came face to face with the Prince!

I felt the stair swing off below me and half distrusted my senses, but I had the presence of mind to take my hat off.

"*Bon jour, Monsieur,*" said he, with a slight hiccough, and I saw that he was flushed and meant to pass with an evasion.   There and then a daft notion to explain myself and my relations with the priest who had planned his assassination came to me, and I stopped and spoke.

"Your Royal Highness——" I began, and at that he grew purple.

"*C'est un drôle de corps!*" said he, and, always speaking in French, said he again:

"You make an error, Monsieur; I have not the honour of Monsieur's acquaintance," and looked at me with a bold eye and a disconcerting.

"Greig," I blurted, a perfect lout, and surely as blind as a mole that never saw his desire, "I had the honour to meet your Royal Highness at Versailles."

"My Royal Highness!" said he, this time in English.   "I think Monsieur mistakes himself." And then, when he saw how crestfallen I was, he smiled and hiccoughed again.   "You are going to call on our good Clancarty," said he.   "In that case please tell him to translate to you the proverb, *Qui plus sait plus se tait.*"

"There is no necessity, Monsieur," I answered promptly.   "Now that I look closer I see I was mistaken. The person I did you the honour to take you for was one in whose opinion (if he took the trouble to think of me at all) I should have liked to re-establish myself, that was all."

In spite of his dissipation there was something noble in his manner—a style of the shoulders and the hands, a poise of the head that I might practise for years and come no closer on than any nowt upon my father's fields. It was that which I remember best of our engagement on the stair, and that at the last of it he put out his hand to bid me good-day.

"My name," says he, "is Monsieur Albany so long as I am in Dunkerque. *À bon entendeur salut!* I hope we may meet again, Monsieur Greig." He looked down at the black boots I had bought me in Rouen. "If I might take the liberty to suggest it," said he, smiling, "I should abide by the others. I have never seen their wearer wanting wit, *esprit*, and prudence—which are qualities that at this moment I desire above all in those that count themselves my friends."

And with that he was gone. I watched him descend the remainder of the stair with much deliberation, and did not move a step myself until the tip of his scabbard had gone round the corner of the close.

CHAPTER XXX

A GUID CONCEIT OF MYSELF LEADS ME FAR ASTRAY

CLANCARTY and Thurot were playing cards, so intent upon that recreation that I was in the middle of the floor before they realised who it was the servant had ushered in.

"*Mon Dieu! Monsieur Blanc-bec! Il n'y a pas de petit chez soi!*" cried Thurot, dropping his hand, and they jumped to their feet to greet me.

"I'll be hanged if you want assurance, child," said Clancarty, surveying me from head to foot as if I were some curiosity. "Here's your exploits ringing about the world, and not wholly to your credit, and you must walk into the very place where they will find the smallest admiration."

"Not meaning the lodging of Captain Thurot," said I. "Whatever my reputation may be with the world, I make bold to think he and you will believe me better than I may seem at the first glance."

"The first glance!" cried his lordship. "Gad, the first glance suggests that Bicêtre agreed with our Scotsman. Sure, they must have fed you on oatmeal. I'd give a hatful of louis d'or to see Father Hamilton, for if he throve so marvellously in the flesh as his secretary he must look like the side of St. Eloi. One obviously grows fat on regicide— fatter than a few poor devils I know do upon devotion to princes."

Thurot's face assured me that I was as welcome there as ever I had been. He chid Clancarty for his badinage, and told me he was certain all along that the first place I should make for after my flight from Bicêtre (of which all the world knew) would be Dunkerque. "And a good thing too, M. Greig," said he.

"Not so good," says I, "but what I must meet on your stair the very man——"

"Stop!" he cried, and put his finger on his lip. "In these parts we know only a certain M. Albany, who is, my faith! a good friend of your own if you only knew it."

"I scarcely see how that can be," said I. "If any man has a cause to dislike me it is his Roy——"

"M. Albany," corrected Thurot.

"It is M. Albany, for whom, it seems, I was the decoy in a business that makes me sick to think on. I would expect no more than that he had gone out there to send the officers upon my heels, and for me to be sitting here may be simple suicide."

Clancarty laughed. " 'Tis the way of youth," said he, "to attach far too much importance to itself. Take our word for it, M. Greig, all France is not scurrying round looking for the nephew of Andrew Greig. Faith, and I wonder at you, my dear Thurot, that has an Occasion here—a veritable Occasion—

and never so much as says bottle. Stap me if I
have a friend come to me from a dungeon without
wishing him joy in a glass of burgundy!"

The burgundy was forthcoming, and his lordship
made the most of it, while Captain Thurot was at
pains to assure me that my position was by no means
so bad as I considered it. In truth, he said, the
police had their own reasons for congratulating
themselves on my going out of their way. They
knew very well, as M. Albany did, that I had been
the catspaw of the priest, who was himself no better
than that same, and for that reason as likely to
escape further molestation as I was myself.

Thurot spoke with authority, and hinted that he
had the word of M. Albany himself for what he said.
I scarcely knew which pleased me best—that I
should be free myself or that the priest should have
a certain security in his concealment.

I told them of Buhot, and how oddly he had shown
his complacence to his escaped prisoner in the tavern
of the Duke of Burgundy's Head. At that they
laughed.

"Buhot!" cried his lordship. "My faith! Ned
must have been tickled to see his escaped prisoner
in such a cosy *cachette* as the Duke's Head, where he
and I, and Andy Greig—ay! and this same priest—
tossed many a glass. *Ciel!* the affair runs like a
play. All it wants to make this the most delightful
of farces is that you should have Father Hamilton
outside the door to come in at a whistle. Art sure
the fat old man is not in your waistcoat pocket?
Anyhow, here's his good health—sure, I owe the

poor soul no grudge, though he made a fool of himself to no purpose."

Thurot wanted to know where the priest was.

I protested I knew no better than himself.

He smiled slyly and winked, and shrugged his shoulders, manifestly unbelieving, but willing to allow something for a sort of chivalry.

"Upon my honour, Captain Thurot," I said, "I have no idea where Father Hamilton is, and here's his own writing to prove it," and with that I handed him the priest's letter.

It convinced him that what I said was true, and then he surprised me by expressing a wish that the unfortunate wretch might manage out of the country. "You may wonder at that, M. Paul," said he "more particularly as I have this cause at my heart, and the Prince that is the back-bone of it there too. But you must know that though I hate the man's calling I liked this priest in a fashion. Set it down to my heart that has no logic and must ever be quarrelling with my head. I am not without a sort of gratitude for this murderous clerk that planned to put an end incontinent to the finest of adventures. This affair of Hamilton's has made his Royal Highness more dear than ever, and to be looked upon as of more consequence than ever, to the court, and to the king of France, who has himself suffered the danger of assassination. Our fat priest, aiming a stupid empty pistol at poor Buhot, has gone far to rid the palaces of these rotten Jesuits, and given Scotland again to the Stuarts."

All this was, at the moment, a sort of Greek to

me, but seemed not at all inconsistent with the treatment Father Hamilton and myself had met with in Bicêtre, the comparative ease of our escape, and the complacence of M. Albany.

Thurot saw my bewilderment and was at pains to make the thing clearer. He began with the premiss that Father Hamilton was a mumming fool, which I could scarce subscribe to, but did not argue with him, and that the priest had been what he called a forced card.

"A forced card?" said I.

A forced card, he explained, was one specially thrust upon a person by a juggler who had a trick to do. The person imposed on took what he thought was his own choice in cards, but all the time was taking the very one the juggler chose for him. In the same way the Jesuits had had Father Hamilton thrust upon them because the juggling government knew he was the least dangerous card in the pack. When he had done his part of the trick, he was permitted to escape in order that he might be followed, and so, perhaps, unconsciously lead to the discovery of his employers. Fleuriau was the man wanted particularly, and it seemed that Fleuriau had been got and now was in a jail himself.

"*Enfin*," concluded Thurot, "the game's played, and Father Hamilton may go to the devil at his leisure, for even M. Albany is desirous that nothing should be done to him."

I swore it was impossible we could have been traced to the Hôtel Dieu after our flight from Bicêtre.

"Bah!" said Thurot, flicking his fingers; "what an innocent is this to be accomplice to an assassin! Why, M. Greig, what do you think your Master Bernard was? He was the spy upon the priest's movements all the time!"

"Bernard?" I cried, astonished.

"Who else?" cried Thurot. "But for Bernard there would have been a bullet for Buhot."

This intelligence greatly disturbed me, for a reason that Thurot nor Clancarty could guess. If the Swiss had been a spy upon the priest he was just as like to be a spy upon myself, and here had I been trusting him with the most delicate secret, the correspondence between Miss Walkinshaw and myself. There was even the probability that he had made use of the same to inform himself upon the future movements of the priest as we sailed over the country in the coach.

What I was to do now that I was back in Dunkerque, and apparently in no danger of molestation, was yet to be decided. I gladly availed myself of Thurot's offer of accommodation, and having visited a *friseur* to have my hair dressed I went later in the afternoon upon a call to Madame. The nearer I came upon her lodging the more did my shyness master me, and I felt the worse because there mingled with it the fear that Bernard might already have exposed our correspondence and made her ridiculous in the eyes of the world. It was true that she herself had chosen him as the vehicle of our letters, but what did she know, poor dear! of the coil of political intrigues all around her? I went up the Rue de la Boucherie counting my steps. If there were more than thirty between the corner of the street and her door, it would mean (I told myself) that all was over between the lady and me; if there were less—well, I must be still in her good favour. With fair play at my spanging I daresay there would have been many more than the thirty paces, but I took the latter half of the street at a moorland stride and reached the stair-foot in twenty-eight. I went up the steps with my breast drumming, and had hardly a breath left in my body when the lady met me on her threshold with a cry of joy.

"Oh laddie! laddie!" she said, "you're just as welcome as the spring," and before I could say a word she had her arms about my neck and gave me the warmest of salutes. I stood a second or two dumfoundered as she smiled up in my face, and then called up my courage in an effort to respond with a similar salute, but no sooner was my arm about her waist than she drew back and waved me off.

"No, no," said she laughing; "there's one retort there must be no swithering over or the chance is gone and there you had it. My salute was but a thanksgiving to see you safe and sound again. Sit you down, Mr. Greig, till I look at you, and tell me your tidings."

"I think I kept you pretty well informed on them in all my letters," said I, and she turned somewhat red.

"Yes, yes!" said she, "but I like my news by word of mouth, too, and I never heard a word of you

since you wrote from the Hôtel Dieu. My poor
Master Paul!"

There was, for some reason or other, as much
amusement as sympathy in her expression, but I
heeded none of that, being taken up by herself.

I think I never saw her look better than on that
day. Her eyes were large and sparkling with what
it was no flattery to think was a pleasure at seeing
me again ; her cheeks glowed, the shoulders her
dress revealed were of satin, like a child's. She
had a voice that warmed one like a cordial, a smile
that was like a blink of sun. I sat on a chair turning my hat and staring.

"Poor Isobel Fortune!" said she, "what a fine
brisk informative good man she lost! Am I to
think he never got a kiss in his life before and is
frightened at me? I pray you excuse me, kind sir,"
she went on, and swept the floor with an extravagant
courtesy.

I could only smile at her humour and inwardly
curse my own unreadiness.

"Oh!" she cried, "it's leevin' after all!" She
began to walk round my chair and comment upon
my dress that was considerably more ornamental
than when she had seen me last. "H'm—Mechlin,
nae less, and point d'Espagne to his hat, and siller
buckles to his shoon. Oh Mr. Greig! Mr. Greig!
am I out of your good graces that you have not
brought the red ones that I like?"

"Confound the red ones!" I cried. "I wore
them all the time because I promised you, and they
were constantly getting me into trouble."

She reddened again and bit her lip, changed the subject, and soon we were in the heart of my adventures. It was "Oh, Mr. Greig!" and "*Mon Dieu*, M. Greig!" and "Poor Mr. Greig!" but somehow I could not conceal from myself that my narrative fell flat. Even the most sensational parts of it had no surprise for her; the attack on the Prince she hurried me over rather ungraciously, and I could only conclude that my letters had taken the edge off the interest in my exploits. For the priest she had scarcely less condemnation than Clancarty had had, and was not even surprised when I passed on Thurot's assurance that Father Hamilton's term of imprisonment at Bicêtre was considered sufficient punishment for his crime. All the time I was telling her these things, I wondered how I could introduce Bernard and his espionage.

She saved me the trouble by breaking in upon my narrative to say the Swiss was on his way back to Dunkerque.

"I hope I may never come across him, then," said I, "for the man's no better than a rogue."

She shrugged her shoulders in the French manner.

"Well," said she, "if I am to be honoured by your visits you must make up your mind to tolerate the sight and the service of Bernard, for he comes back to my employ again. I find I cannot do without him; this fellow I have now is a cuif, as we say at home, and I'm only too glad to get my Bernard back."

"If you want a spy he certainly has all the

qualifications," I said, expecting to stagger her, and fearing I was precipitating an unpleasant revelation for myself.

"Spy!" said she, eyeing me quickly. "I know all about that. And he apparently spied to very good purpose, too. I have no fault to find with him. You foolish fellow, he was there wholly in my interest!"

At this time I cannot but marvel at the vanity and blindness that made me think this confession of the lady's had some relation to my place in her regards. I had accepted Bernard's service with the priest without too closely considering how it happened that he was dismissed in disgrace for drunkenness, and yet retained the confidence of his mistress to that degree that she would trust him in the matter of our correspondence. Now, I thought, I had my explanation—the lady had such an interest in myself and my affairs that she had sacrificed her domestic arrangements for the time being!

"You—you—are too good," I stammered.

"Mercy on us! what's this of it?" cried she in a way that made me keep my mouth shut out of caution, though I still cherished my conceit. I fancied she jumped at my thoughts, for she became confused herself and then more merry than ever. She sent me off at the long run pretty well content with myself, though now and then I found the fear intrude that a good part of the merriment was at my own expense.

CHAPTER XXXI

THE BARD OF LOVE WHO WROUGHT WITH
OLD MATERIALS

AND now I will tell of how I set about trimming up an old song for a new purpose. The thing is no way creditable to me, and I cannot pretend to find much excuse in the fact that many a better man than I, and bards more notable, have given one name or another (as the occasion suited) to the women of their imagining.

Only once since I had torn up my stanzas in the house of Hazel Den had I indulged in shaping rhyme; it was in Versailles the day that Buhot disturbed me, and—to make a breast of it—a good deal of my poem was the same that I had torn to pieces and cast upon the washing-green. A boy's love, I take it, is very much an abstract business after all, unwittingly engaged upon himself more than on the one who is its impulse. However that may be, 'tis certain my old poem made a great deal of myself and little of Miss Isobel, so that it was all the easier furbished up for Clementina.

Of that lady I saw little for a week after my return, for she had given me to understand that she

would be much engaged, but I saw plenty of her
infancy. There was great to-do in Dunkerque in
these days, but one there was walked through
it like a desert. I would dare to go at nights and
watch the glow of her window from the other side
of the street, but by day I durst not venture there
lest I should look ridiculous in my insistence, and so
I sought the dunes, travelling over them like a man
that trod on air, chaunting my stanzas to myself.
There was more of the leaping Linn of Earn than
the noisy Straits of Dover in them, and something
more of the homely oaten reed in the performance
than properly suited this new lady of my dream as
I see now when I return to them, but at the time
that fact escaped me. It was herself that showed
me how.

I was frequent on the dunes as I have said, and
there was one particular grassy cove where I would
lie for hours in a seclusion. Who should come to
discover me there one day but the lady herself? At
the time the thing seemed providential, but a remark
that Thurot let drop long after makes me think he
had a hand in it, and that our rencontre in this
lonely place was designed.

At all events, she came like a fairy (as I thought,
though I confess the association extravagant considering everything), and cried, "Oh, Mr. Greig!"
with the accent of astonishment, and hoped she had
not (in the homely phrase) spoiled my tryst with
any one. We sat in a drift of sand, breathing
the inebriating sea. The sun was shining, fields
behind us rang with birds. A great day, and

yet half filled with silent spaces, for she looked on the sea and I on her, and there was no need for a word to say. But finally we came to talk upon my prospects.

I ruefully confessed myself ashamed of my dependence upon Thurot, and swore I would herd swine for an honest living, but that meanwhile Thurot bade me wait the ripening of some plans he had for me.

"Yes, yes! I know about that," said she, "he has a scheme for you to join the army, and I think indeed it is the one career for a man of spirit."

"The one career for me just now," I said quickly, "is whichever will keep me in Dunkerque," and I felt appalled at my own temerity.

She reddened slightly as if she understood, but hurried on to enlarge upon the opportunities that the profession offered. It was Thurot's idea, it seemed; he had spoken to her upon the matter, and she had a friend who was able to promise an early appointment to a lieutenancy in the Regiment d'Auvergne.

"The Regiment d'Auvergne!" I said. "I had preferred it had been with some of the Scots corps, though none could be happier than I to do a decent day's darg in any corps."

Just as I said it there came upon the sunny air the roar of a cannon fired further along the coast. It shivered at once my career of cards, for it was something more than a cannon shot to me, it was no less than a threat at Scotland. From where we sat together I could see the outmost of a train of boats that were destined to make the descent upon my native land.

"There goes the one argument against such a career for me!" I said. "Soldiering might suit with my fancy very well, but I have not forgotten Scotland enough to join in an attack on her."

"And do you think I have forgotten, Mr. Greig?" cried she warmly. "Fie! Fie! that is to give me small credit for constancy to what I love. The very reason why we chose the Regiment d'Auvergne for you was because it will have no share in this invasion, if ever it takes place."

I think she would have had little difficulty in making me jump at the opportunity but for the knowledge that I had myself gathered, in a casual conversation with Thurot some days previously, that this same Regiment d'Auvergne was stationed in the other end of France, many a weary league away from where my interests lay. Nor did the fact that I should have a countryman for major of that mountain corps in any way mitigate my objections to the same.

I must have shown my repugnance in my face.

"Then," said she shortly, denting the sand with her heel, "I'm to conclude that M. Thurot's scheme for his guest has come to nothing."

"It is a good enough scheme," I said, "but it might be amended. If the Regiment d'Avergne was anywhere else than where it is; if it was, more correctly, in Dunkerque or there was no one here to think of, I should take what offered and thankful to get it, but—but——"

"Don't be a gowk!" said she quickly.

"Gowk or no," said I. "I would prefer some other appointment."

"But this one's yours," she hastened to tell me. "I took the trouble to secure it for you yesterday."

"Indeed!" I cried, with just as much amazement as chagrin. "And whom am I to thank besides yourself for this brisk interest in my poor affairs?"

"Never mind!" said she. "Consider it wholly the act of one that likes you."

"Meaning yourself?"

"Oh, laddie, ye maun spare my blushes!" she said laughingly.

"It is a poor word 'likes,'" I said. "There's one that has just the same number of letters but sounds ever so much bonnier, and that's the one I would sooner hear you use. Here am I," I went on rising on the sands and finding myself awkwardly on my knees before her though that was not the intention, "and I'm thinking night and day of you and seeking lonely places that I may think on you, and writing silly verses for you, and counting Dunkerque the dearest place in the world just because you are in it, and you must take the first occasion that offers to drive me for the second time to the other end of the country."

"Verses!" she cried, with sparkling eyes. "Oh you must be showing me these. It would take a heap of verses to make up for the stilted sentences of your letters."

"Stilted!" I cried. "It was because I dare not put my heart in a single one of them."

"If your heart's in the verses, Paul," said she, "then they must be very fine verses indeed. Show me them."

"No, no," I said, "I dare not," and I sank again upon the sand, vexed at my confidence and dreading her irony.

"Now show them to me," she repeated softly.

"What interest can they have for you?" I said. "You would only laugh at my boldness."

"The boldness that takes the wings of poetry," said she, "will never offend a woman. That's if the verses are anyway decently done."

"They could never be well enough done for the subject," I said.

"Of course not," said she, "but I cannot be the judge of that until I read them myself. And if I'm not to have the privilege I must just be going."

"There they are then," said I, drawing them from my pocket and casting them on her knees.

"Foolish Paul!" she said, looking at my trembling fingers and my agitated face. "Shall I read them now or take them home with me?"

"You can read them now," I said, willing to bring matters to a head. She unrolled the manuscript and began to read. The words seemed much finer on her lips than ever they had been in my mind, but yet I owned them insufficient and felt ashamed.

"O maid of the mountain, if fortune were mine,
  A hero half-hearted no longer I'd pine,
  But ride on some morning across to your home,
  Saying 'Sweet one, my darling, art willing to come?'"

"Well, that's to the point at least," said she,

smoothing out the page. "There's nae time wasted in preliminaries. And yet I canna but think I wad mak' a bonny-like object cockit up on a pillion."

I tore a tuft of grass between my fingers and prayed her to go on.

" O then would the harp-string sound sweet in the hall,
   (Though the voice of my loved one were sweeter than all,)
   The flambeau would flicker on target and spear,
   (Though the eyes of my love were more dazzling and clear,)

" And there would be strawberries plucked from the dew,
   And the trout of the river made ready for you ;
   If you tired of the milk and the curd of the fold,
   I'd buy of the wine, love, with ruddy round gold."

" I've no great *gout* o' the bill-of-fare, Mr. Paul," she interposed. " It wants variety. A man that keepit a coffee-hoose on thae lines wadna be muckle fashed wi' customers."

" The looms of the valley would weave for your gowns,
   And I'd send for rich jewels to all the far towns,—

" Come now, that's no' sae Hielan'. It's weel put down, and shows a kind of an understandin' o' us."

" The maids of the valley would wait by your side,
   And all my stout gallants your errands would ride."

" H'm," said she suspiciously ; " whatna valley's this ? It seems to myself to smack a little o' Clydesdale and the heather o' Ballageich. But let us on wi' the ballad ! "

" But far have I wandered, 'tis heather no more,
   And I a poor exile just rap at your door,
   Just rap at your door ; fame nor fortune is here,
   But only the love of your true chevalier."

She crushed the paper in her hand and gave a sob.

"Oh God!" she cried, "have they all but the one story?" and she looked as if she were to burst in tears. This was scarcely what I had expected from my duans.

"Now what can I have done that's vexed you?" I cried, upon my knees again and this time meaning it and ready to make the uttermost fool of myself in the way of grovelling. When she saw my intention she jumped to her feet.

"Oh, what a shame! What a shame!" she cried, "that I should listen for a single moment to a bairn new from his mother's side. And it is just my deserts that he should punish me as you have done."

I made to speak.

"Hush!" she commanded. "Not a word that you'll think on again with regret. Your poem is doubtless a good enough poem, though I am no judge of such things to venture an opinion, and there's a good deal of sense in the last stanza (though that is not to say it is lacking in the others), but I'm sure it's not half good enough for her it was intended for, and that was never Clementina Walkinshaw, but one that more deserved your rhyming."

I made to protest, full of shame at her discovery.

"No! no!" she cried, "I am no more to you than the echo of a voice among the hills. Do not tell me that her for whose sake you steeped your hands in blood is clean gone from your mind already, or else

I am bound to think the fancy of Paul Greig a very fickle thing indeed. When you have travelled the world a little more you will know yourself better, and you will thank me that I laughed at your whim and saw well enough I was but the proxy for another in your passionate eyes. Fie! Paul Greig, the sooner you are eidently at work the better, and shaping a fortune instead of fine phrases."

I was properly abashed, but still unwise.

"I love your very chiding!" I cried.

At that she stamped her foot and thrust her hair behind her ears. Her eyes flashed and her lips curled.

"You are surely the blindest fool ever stepped off heather," she cried, "that thinks me a suitable object for your love or that I'm without a preference of my own. Put your ballad in your pocket, Mr. Greig. To be honest with you, I could find it in my heart to wish it were really meant for me or that I deserved it, but when I want ballads I must seek for another maker of them."

CHAPTER XXXII

THE DUEL IN THE AUBERGE GARDEN

WHOEVER it was that moved at the instigation of Madame on my behalf, he put speed into the business, for the very next day I was told my sous-lieutenancy was waiting at the headquarters of the regiment. A severance that seemed almost impossible to me before I learned from the lady's own lips that her heart was elsewhere engaged was now a thing to long for eagerly, and I felt that the sooner I was out of Dunkerque and employed about something more important than the tying of my hair and the teasing of my heart with thinking, the better for myself. Teasing my heart, I say, because Miss Walkinshaw had her own reasons for refusing to see me any more, and do what I might I could never manage to come face to face with her. Perhaps on the whole it was as well, for what in the world I was to say to the lady, supposing I were privileged, it beats me now to fancy. Anyhow, the opportunity never came my way, though, for the few days that elapsed before I departed from Dunkerque, I spent hours in the Rue de la Boucherie sipping sirops on the terrace of the Café Coignet

K

opposite her lodging, or at night on the old game of humming ancient love-songs to her high and distant window.   All I got for my pains were brief and tantalising glimpses of her shadow on the curtains ; an attenuate kind of bliss it must be owned, and yet counted by Master Red-Shoes (who suffered from nostalgia, not from love, if he had had the sense to know it) a very delirium of delight.

One night there was an odd thing came to pass. But, first of all, I must tell that more than once of an evening, as I would be in the street and staring across at Miss Walkinshaw's windows, I saw his Royal Highness in the neighbourhood.   His cloak might be voluminous, his hat dragged down upon the very nose of him, but still the step was unmistakable.   If there had been the smallest doubt of it, there came one evening when he passed me so close in the light of an oil lamp that I saw the very blotches on his countenance.   What was more, he saw and recognised me, though he passed without any other sign than the flash of an eye and a half-step of hesitation.

" H'm," thinks I, "here's Monsieur Albany looking as if he might, like myself, be trying to content himself with the mere shadows of things."

He saw me more than once, and at last there came a night when a fellow in drink came staving down the street on the side I was on and jostled me in the by-going without a word of apology.

" *Pardonnez, Monsieur !* " said I in irony, with my hat off to give him a hint at his manners.

He lurched a second time against me and put up

his hand to catch my chin, as if I were a wench, "*Mon Dieu! Monsieur Blanc-bec*, 'tis time you were home," said he in French, and stuttered some ribaldry that made me smack his face with an open hand.

At once he sobered with suspicious suddenness if I had had the sense to reflect upon it, and gave me his name and direction as one George Bonnat, of the Marine. "Monsieur will do me the honour of a meeting behind the Auberge Cassard after *petit déjeuner* to-morrow," said he, and named a friend. It was the first time I was ever challenged. It should have rung in the skull of me like an alarm, but I cannot recall at this date that my heart beat a stroke the faster, or that the invitation vexed me more than if it had been one to the share of a bottle of wine.

" It seems a pretty ceremony about a cursed impertinence on the part of a man in liquor," I said, " but I'm ready to meet you either before or after *petit déjeuner*, as it best suits you, and my name's Greig, by your leave."

" Very well, Monsieur Greig," said he ; "except that you stupidly impede the pavement and talk French like a Spanish cow (*comme une vache espagnole*), you seem a gentleman of much accommodation. Eight o'clock then, behind the *auberge*," and off went Sir Ruffler, singularly straight and business-like, with a profound *congé* for the unfortunate wretch he planned to thrust a spit through in the morning.

I went home at once, to find Thurot and Clancarty

at lansquenet. They were as elate at my story as if I had been asked to dine with Louis.

"Gad, 'tis an Occasion!" cried my lord, and helped himself, as usual, with a charming sentiment: "*À demain les affaires sérieuses;* to-night we'll pledge our friend!"

Thurot evinced a flattering certainty of my ability to break down M. Bonnat's guard in little or no time. "A crab, this Bonnat," said he. "Why he should pick a quarrel with you I cannot conceive, for 'tis well known the man is M. Albany's creature. But, no matter, we shall tickle his ribs, M. Paul. *Ma foi!* here's better gaming than your pestilent cards. I'd have every man in the kingdom find an affair for himself once a month to keep his spleen in order."

"This one's like to put mine very much out of order with his iron," I said, a little ruefully recalling my last affair.

"What!" cried Thurot, "after all my lessons! And this Bonnat a crab too! Fie! M. Paul. And what an he pricks a little? a man's the better for some iron in his system now and then. Come, come, pass down these foils, my lord, and I shall supple the arms of our Paul."

We had a little exercise, and then I went to bed. The two sat in my room, and smoked and talked till late in the night, while I pretended to be fast asleep. But so far from sleep was I, that I could hear their watches ticking in their fobs. Some savagery, some fearful want of soul in them, as evidenced by their conversation, horrified me. It was no great matter that I was to risk my life upon a drunkard's folly, but for the first time since I had come into the port of Dunkerque, and knew these men beside my bed, there intruded a fiery sense of alienation. It seemed a dream—a dreadful dream, that I should be lying in a foreign land, upon the eve, perhaps, of my own death or of another manslaughter, and in a correspondence with two such worldly men as those that sat there recalling combats innumerable with never a thought of the ultimate fearful retribution. Compared with this close room, where fumed the wine and weed, and men with never a tie domestic were paying away their lives in the small change of trivial pleasures, how noble and august seemed our old life upon the moors!

When they were gone I fell asleep and slept without a break till Thurot's fingers drummed reveille on my door. I jumped into the sunshine of a lovely day that streamed into the room, soused my head in water and in a little stood upon the street with my companion.

"*Bon matin*, Paul!" he cried cheerfully. "Faith, you sleep *sur les deux oreilles*, and we must be marching briskly to be at M. Bonnat's rendezvous at eight o'clock."

We went through the town and out upon its edge at the Calais road. The sky was blue like another sea; the sea itself was all unvexed by wave; a sweeter day for slaughtering would pass the wit of man to fancy. Thurot hummed an air as he walked along the street, but I was busy thinking of another morning in Scotland, when I got a bitter

lesson I now seemed scandalously soon to have forgotten. By-and-by we came to the inn. It stood
by itself upon the roadside, with a couple of work-
men sitting on a bench in front dipping their morning
crusts in a common jug of wine. Thurot entered
and made some inquiry; came out radiant. "Monsieur is not going to disappoint us, as I feared,"
said he; and led me quickly behind the *auberge*.
We passed through the yard, where a servant-girl
scoured pots and pans and sang the while as if the
world were wholly pleasant in that sunshine; we
crossed a tiny rivulet upon a rotten plank and found
ourselves in an orchard. Great old trees stood
silent in the finest foggy grass, their boughs all
bursting out into blossom, and the air scent-thick-
ened; everywhere the birds were busy; it seemed
a world of piping song. I thought to myself there
could be no more incongruous place nor season for
our duelling, and it was with half a gladness I
looked around the orchard, finding no one there.

"Bah! our good Bonnat's gone!" cried Thurot,
vastly chagrined and tugging at his watch. "That
comes of being five minutes too late, and I cannot,
by my faith, compliment the gentleman upon his
eagerness to meet you."

I was mistaken but for a second; then I spied my
fiery friend of the previous evening lying on his
back beneath the oldest of the trees, his hat tilted
over his eyes, as if he had meant to snatch a little
sleep in spite of the dazzling sunshine. He rose to
his feet on our approach, swept off his hat cour-
teously, and hailed Thurot by name.

"What, you, Antoine! I am ravished! For, look you, the devil's in all my friends that I can get none of them to move a step at this hour of the morning, and I have had to come to M. Greig without a second. Had I known his friend was Captain Thurot I should not have vexed myself. Doubtless M. Greig has no objection to my entrusting my interests as well as his own in the hands of M. le Capitaine?"

I bowed my assent. Captain Thurot cast a somewhat cold and unsatisfied eye upon the ruffler, protesting the thing was unusual.

Bonnat smiled and shrugged his shoulders, put off his coat with much deliberation, and took up his place upon the sward, where I soon followed him.

"Remember, it is no fool, this crab," whispered Captain Thurot as he took my coat from me. "And 'tis two to one on him who prefers the parry to the attack."

I had been reading Molière's "Bourgeois Gentilhomme" the previous morning, and as I faced my assailant I had the fencing-master's words as well as Captain Thurot's running in my ears: "To give and not receive is the secret of the sword." It may appear incredible, but it seemed physically a trivial affair I was engaged upon until I saw the man Bonnat's eye. He wore a smile, but his eye had the steely glint of murder! It was as unmistakable as if his tongue confessed it, and for a second I trembled at the possibilities of the situation. He looked an unhealthy dog; sallow

exceedingly on the neck, which had the sinews so
tight they might have twanged like wire, and on his
cheeks, that he seemed to suck in with a gluttonous
exultation such as a gross man shows in front of a
fine meal.

"Are you ready, gentlemen?" said Thurot; and
we nodded. "Then in guard!" said he.

We saluted, fell into position and thrust simul-
taneously in tierce, parrying alike, then opened
more seriously.

In Thurot's teaching of me there was one lesson
he most unweariedly insisted on, whose object was
to keep my point in a straight line and parry in the
smallest possible circles. I had every mind of it
now, but the cursed thing was that this Bonnat
knew it too. He fenced, like an Italian, wholly
from the wrist, and, crouched upon his knees, hus-
banded every ounce of energy by the infrequency
and the brevity of his thrusts. His lips drew back
from his teeth, giving him a most villainous aspect,
and he began to press in the lower lines.

In a side-glance hazarded I saw the anxiety of
Thurot's eye and realised his apprehension. I broke
ground, and still, I think, was the bravo's match but
for the alarm of Thurot's eye. It confused me so
much that I parried widely and gave an opening for
a thrust that caught me slightly on the arm, and
dyed my shirt-sleeve crimson in a moment.

"Halt!" cried Thurot, and put up his arm.

I lowered my weapon, thinking the bout over, and
again saw murder in Bonnat's eye. He lunged
furiously at my chest, missing by a miracle.

"*Scélérat!*" cried Thurot, and, in an uncontrollable fury at the action, threw himself upon Bonnat and disarmed him.

They glared at each other for a minute, and Thurot finally cast the other's weapon over a hedge. "So much for M. Bonnat!" said he. "This is our valiant gentleman, is it? To stab like an assassin!"

"*Oh, malédiction!*" said the other, little abashed, and shrugging his shoulders as he lifted his coat to put it on. "Talking of assassination, I but did the duty of the executioner in his absence, and proposed to kill the man who meditated the same upon the Prince."

"The Prince!" cried Thurot. "Why 'tis the Prince's friend, and saved his life!"

"I know nothing about that," said Bonnat; "but do you think I'd be out here at such a cursed early hour fencing if any other than M. Albany had sent me? *Pardieu!* the whole of you are in the farce, but I always counted you the Prince's friend, and here you must meddle when I do as I am told to do!"

"And you tell me, Jean Bonnat, that you take out my friend to murder him by M. Albany's command?" cried Thurot incredulous.

"What the devil else?" replied the bravo. "'Tis true M. Albany only mentioned that M. des Souliers Rouges was an obstruction in the Rue de la Boucherie and asked me to clear him out of Dunkerque, but 'twere a tidier job to clear him altogether. And here is a great pother about an English hog!"

I was too busily stanching my wound, that was

scarce so serious as it appeared, to join in this dispute, but the allusion to the Prince and the Rue de la Boucherie extremely puzzled me. I turned to Bonnat with a cry for an explanation.

"What!" I says, "does his Royal Highness claim any prerogative to the Rue de la Boucherie? I'm unconscious that I ever did either you or him the smallest harm, and if my service—innocent enough as it was—with the priest Hamilton was something to resent, his Highness has already condoned the offence."

"For the sake of my old friend M. le Capitaine here I shall give you one word of advice," said Bonnat, "and that is, to evacuate Dunkerque as sharply as you may. M. Albany may owe you some obligement, as I've heard him hint himself, but nevertheless your steps will be safer elsewhere than in the Rue de la Boucherie."

"There is far too much of the Rue de la Boucherie about this," I said, "and I hope no insult is intended to certain friends I have or had there."

At this they looked at one another. The bravo (for so I think I may at this time call him) whistled curiously and winked at the other, and, in spite of himself, Captain Thurot was bound to laugh.

"And has M. Paul been haunting the Rue de la Boucherie, too?" said he. "That, indeed, is to put another face on the business. 'Tis, *ma foi!* to expect too much of M. Albany's complaisance. After that there is nothing for us but to go home. And, harkee! M. Bonnat, no more Venetian work, or, by St. Denys, I shall throw you into the harbour."

"You must ever have your joke, my noble M. le Capitaine," said Bonnat brazenly, and tucked his hat on the side of the head. "M. Blanc-bec there handles *arme blanche* rather prettily, thanks, no doubt, to the gallant commander of the *Roi Rouge*, but if he has a mother let me suggest the wisdom of his going back to her." And with that and a *congé* he left us to enter the *auberge*.

Thurot and I went into the town. He was silent most of the way, ruminating upon this affair, which it was plain he could unravel better than I could, yet he refused to give me a hint at the cause of it. I pled with him vainly for an explanation of the Prince's objection to my person. "I thought he had quite forgiven my innocent part in the Hamilton affair," I said.

"And so he had," said Thurot. "I have his own assurances."

"'Tis scarcely like it when he sets a hired assassin on my track to lure me into a duel."

"My dear boy," said Thurot, "you owe him all—your escape from Bicêtre, which could easily have been frustrated; and the very prospect of the lieutenancy in the Regiment d'Auvergne."

"What! he has a hand in this?" I cried.

"Who else?" said he. "'Tis not the fashion in France to throw unschooled Scots into such positions out of hand, and only princes may manage it. It seems, then, that we have our Prince in two moods, which is not uncommon with the same gentleman. He would favour you for the one reason, and for the other he would cut your throat.

M. Tête-de-fer is my eternal puzzle. And the deuce is that he has, unless I am much mistaken, the same reason for favouring and hating you."

" And what might that be ? " said I.

" Who, rather ? " said Thurot, and we were walking down the Rue de la Boucherie. " Why, then, if you must have pointed out to you what is under your very nose, 'tis the lady who lives here. She is the god from the machine in half a hundred affairs no less mysterious, and I wish she were anywhere else than in Dunkerque. But, anyway, she sent you with Hamilton, and she has secured the favour of the Prince for you, and now—though she may not have attempted it—she has gained you the same person's enmity."

I stopped in the street and turned to him.

"All this is confused enough to madden me," I said, "and rather than be longer in the mist I shall brave her displeasure, compel an audience, and ask her for an explanation."

" Please yourself," said Thurot, and seeing I meant what I said he left me.

CHAPTER XXXIII

It was under the lash of a natural exasperation I went up Mademoiselle's stairs determined on an interview. Bernard (of all men in the world!) responded to my knock. I could have thrashed him with a cane if the same had been handy, but was bound to content myself with the somewhat barren comfort of affecting that I had never set eyes on him before. He smiled at first, as if not unpleased to see me, but changed his aspect at the unresponse of mine.

"I desire to see Miss Walkinshaw," said I.

The rogue blandly intimated that she was not at home. There is more truth in a menial eye than in most others, and this man's fashionable falsehood extended no further than his lips. I saw quite plainly he was acting upon instructions, and, what made it the more uncomfortable for him, he saw that I saw.

"Very well, I shall have the pleasure of waiting in the neighbourhood till she returns," I said, and leaned against the railing. This frightened him somewhat, and he hastened to inform me that he did not know when she might return.

"It does not matter," I said coolly, inwardly pleased to find my courage much higher in the circumstances than I had expected. "If it's midnight she shall find me here, for I have matters of the first importance upon which to consult her."

He was more disturbed than ever, hummed and hawed and hung upon the door-handle, making it very plainly manifest that his instructions had not gone far enough, and that he was unable to make up his mind how he was further to comport himself to a visitor so persistent. Then, unable to get a glance of recognition from me, and resenting further the inconvenience to which I was subjecting him, he rose to an impertinence—the first (to do him justice) I had ever found in him.

"Will Monsieur," said he, "tell me who I shall say called?"

The thrust was scarcely novel. I took it smiling, and "My good rogue," said I, "if the circumstances were more favourable I should have the felicity of giving you an honest drubbing." He got very red. "Come, Bernard," I said, adopting another tone, "I think you owe me some consideration. And will you not, in exchange for my readiness to give you all the information you required some time ago for your employers, tell me the truth and admit that Mademoiselle is within?"

He was saved an answer by the lady herself.

"La! Mr. Greig!" she cried, coming to the door and putting forth a welcoming hand. "My good Bernard has no discrimination, or he should except my dear countryman from my general orders against all visitors." So much in French; and then, as she led the way to her parlour, "My dear man of Mearns, you are as dour as—as dour as——"

"As a donkey," I finished, seeing she hesitated for a likeness. "And I feel very much like that humble beast at this moment."

"I do not wonder at it, " said she, throwing herself in a chair. "To thrust yourself upon a poor lonely woman in this fashion!"

"I am the ass—I have been the ass—it would appear, in other respects as well."

She reddened, and tried to conceal her confusion by putting back her hair, that somehow escaped in a strand about her ears. I had caught her rather early in the morning; she had not even the preparation of a *petit lever*, and because of a certain chagrin at being discovered scarcely looking her best her first remarks were somewhat chilly.

"Well, at least you have persistency, I'll say that of it," she went on, with a light laugh, and apparently uncomfortable. "And for what am I indebted to so early a visit from my dear countryman?"

"It was partly that I might say a word of thanks personally to you for your offices in my poor behalf. The affair of the Regiment d'Auvergne is settled with a suddenness that should be very gratifying to myself, for it looks as if King Louis could not get on another day wanting my distinguished services. I am to join the corps at the end of the month, and must leave Dunkerque forthwith. That being so, it was only proper I should come in my own person to thank you for your good offices."

"Do not mention it," she said hurriedly. "I am only too glad that I could be of the smallest service to you."

"I cannot think," I went on, "what I can have done to warrant your displeasure with me."

"Displeasure!" she replied. "Who said I was displeased?"

"What am I to think, then? I have been refused the honour of seeing you for this past week."

"Well, not displeasure, Mr. Greig," she said, trifling with her rings. "Let us be calling it prudence. I think that might have suggested itself as a reason to a gentleman of Mr. Greig's ordinary intuitions."

"It's a virtue, this prudence, a Greig could never lay claim to," I said. "And I must tell you that, where the special need for it arises now, and how it is to be made manifest, is altogether beyond me."

"No matter," said she, and paused. "And so you are going to the frontier, and are come to say good-bye to me?"

"Now that you remind me that is exactly my object," I said, rising to go. She did not have the graciousness even to stay me, but rose too, as if she felt the interview could not be over a moment too soon. And yet I noticed a certain softening in her manner that her next words confirmed.

"And so you go, Mr. Greig?" she said. "There's but the one thing I would like to say to my friend, and that's that I should like him not to think unkindly of one that values his good opinion—if she were worthy to have it. The honest and unsuspecting come rarely my way nowadays, and now that I'm to lose them I feel like to greet." She was indeed inclined to tears, and her lips were twitching, but I was not enough rid of my annoyance to be moved much by such a demonstration.

"I have profited much by your society, Miss Walkinshaw," I said. "You found me a boy, and what way it happens I do not know, but it's a man that's leaving you. You made my stay here much more pleasant than it would otherwise have been, and this last kindness—that forces me away from you—is one more I have to thank you for."

She was scarcely sure whether to take this as a compliment or the reverse, and, to tell the truth, I meant it half and half.

"I owed all the little I could do to my countryman," said she.

"And I hope I have been useful," I blurted out, determined to show her I was going with open eyes.

Somewhat stricken she put her hand upon my arm. "I hope you will forgive that, Mr. Greig," she said, leaving no doubt that she had jumped to my meaning.

"There is nothing to forgive," I said shortly. "I am proud that I was of service, not to you alone but to one in the interests of whose house some more romantical Greigs than I have suffered. My only complaint is that the person in question seems scarcely to be grateful for the little share I had unconsciously in preserving his life."

"I am sure he is very grateful," she cried hastily, and perplexed. "I may tell you that he was the means of getting you the post in the regiment."

"So I have been told," I said, and she looked a little startled. "So I have been told. It may be that I'll be more grateful by-and-by, when I see what sort of a post it is. In the meantime, I have my gratitude greatly hampered by a kind of inconsistency in the—in the person's actings towards myself!"

"Inconsistency!" she repeated bitterly. "That need not surprise you! But I do not understand."

"It is simply that—perhaps to hasten me to my duties—his Royal Highness this morning sent a ruffian to fight me."

I have never seen a face so suddenly change as hers did when she heard this; for ordinary she had a look of considerable amiability, a soft, kind eye, a ready smile that had the hint (as I have elsewhere said) of melancholy, a voice that, especially in the Scots, was singularly attractive. A temper was the last thing I would have charged her with, yet now she fairly flamed.

"What is this you are telling me, Paul Greig?" she cried, her eyes stormy, her bosom beginning to heave.

"Oh, just that M. Albany (as he calls himself) has some grudge against me, for he sent a man—Bonnat —to pick a quarrel with me, and by Bonnat's own confession the duel that was to ensue was to be *à outrance*. But for the intervention of a friend, half an hour ago, there would have been a vacancy already in the Regiment d'Auvergne."

"Good heavens!" she cried. "You must be mistaken. What object in the wide world could his Royal Highness have in doing you any harm? You were an instrument in the preservation of his life."

I bowed extremely low, with a touch of the courts I had not when I landed first in Dunkerque.

"I have had the distinguished honour, Miss Walkinshaw," I said. "And I should have thought that enough to counterbalance my unfortunate and ignorant engagement with his enemies."

"But why, in Heaven's name, should he have a shred of resentment against you?"

"It seems," I said, "that it has something to do with my boldness in using the Rue de la Boucherie for an occasional promenade."

She put her two hands up to her face for a moment, but I could see the wine-spill in between, and her very neck was in a flame.

"Oh, the shame! the shame!" she cried, and began to walk up and down the room like one demented. "Am I to suffer these insults for ever in spite of all that I may do to prove—to prove——" She pulled herself up short, put down her hands from a face exceedingly distressed, and looked closely at me. "What must you think of me, Mr. Greig?" she asked suddenly in quite a new key.

"What do I think of myself to so disturb you?" I replied. "I do not know in what way I have vexed you, but to do so was not at all in my intention. I must tell you that I am not a politician, and that since I came here these affairs of the Prince

and all the rest of it are quite beyond my understanding. If the cause of the white cockade brought
you to France, Miss Walkinshaw, as seems apparent,
I cannot think you are very happy in it nowadays,
but that is no affair of mine."

She stared at me. "I hope," said she, "you are
not mocking me?"

"Heaven forbid!" I said. "It would be the last
thing I should presume to do, even if I had a reason.
I owe you, after all, nothing but the deepest gratitude."

Beyond the parlour we stood in was a lesser room
that was the lady's boudoir. We stood with our
backs to it, and I know not how much of our conversation had been overheard when I suddenly
turned at the sound of a man's voice, and saw his
Royal Highness standing in the door!

I could have rubbed my eyes out of sheer
incredulity, for that he should be in that position
was as if I had come upon a ghost. He stood with
a face flushed and frowning, rubbing his eyes, and
there was something in his manner that suggested
he was not wholly sober.

"I'll be cursed," said he, "if I haven't been
asleep. Deuce take Clancarty! He kept me at
cards till dawn this morning, and I feel as if I had
been all night on heather. *Pardieu*——!"

He pulled himself up short and stared, seeing me for
the first time. His face grew purple with annoyance.

"A thousand pardons!" he cried with sarcasm,
and making a deep bow. "I was not aware that I
intruded on affairs."

Miss Walkinshaw turned to him sharply.

"There is no intrusion," said she, "but honesty, in the person of my dear countryman, who has come to strange quarters with it. Your Royal Highness has now the opportunity of thanking this gentleman."

"I' faith," said he, "I seem to be kept pretty constantly in mind of the little I owe to this gentleman in spite of himself. Harkee, my good Monsieur, I got you a post; I thought you had been out of Dunkerque by now."

"The post waits, M. Albany," said I, "and I am going to take it up forthwith. I came here to thank the person to whose kindness I owe the post, and now I am in a quandary as to whom my thanks should be addressed."

"My dear Monsieur, to whom but to your countrywoman? We all of us owe her everything, and—egad!—are not grateful enough," and with that he looked for the first time at her with his frown gone.

"Yes, yes," she cried; "we may put off the compliments till another occasion. What I must say is that it is a grief and a shame to me that this gentleman, who has done so much for me—I speak for myself, your Royal Highness will observe—should be so poorly requited."

"Requited!" cried he. "How now? I trust Monsieur is not dissatisfied." His face had grown like paste, his hand, that constantly fumbled at his unshaven chin, was trembling. I felt a mortal pity for this child of kings, discredited and debauched, and yet I felt bound to express myself upon the trap that he had laid for me, if Bonnat's words were true.

"I have said my thanks, M. Albany, very stammeringly for the d'Auvergne office, because I can only guess at my benefactor. My gratitude——"

"Bah!" cried he. "'Tis the scurviest of qualities. A benefactor that does aught for gratitude had as lief be a selfish scoundrel. We want none of your gratitude, Monsieur Greig."

"'Tis just as well, M. Albany," I cried, "for what there was of it is mortgaged."

"*Comment?*" he asked, uneasily.

"I was challenged to a duel this morning with a man Bonnat that calls himself your servant," I replied, always very careful to take his own word for it and assume I spoke to no prince, but simply M. Albany. "He informed me that you had, Monsieur, some objection to my sharing the same street with you, and had given him his instructions."

"Bonnat," cried the Prince, and rubbed his hand across his temples. "I'll be cursed if I have seen the man for a month. Stay!—stay—let me think! Now that I remember, he met me last night after dinner, but—but——"

"After dinner! Then surely it should have been in a more favourable mood to myself, that has done M. Albany no harm," I said. "I do not wonder that M. Albany has lost so many of his friends if he settles their destinies after dinner."

At first he frowned at this and then he laughed outright.

"*Ma foi!*" he cried, "here's another Greig to call

me gomeral to my face," and he lounged to a chair where he sunk in inextinguishable laughter.

But if I had brought laughter from him I had precipitated anger elsewhere.

"Here's a pretty way to speak to his Royal Highness," cried Miss Walkinshaw, her face like thunder. "The manners of the Mearns shine very poorly here. You forget that you speak to one that is your prince, in faith your king!"

"Neither prince nor king of mine, Miss Walkinshaw," I cried, and turned to go. "No, if a hundred thousand swords were at his back. I had once a notion of a prince that rode along the Gallowgate, but I was then a boy, and now I am a man—which you yourself have made me."

With that I bowed low and left them. They neither of them said a word. It was the last I was to see of Clementina Walkinshaw and the last of Charles Edward.

CHAPTER XXXIV

OF MY WINTER CAMPAIGN IN PRUSSIA, AND ANOTHER
MEETING WITH MACKELLAR OF KILBRIDE

I HAVE no intention here of narrating at large what
happened in my short career as a soldier of the
French Army, curious though some of the things
that befell me chanced to be. They may stand for
another occasion, while I hurriedly and briefly
chronicle what led to my second meeting with Mac-
Kellar of Kilbride, and through that same to the
restoration of the company of Father Hamilton, the
sometime priest of Dixmunde.

The Regiment d'Auvergne was far from its native
hills when first I joined it, being indeed on the
frontier of Austria. 'Twas a corps not long em-
bodied, composed of a preposterous number of mere
lads as soft as kail, yet driven to miracles of exertion by drafted veteran officers of other regiments
who stiffened their command with the flat of the
sword. As for my lieutenancy it was nothing to be
proud of in such a battalion, for I herded in a mess
of foul-mouthed scoundrels and learned little of the
trade of soldiering that I was supposed to be taught
in the interval between our departure from the

frontier and our engagement on the field as allies with the Austrians. Of the Scots that had been in the regiment at one time there was only one left—a major named MacKay, that came somewhere out of the Reay country in the shire of Sutherland, and was reputed the drunkenest officer among the allies, yet comported himself, on the strength of his Hielan' extraction, towards myself, his Lowland country-man, with such a ludicrous haughtiness I could not bear the man—no, not from the first moment I set eyes on him!

He was a pompous little person with legs bowed through years of riding horse, and naturally he was the first of my new comrades I introduced myself to when I joined the colours. I mind he sat upon a keg of bullets, looking like a vision of Bacchus, somewhat soiled and pimply, when I entered to him and addressed him, with a certain gladness, in our tongue.

"Humph!" was what he said. "Another of his Royal Highness's Sassenach friends! Here's a wheen of the lousiest French privates ever shook in their breeks in front of a cannon, wanting smeddum and courage drummed into them with a scabbard, and they send me Sassenachs to do the business with when the whole hearty North of Scotland is crawling with the stuff I want particularly."

"Anyway, here I am, major," said I, slightly taken aback at this, "and you'll have to make the best of me."

"Pshaw!" cried he vulgarly and cracked his thumb. "I have small stomach for his Royal Highness's recommendations; I have found in the past that he sends to Austria—him and his friends—only the stuff he has no use for nearer the English Channel, where it's I would like to be this day. They're talking of an invasion, I hear; wouldn't I like to be among the first to have a slap again at Geordie?"

My birse rose at this, which I regarded as a rank treason in any man that spoke my own language even with a tartan accent.

"A slap at Geordie!" I cried. "You made a bonny-like job o't when you had the chance!"

It was my first and last confabulation of a private nature with Major Dugald MacKay. Thereafter he seldom looked the road I was on beyond to give an order or pick a fault, and, luckily, though a pleasant footing with my neighbours has ever been my one desire in life, I was not much put up or down by the ill-will of such a creature.

Like a break in a dream, a space of all unfriended travelling, which is the worst travelling of all, appears my time of marching with the Regiment d'Auvergne. I was lost among aliens—aliens in tongue and sentiment, and engaged, to tell the truth, upon an enterprise that never enlisted the faintest of my sympathy. All I wished was to forget the past (and that, be sure, was the one impossible thing), and make a living of some sort. The latter could not well be more scanty, for my pay was a beggar's, and infrequent at that, and finally it wholly ceased.

I saw the world, so much of it as lies in Prussia, and may be witnessed from the ranks of a marching regiment of the line; I saw life—the life of the tent and the bivouac, and the unforgettable thing of it was death—death in the stricken field among the grinding hoofs of horses, below the flying wheels of the artillery.

And yet if I had had love there—some friend to talk to when the splendour of things filled me; the consciousness of a kind eye to share the pleasure of a sunshine or to light at a common memory; or if I had had hope, the prospect of brighter days and a restitution of my self-respect, they might have been much happier these marching days that I am now only too willing to forget. For we trod in many pleasant places even when weary, by summer fields jocund with flowers, and by autumn's laden orchards. Stars shone on our wearied columns as we rested in the meadows or on the verge of woods, half satisfied with a gangrel's supper and sometimes joining in a song. I used to feel then that here was a better society after all than some I had of late been habituated with upon the coast. And there were towns we passed through: 'twas sweet exceedingly to hear the echo of our own loud drums, the tarantara of trumpets. I liked to see the folks come out although they scarce were friendly, and feel that priceless zest that is the guerdon of the corps, the crowd, the mob—that I was something in a vastly moving thing even if it was no more than the regiment of raw lads called d'Auvergne.

We were, for long in our progress, no part of the main army, some strategy of which we could not guess the reasoning, making it necessary that we should move alone through the country; and to the interest of our progress through these foreign scenes was added the ofttimes apprehension that we might some day suffer an alarm from the regiments of the great Frederick.   Twice we were surprised by night and our pickets broken in, once a native guided us to a *guet-apens*—an ambuscade—where, to do him justice, the major fought like a lion, and by his spirit released his corps from the utmost danger. A war is like a harvest; you cannot aye be leading in, though the common notion is that in a campaign men are fighting even-on.   In the cornfield the work depends upon the weather; in the field of war (at least with us 'twas so) the actual strife must often depend upon the enemy, and for weeks on end we saw them neither tail nor horn, as the saying goes. Sometimes it seemed as if the war had quite forgotten us, and was waging somewhere else upon the planet far away from Prussia.

We got one good from the marching and the waiting; it put vigour in our men.   Day by day they seemed to swell and strengthen, thin faces grew well-filled and ruddy, slouching steps grew confident and firm.   And thus the Regiment d'Auvergne was not so badly figured when we fought the fight of Rosbach that ended my career of glory.

Rosbach !— its name to me can still create a tremor.   We fought it in November month in a storm of driving snow.   Our corps lay out upon the right of Frederick among fields that were new-ploughed for wheat and broken up by ditches.   The d'Auvergnes charged with all the fire of veterans; they were smashed by horse, but rose and fell and rose again though death swept across them like breath from a furnace, scorching and shrivelling all before it. The Prussian and the Austrian guns went rat-a-pat like some gigantic drum upon the braes, and nearer the musketry volleys mingled with the plunge of horse and shouting of commanders so that each sound individually was indistinguishable, but all was blended in one unceasing melancholy hum.

That drumming on the braes and that long melancholy hum are what most vividly remains to me of Rosbach, for I fell early in the engagement, struck in the charge by the sabre of a Prussian horseman that cleft me to the skull in a slanting stroke and left me incapable, but not unconscious, on the field.

I lay for hours with other wounded in the snow The battle changed ground; the noises came from the distance: we seemed to be forgotten. I pitied myself exceedingly. Finally I swounded.

When I came to myself it was night and men with lanterns were moving about the fields gathering us in like blackcock where we lay. Two Frenchmen came up and spoke to me, but what they said was all beyond me for I had clean forgotten every word of their language though that morning I had known it scarcely less fully than my own. I tried to speak in French, it seems, and thought I did so, but in spite of me the words were the broadest lallands Scots such as I had not used since I had run, a bare-legged boy, about the braes of home. And otherwise my faculties were singularly acute, for I remember how keenly I noticed the pitying eye of the younger of the two men.

What they did was to stanch my wound and go away. I feared I was deserted, but by-and-by they returned with another man who held the lantern close to my face as he knelt beside me.

"By the black stones of Baillinish!" said he in an unmistakable Hielan' accent, "and what have I here the night but the boy that harmed the bylie? You were not in your mother's bosom when you got that stroke!"

I saw his smile in the light of his lanthorn, 'twas no other than MacKellar of Kilbride!

He was a surgeon in one of the corps; had been busy at his trade in another part of the field when the two Frenchmen who had recognised me for a Scot had called him away to look to a compatriot.

Under charge of Kilbride (as, in our country fashion, I called him) I was taken in a waggon with several other wounded soldiers over the frontier into Holland, that was, perhaps, the one unvexed part of all the Continent of Europe in these stirring days.

I mended rapidly, and cheery enough were these days of travel in a cart, so cheery that I never considered what the end of them might be, but was content to sit in the sunshine blithely conversing with this odd surgeon of the French army who had been roving the world for twenty years like my own

Uncle Andrew, and had seen service in every army in Europe, but yet hankered to get back to the glens of his nativity, where he hoped his connection with the affair of Tearlach and the Forty-five would be forgotten.

"It's just this way of it, Hazel Den," he would say to me, "there's them that has got enough out of Tearlach to make it worth their while to stick by him and them that has not. I am of the latter. I have been hanging about Paris yonder for a twelve-month on the promise of the body that I should have a post that suited with my talents, and what does he do but get me clapped into a scurvy regiment that goes trudging through Silesia since Whit-sunday, with never a sign of the paymaster except the once and then no more than a tenth of what was due to me. It is, maybe, glory, as the other man said; but my sorrow, it is not the kind that makes a clinking in your pouches."

He had a comfortable deal of money to have so poor an account of his paymaster, and at that I hinted.

"Oh! Allow me for that!" he cried with great amusement at my wonder. "Fast hand at a feast and fast feet at a foray is what the other man said, and I'm thinking it is a very good observation, too. Where would I be if I was lippening on the pay-master?"

"Man! you surely have not been stealing?" said I, with such great innocency that he laughed like to end.

"Stealing!" he cried. "It's no theft to lift a purse in an enemy's country."

"But these were no enemies of yours?" I protested, "though you happen to be doctoring in their midst."

"Tuts! tuts, man!" said he shortly. "When the conies quarrel the quirky one (and that's Sir Fox if ye like to ken) will get his own. There seems far too much delicacy about you, my friend, to be a sporran-soldier fighting for the best terms an army will give you. And what for need you grumble at my having found a purse in an empty house when it's by virtue of the same we're at this moment making our way to the sea?"

I could make no answer to that, for indeed I had had, like the other three wounded men in the cart with me, the full benefit of his purse, wherever he had found it, and but for that we had doubtless been mouldering in a Prussian prison.

It will be observed that MacKellar spoke of our making for the sea, and here it behoves that I should tell how that project arose.

When we had crossed the frontier the first time it was simply because it seemed the easiest way out of trouble, though it led us away from the remnants of the army. I had commented upon this the first night we stopped within the Netherlands, and the surgeon bluntly gave me his mind on the matter. The truth was, he said, that he was sick of his post and meant to make this the opportunity of getting quit of it.

I went as close as I dared upon a hint that the thing looked woundily like a desertion. He picked me up quick enough and counselled me to follow his example, and say farewell to so scurvy a service as that I had embarked on. His advices might have weighed less with me (though in truth I was sick enough of the Regiment d'Auvergne and a succession of defeats) if he had not told me that there was a certain man at Helvoetsluys he knew I should like to see.

"And who might that be?" I asked.

"Who but his reverence himself?" said Kilbride, who dearly loved an effect. "Yon night I met you in the Paris change-house it was planned by them I was with, one of them being Buhot himself of the police, that the old man must be driven out of his nest in the Hôtel Dieu, seeing they had got all the information they wanted from him, and I was one of the parties who was to carry this into effect. At the time I fancied Buhot was as keen upon yourself as upon the priest, and I thought I was doing a wonderfully clever thing to spy your red shoes and give you a warning to quit the priest, but all the time Buhot was only laughing at me, and saw you and recognised you himself in the change-house. Well, to make the long tale short, when we went to the hospital the birds were both of them gone, which was more than we bargained for, because some sort of trial was due to the priest though there was no great feeling against him. Where he had taken wing to we could not guess, but you will not hinder him to come on a night of nights (as we say) to the lodging I was tenanting at the time in the Rue Espade, and throw himself upon my mercy. The muckle hash! I'll allow the insolency of the thing

L

tickled me greatly. The man was a fair object, too;
had not tasted food for two days, and captured my
fancy by a tale I suppose there is no trusting, that
he had given you the last few *livres* he had in the
world."

"That was true enough about the *livres*," I said
with gratitude.

"Was it, faith?" cried Kilbride. "Then I'm
glad I did him the little service that lay in my power,
which was to give him enough money to pay for
posting to Helvoetsluys, where he is now, and grateful enough so far as I could gather from the last
letters I had from him, and also mighty anxious to
learn what became of his secretary."

"I would give the last plack in my pocket to see
the creature," said I.

"Would you indeed?" said Kilbride. "Then
here's the road for you, and it must be a long fur-
lough whatever of it from the brigade of Marshal
Clermont."

CHAPTER XXXV

BRINGS ME TO HELVOETSLUYS IN WINTER WEATHER

KILBRIDE and I parted company with the others once we had got within the lines of Holland; the cateran (as I would sometimes be calling him in a joke) giving them as much money as might take them leisuredly to the south they meant to make for, and he and I proceeded on our way across the country towards the mouth of the River Maas.

It was never my lot before nor since to travel with a more cheerful companion. Not the priest himself had greater humour in his composition, and what was more it was a jollity I was able the better to understand, for while much of Hamilton's *esprit* missed the spark with me because it had a foreign savour, the pawkiness of Kilbride was just the marrow of that I had seen in folks at home. And still the man was strange, for often he had melancholies. Put him in a day of rain and wind and you would hear him singing like a laverock the daftest songs in Erse; or give him a tickle task at haggling in the language of signs with a broad-bottomed bargeman, or the driver of a rattel-van, and the fun would froth in him like froth on boiling milk.

Indeed, and I should say like cream, for this Mac-Kellar man had, what is common enough among the clans in spite of our miscalling, a heart of jeel for the tender moment and a heart of iron for the hard. But black, black, were his vapours when the sun shone, which is surely the poorest of excuses for dolours. I think he hated the flatness of the land we travelled in. To me it was none amiss, for though it was winter I could fancy how rich would be the grass of July in the polders compared with our poor stunted crops at home, and that has ever a cheerful influence on any man that has been bred in Lowland fields. But he (if I did not misread his eye) looked all ungratefully on the stretching leagues that ever opened before us as we sailed on water-ways or jolted on the roads.

"I do not ken how it may be with you, Mr. Greig," he said one day as, somewhere in Brabant, our sluggish vessel opened up a view of canal that seemed to stretch so far it pricked the eye of the setting sun, and the windmills whirled on either hand ridiculous like the games of children—"I do not ken how it may be with you, but I'm sick of this country. It's no better nor a bannock, and me so fond of Badenoch!"

"Indeed and there's a sameness about every part of it," I confessed, "and yet it has its qualities. See the sun on yonder island—'tis pleasant enough to my notion, and as for the folk, they are not the cut of our own, but still they have very much in common with folks I've seen in Ayr."

He frowned at that unbelievingly, and cast a sour

eye upon some women that stood upon a bridge.
"Troth!" said he, "you would not compare these
limmers with our own. I have not seen a light foot
and a right dark eye since ever I put the back of
me to the town of Inverness in the year of 'Fifty-
six.'"

"Nor I since I left the Mearns," I cried, suddenly
thinking of Isobel and forgetting all that lay between
that lass and me.

"Oh! oh!" cried Kilbride. "And that's the way
of it? There's more than Clemie Walkinshaw, is
there? I was ill to convince that a nephew of Andy
Greig's began the game at the age of twenty-odd
with a lady that might have been his mother."

I felt very much ashamed that he should have any
knowledge of this part of my history, and seeing it
he took to bantering me.

"Come, come!" said he, "you must save my
reputation with myself for penetration, for I aye
argued with Buhot that your tanglement with
madame was something short of innocency for all
your mim look, and he was for swearing the lady
had found a fool."

"I am beat to understand how my affairs came to
be the topic of dispute with you and Buhot?" said I,
astonished.

"And what for no'?" said he. "Wasn't the
man's business to find out things, and would you
have me with no interest in a ploy when it turned
up? There were but the two ways of it—you were
all the gomeral in love that Buhot thought you, or
you were Andy Greig's nephew and willing to win

the woman's favour (for all her antiquity) by keeping
Buhot in the news of Hamilton's movements."

"Good God!" I cried, "that was a horrible
alternative!" even then failing to grasp all that he
implied.

"Maybe," he said pawkily; "but you cannot deny
you kept them very well informed upon your master's
movements, otherwise it had gone very hard perhaps
with his Royal Highness."

"Me!" I cried. "I would have as soon informed
upon my father. And who was there to inform?"

Kilbride looked at me curiously as if he half
doubted my innocence. "It is seldom I have found
the man Buhot in a lie of the sort," said he, "but
he led me to understand that what information he
had of the movements of the priest came from yourself."

I jumped to my feet, and almost choked in denying it.

"Oh, very well, very well!" said Kilbride coolly.
"There is no need to make a *fracas* about the matter.
I am just telling you what Buhot told me. And troth!
it was a circumstantial story he had of it; for he
said that the Marshal Duke de Bellisle, and Monsieur
Florentin, and Monsieur Berrier, and all the others
of the Cabinet, had Fleuriau's name and direction
from yourself, and found the plot had some connection with the affair of Damiens. George Kelly, the
Prince's secretary, was another man that told me."
He gazed along the deck of the scow we sat in, as
if thinking hard, and then turned to me with a
hesitating suggestion. "Perhaps," said he, "you

are forgetting. Perhaps you wrote the woman and told her innocently enough, and that would come to the same thing."

I was overwhelmed with confusion at the idea, though the possibility of my letters being used had once before occurred to me.

"Well, if you must know, it is true I wrote some letters to Miss Walkinshaw," I confessed shamefacedly. "But they were very carefully transmitted by Bernard the Swiss to her, for I got her answers back."

He burst out laughing.

"For simplicity you beat all!" cried he. "You sent your news through the Swiss, that was in Buhot's pay, and took the charge from Hamilton's pistols, and did his part in helping you to escape from jyle with a great degree of humour as those of us who knew what was afoot had to agree, and you think the man would swither about peeping into a letter you entrusted to him, particularly if it was directed to hersel'! The sleep-bag was under your head sure enough, as the other man said."

"And I was the unconscious wretch that betrayed our hiding in the Hôtel Dieu!" I cried with much chagrin, seeing at a flash what all this meant. "If I had Bernard here I could thraw his neck."

"Indeed," said he, "and what for should it be Bernard? The man but did what he was told, and there, by my troth! when I think of it, I'm no' so sure that he was any different from yourself."

"What do you mean?" said I.

"Oh, just that hersel' told you to keep her informed

of your movements and you did so. In Bernard and you she had a pair of spies instead of only the one had she trusted in either."

"And what in all the world would she be doing that for?"

"What but for her lover the prince?" said he with a sickening promptness that some way left me without a doubt he spoke with knowledge. "Foul fa' the day he ever clapt eyes on her! for she has the cunning of the fox, though by all accounts a pleasant person. They say she has a sister that's in the service of the queen at St. James's, and who kens but for all her pretended affection for Tearlach she may be playing all the time into the hands of his enemies? She made you and this Bernard the means of putting an end to the Jesuit plot upon his Royal Highness by discovering the source of it, and now the Jesuits, as I'm told, are to be driven furth the country and putten to the horn."

I was stunned by this revelation of what a tool I had been in the hands of one I fancied briefly that I was in love with. For long I sat silent pondering on it, and at last unable to make up my mind whether I should laugh or swear. Kilbride, while affecting to pay no heed to me, was keen enough to see my perturbation, and had, I think, a sort of pride that he had been able to display such an astuteness.

"I'm afraid," said I at last, "there is too much probability in all that you have said and thought. I am a stupendous ass, Mr. MacKellar, and you are a very clever man."

"Not at all, not at all!" he protested hurriedly. "I have just some natural Hielan' interest in affairs of intrigue, and you have not (by your leave) had my advantages of the world, for I have seen much of the evil as well as the good of it, and never saw a woman's hand in aught yet but I wondered what mischief she was planning. There's much, I'm telling you, to be learned about a place like Fontainebleau or Versailles, and I advantaged myself so well of my opportunities there that you could not drive a hole but I would put a nail in it, as the other man said."

"Well," said I, "my hope is that I may never meet the woman again, and that's without a single angry feeling to her."

"You need not fear about that," said he. "The thing that does not lie in your road will never break your leg, as the other man said, and I'll be surprised if she puts herself in your way again now that her need for you is done. A score of your friends in Dunkerque could have told you that she was daft about him. I might be vexed for you if I did not know from your own mouth of the other one in Mearns."

"We'll say nothing about that," I says, "for that's a tale that's by wi'. She's lost to me."

He gave a little chuckle and had that turn in the eye that showed he had a curious thought.

"What are you laughing at?" I asked.

"Oh, just an old word we have in the Language, that with a two-deer stag-hound it will be happening often that a stag's amissing."

"There's another thing I would like you to tell me out of your experience," I said, "and that is the reason for the Prince's doing me a good turn with the one hand and a bad one with the other; using his efforts to get me the lieutenancy and at the same time putting a man on my track to quarrel with me?"

"It's as plain as the nose on your face," he cried. "It was no great situation he got you when it was in the Regiment d'Auvergne, as you have discovered, but it would be got I'll warrant on the pressure of the Walkinshaw one. Just because she had that interest in you to press him for the post, and you were in the trim to keep up a correspondence with her (though in his own interest, as he must know, so far as she was concerned), he would want you out of the road. Love is like lairdship, Hazel Den, and it puts up very poorly with fellowship, as the other man said."

I thought of the occasions when his Royal Highness had seen me at night in front of a certain window in the Rue de la Boucherie, and concluded that Kilbride in this too had probably hit the mark.

And so we passed through Holland in many changes of weather that finally turned to a black frost, which covered the canals with ice whereon skated the Dutch folks very pleasantly, but we were the losers, as the rest of our journey had to be made by post.

It was well on in the winter when we got to Helvoetsluys.

CHAPTER XXXVI

FATHER HAMILTON IS THREATENED BY THE JESUITS
AND WE ARE FORCED TO FLY AGAIN

THE priest, poor man! aged a dozen years by his anxieties since I had seen him last, was dubious of his senses when I entered where he lodged, and he wept like a bairn to see my face again.

"Scotland! Scotland! beshrew me, child, and I'd liefer have this than ten good dinners at Verray's!" cried he, and put his arms about my shoulders and buried his face in my waistcoat to hide his uncontrollable tears.

He was quartered upon a pilot of the Schelde and Hollands Deep, whose only child he made a shift to tutor in part payment of his costs, and the very moment that we had come in upon him he was full of a matter that had puzzled him for weeks before we came to Helvoetsluys. 'Twas a thing that partly hurt his pride, though that may seem incredible, and partly gave him pleasure, and 'twas merely that when he had at last found his concealment day and night in the pilot's house unendurable, and ventured a stroll or two upon the dunes in broad sunshine, no one paid any attention to him. There were soldiers and sailors that must have some suspicions of his identity, and he had himself read his own story and description in one of the gazettes, yet never a hand was raised to capture him.

"*Ma foi!* Paul," he cried to me in a perplexity. "I am the most marvellous priest unfrocked, invisible to the world as if I had Mambrino's helmet. Sure it cannot be that I am too stale quarry for their hunting! My *amour propre* baulks at such conclusion. I that have—heaven help me!—loaded pistols against the Lord's anointed, might as well have gone shooting sparrows for all the infamy it has gained me. But yesterday I passed an officer of the peace that cried '*Bon jour*, father,' in villainous French with a smile so sly I could swear he knew my history from the first breeching. I avow that my hair stirred under my hat when he said it."

MacKellar stood by contemptuous of the priest's raptures over his restored secretary.

"Goodness be about us!" he said, "what a pity the brock should be hiding when there's nobody hunting him! The first squirt of the haggis is always the hottest, as the other man said. If they were keen on your track at the start of it—and it's myself has the doubt of that same—you may warrant they are slack on it now. It's Buhot himself would be greatly put about if you went to the jail and put out your hands for the manacles."

Father Hamilton looked bewildered.

"Expiscate, good Monsieur MacKellar," said he.

"Kilbride just means," said I, "that you are in

the same case as myself, and that orders have gone out that no one is to trouble you."

He believed it, and still he was less cheerful than I looked for. " Indeed, 'tis like enough," he sighed. " I have put my fat on a trap for a fortnight back to catch my captors and never a rat of them will come near me, but pass with sniffing noses. And yet on my word I have little to rejoice for. My friends have changed coats with my enemies because they swear I betrayed poor Fleuriau. I'd sooner die on the rack——"

" Oh, Father Hamilton ! " I could not help crying, with remorse upon my countenance. He must have read the story in a single glance at me, for he stammered and took my hand.

" What ! there too, Scotland ! " he said. " I forswear the company of innocence after this. No matter, 'tis never again old Dixmunde parish for poor Father Hamilton that loved his flock well enough and believed the best of everybody and hated the confessional because it made the world so wicked. My honey-bees will hum next summer among another's flowers, and my darling blackbirds will be all starving in this pestilent winter weather. Paul, Paul, hear an old man's wisdom—be frugal in food, and raiment, and pleasure, and let thy ambitions flutter, but never fly too high to come down at a whistle. But here am I, old Pater Dull, prating on foolish little affairs, and thou and our honest friend here new back from the sounding of the guns. Art a brave fighter, lad ? I heard of thee in the grenadier company of d'Auvergne."

"We did the best part of our fighting with our shanks, as the other man said," cried Kilbride. "But Mr. Greig came by a clout that affected his mind and made him clean forget the number of his regiment, and that is what for the lowlands of Holland is a very pleasant country just now."

"Wounded!" cried the priest, disturbed at this intelligence. "Had I known on't I should have prayed for thy deliverance."

"I have little doubt he did that for himself," said Kilbride. "When I came on him after Rosbach he was behind a dyke, that is not a bad alternative for prayer when the lead is in the air."

We made up our minds to remain for a while at Helvoet, but we had not determined what our next step should be, when in came the priest one day with his face like clay and his limbs trembling.

"Ah, Paul!" he cried, and fell into a chair; "here's Nemesis, daughter of Nox, a scurvy Italian, and wears a monkish cowl. I fancied it were too good to be true that I should be free from further trials."

"Surely Buhot has not taken it into his head to move again," I cried. "That would be very hirpling justice after so long an interval. And in any case they could scarcely hale you out of the Netherlands."

"No, lad, not Buhot," said he, perspiring with his apprehensions, "but the Society. There's one Gordoletti, a pretended Lutheran that hails from Jena, that has been agent between the Society and myself before now, and when I was out there he followed me upon the street with the eyes of a viper.

I'll swear the fellow has a poignard and means the letting of blood. I know how 'twill be—a watch set upon this building, Gordoletti upon the steps some evening; a jostle, a thrust, and a speeding shade. A right stout shade too! if spirits are in any relation of measure to the corporeal clay. Oh, lad, what do I say? my sinner's wit must be evincing in the front of doom itself."

I thought he simply havered, but found there was too real cause for his distress. That afternoon the monk walked up and down the street without letting his eyes lose a moment's sight of the entrance to the pilot's house where Father Hamilton abode. I could watch him all the better because I shared a room with Kilbride on the same side of the street, and even to me there was something eerie in the sight of this long thin stooping figure in its monkish garment, slouching on the stones or hanging over the parapet of the bridge, his eyes, lambent black and darting, over his narrow chafts. Perhaps it was but fancy, yet I thought I saw in the side of his gown the unmistakable bulge of a dagger. He paced the street for hours or leaned over the parapet affecting an interest in the barges, and all the time the priest sat fascinated within, counting his sentence come.

"Oh, by my faith and it is not so bad as that," I protested on returning to find him in this piteous condition. "Surely there are two swords here that at the worst of it can be depended on to protect you."

He shook his head dolefully. "It is no use, Paul," he cried. "The poignard or the phial—'tis

all the same to them or Gordoletti, and hereafter I
dare not touch a drop of wine or indulge in a
meagre soup."

"But surely," I said, "there may be a mistake,
and this Gordoletti may have nothing to do with
you."

"The man wears a cowl—a monkish cowl—and
that is enough for me. A Jesuit out of his customary *soutane* is like the devil in dancing shoes—
be sure his lordship means mischief. Oh! Paul,
I would I were back in Bicêtre and like to die there
cleaner than on the banks of a Dutch canal. I
protest I hate to think of dying by a canal."

Still I was incredulous that harm was meant to
him, and he proceeded to tell me the Society of
Jesus was upon the brink of dissolution, and des-
perate accordingly. The discovery of Fleuriau's plot
against the Prince had determined the authorities
upon the demolition and extinction of the Jesuits
throughout the whole of the King's dominion. Their
riches and effects and churches were to be seized
to the profit and emolument of the Crown ; the
reverend Fathers were to be banished furth of
France for ever. Designs so formidable had to be
conducted cautiously, and so far the only evidence
of a scheme against the Society was to be seen in
the Court itself, where the number of priests of the
order was being rapidly diminished.

I thought no step of the civil power too harsh
against the band of whom the stalking man in the
cowl outside was representative, and indeed the
priest at last half-infected myself with his terrors.
We sat well back from the window looking out upon

the street till it was dusk. There was never a moment when the assassin (as I still must think him) was not there, his interest solely in the house we sat in. And when it was wholly dark, and a single lamp of oil swinging on a cord across the thoroughfare lit the passage of the few pedestrians that went along the street, Gordoletti was still close beneath it, silent, meditating, and alert.

MacKellar came in from his coffee-house. We sat in darkness, except for the flicker of a fire of peat. He must have thought the spectacle curious.

"My goodness!" cried he, "candles must be unco dear in this shire when the pair of you cannot afford one between you to see each other yawning. I'm of a family myself that must be burning a dozen at a time and at both ends to make matters cheery, for it's a gey glum world at the best of it."

He stumbled over to the mantel-shelf where there was customarily a candle; found and lit it, and held it up to see if there was any visible reason for our silence.

The priest's woebegone countenance set him into a shout of laughter. His amusement scarcely lessened when he heard of the ominous gentleman in the cowl.

"Let me see!" he said, and speedily devised a plan to test the occasion of Father Hamilton's terrors. He arranged that he should dress himself in the priest's garments, and as well as no inconsiderable difference in their bulk might let him, simulate the priest by lolling into the street.

"A brave plan verily," quo' the priest, "but am I

a bowelless rogue to let another have my own particular poignard? No, no, Messieurs, let me pay for my own *pots cassés* and run my own risks in my own *soutane*."

With that he rose to his feet and was bold enough to offer a trial that was attended by considerable hazard.

It was determined, however, that I should follow close upon the heels of Kilbride in his disguise, prepared to help him in the case of too serious a surprise.

The night was still. There were few people in the street, which was one of several that led down to the quays. The sky had but a few wan stars. When MacKellar stepped forth in the priest's hat and cloak, he walked slowly towards the harbour, ludicrously imitating the rolling gait of his reverence, while I stayed for a little in the shelter of the door. Gordoletti left his post upon the bridge and stealthily followed Kilbride. I gave him some yards of law and followed Gordoletti.

Our footsteps sounded on the stones; 'twas all that broke the evening stillness except the song of a roysterer who staggered upon the quays. The moment was fateful in its way and yet it ended farcically, for ere he had gained the foot of the street Kilbride turned and walked back to meet the man that stalked him. We closed upon the Italian to find him baffled and confused.

"Take that for your attentions!" cried Kilbride, and buffeted the fellow on the ear, a blow so secular and telling from a man in a frock that Gordoletti must have thought himself bewitched, for he gave a howl and took to his heels. Kilbride attempted to stop him, but the cassock escaped his hands and his own unwonted costume made a chase hopeless. As for me, I was content to let matters remain as they were now that Father Hamilton's suspicions seemed too well founded.

It did not surprise me that on learning of our experience the priest should determine on an immediate departure from Helvoetsluys. But where he was to go was more than he could readily decide. He proposed and rejected a score of places—Bordeaux, Flanders, the Hague, Katwyk farther up the coast, and many others—weighing the advantages of each, enumerating his acquaintances in each, discovering on further thought that each and every one of them had some feature unfavourable to his concealment from the Jesuits.

"You would be as long tuning your pipes as another would be playing a tune," said Kilbride at last. "There's one thing sure of it, that you cannot be going anywhere the now without Mr. Greig and myself, and what ails you at Dunkerque in which we have all of us acquaintances?"

A season ago the suggestion would have set my heart in flame; but now it left me cold. Yet I backed up the proposal, for I reflected that (keeping away from the Rue de la Boucherie) we might there be among a good many friends. Nor was his reverence ill to influence in favour of the proposal.

The next morning saw us, then, upon a hoy that sailed for Calais and was bargained to drop us at Dunkerque.

CHAPTER XXXVII

I OVERHEAR THE PLAN OF BRITAIN'S INVASION

I BEGAN these chronicles with a homily upon the
pregnancy of chance that gives the simplest of our
acts ofttimes far-reaching and appalling conse-
quences. It is clear that I had never become the
Spoiled Horn and vexed my parents' lives had not a
widow woman burned her batch of scones, and
though perhaps the pair of shoes in the chest be-
queathed to me by my Uncle Andrew were without
the magic influence he and I gave credit for, it is
probable that I had made a different flight from Scotland had they not led me in the way of Daniel Risk.

And even now their influence was not ended.
During the months I had spent at soldiering the red
shoes reposed among my baggage; even when I had
changed from the uniform of the Regiment d'Auvergne
upon the frontier of Holland, and made myself again
a common citizen of Europe, I had some freit (as we
say of a superstition) against resuming the shoes
that had led me previously into divers perils. But
the day we left Helvoet in the Hollands Deep hoy, I
was so hurried in my departure that the red shoes
were the only ones I could lay hands on. As luck

would have it, when I entered Dunkerque for the last time in my history some days after, I was wearing the same leather as on the first day of my arrival there, and the fact led, by a singularity of circumstances, to my final severance from many of those companions—some of them pleasant and unforgetable—I had made acquaintance with in France.

It was thus that the thing happened.

When we entered Dunkerque, the priest, Kilbride, and I went to an inn upon the sea front. Having breakfasted I was deputed to go forth and call upon Thurot, explain our circumstances, take his counsel, and return to the hoy where my two friends would return to wait for me. He was out when I reached his lodging, but his Swiss—a different one from what he had before when I was there—informed me that his master was expected back at any moment, and invited me to step in and wait for him. I availed myself of the opportunity.

Our voyage along the coast had been delayed by contrary winds, so that now it was the Sabbath; the town was by-ordinary still (though indeed Sabbath nor Saturday made much difference, as a rule, on the gaiety of Dunkerque), and wearied by the sea travel that had just concluded I fell fast asleep in Captain Thurot's chair.

I was wakened by a loud knocking at the outer door, not the first, as it may be remembered, that called me forth from dreams to new twists of fortune, and I started to my feet to meet my host.

What was my chagrin to hear the Prince's voice in converse with him on the stair!

"Here is a pretty pickle!" I told myself.
"M. Albany is the last man on earth I would choose to
meet at this moment," and without another reflection
I darted into the adjoining room and shut the door.
It was Thurot's bed-chamber, with a window that
looked out upon the court where fowls were cack-
ling. I was no sooner in than I somewhat rued my
precipitation, for the manlier course indubitably had
been to bide where I was. But now there was no
retreating, so I sat with what patience I could command to wait my discovery by the tenant of the place
after his royal visitor was gone.

It was the Sabbath day as I have said, and the
chimes of St. Eloi were going briskly upon some
papist canticle, but not so loud that I could not hear,
in spite of myself, all that went on in the next
room.

At first I paid no heed, for the situation was
unworthy enough of itself without any attempt on
my part to be an eavesdropper. But by-and-bye,
through the banging of the bells of St. Eloi, I heard
M. Albany (still to give the man his by-name)
mention the name Écosse.

Scotland! The name of her went through me
like a pang!

They spoke in French of course; I think I could
have understood them had it been Chinese. For
they discussed some details of the intended invasion
that still hung fire, and from the first of M. Albany's
sentences I learned that the descent was determined
upon Scotland. 'Twas that which angered me and
made me listen for the rest with every sense of the

spy and deterred by never a scruple. At first I had fancied Thurot would learn from his servant I was in the house, and leave me alone till his royal guest's departure from an intuition that I desired no meeting, but it was obvious now that no such consideration would have induced him to let me hear the vast secret they discussed.

"Twenty thousand men are between Brest and Vannes," said M. Albany. "We shall have them in frigates in a fortnight from to-day, and then, *mon Capitaine*, affairs shall move briskly."

"And still," said Thurot, who had some odd tone of dissatisfaction in his voice, "I had preferred it had been the South of England. Dumont has given us every anchorage and sounding on the coast between Beachy Head and Arundel, and from there we could all the sooner have thrust at the heart of England. This Scotland——"

"Bah! Captain Thurot," cried his Royal Highness impatiently, "you talk like a fool. At the heart, indeed! With all habitable England like a fat about it, rich with forts and troops and no more friendship for us than for the Mameluke! No, no, Thurot, I cry Scotland; all the chances are among the rocks, and I am glad it has been so decided on."

"And still, with infinite deference, your Royal Highness, this same West of Scotland never brought but the most abominable luck to you and yours," continued Thurot. "Now, Arundel Bay——"

"Oh! to the devil with Arundel Bay!" cried M. Albany; "'tis settled otherwise, and you must

take it as you find it. Conflans and his men shall land
upon the West—*mon Dieu!* I trust they may escape
its fangs; and measures will be there taken with
more precaution and I hope with more success than
in Seventeen Forty-five. Thence they will march to
England, sweeping the whole country before them,
and not leaving behind them a man or boy who can
carry a musket. Thus they must raise the army to
fifty or sixty thousand men, strike a terror into
England, and carry all with a high hand. I swear
'tis a fatted hog this England: with fewer than ten
thousand Highlanders I have made her thrill at the
very vitals."

Thurot hummed. Plainly there was much in the
project that failed to meet his favour.

"And Conflans?" said he.

His Royal Highness laughed.

"Ha! Captain," said he, "I know, I know.
'Twould suit you better if a certain Tony Thurot
had command."

"At least," said Thurot, "I am in my prime,
while the Marshal is beyond his grand climacteric."

"And still, by your leave, with the reputation of
being yet the best—well, let us say among the best
—of the sea officers of France. Come, come, Captain, there must be no half-hearts in this venture;
would to Heaven I were permitted to enjoy a share
in it! And on you, my friend, depends a good half
of the emprise and the *gloire*."

"*Gloire!*" cried Thurot. "With every deference
to your Royal Highness I must consider myself
abominably ill-used in this matter. That I should

be sent off to Norway and hound-in wretched Swedes with a personage like Flaubert! Oh, I protest, 'tis beyond all reason! Is it for that I have been superseded by a man like Conflans that totters on the edge of the grave?"

"I hope 'tis England's grave," retorted M. Albany with unfailing good humour, and I heard the gluck of wine as he helped himself to another glass. "I repeat *gloire*, with every apology to the experience of M. le Corsair. 'Tis your duty to advance with your French and your Swedes upon the North of England, and make the diversion in these parts that shall inconvenience the English army front or rear."

"Oh, curse your diversions!" cried Thurot. "If I have a talent at all 'tis for the main attack. And this Conflans——"

The remainder of the discussion, so far as I remained to hear it, gave no enlargement upon the plan thus laid bare. But in any case my whole desire now was to escape from the house without discovery, for I had news that made my return to Britain imperative.

I opened the window quietly and slipped out. The drop to the court was less than my own height. Into the street I turned with the sober step of leisure, yet my feet tingled to run hard and my heart was stormy. The bells of St. Eloi went on ringing; the streets were growing busy with holiday-makers and the soldiers who were destined to over-run my country. I took there and then the most dreadful hatred of them, and scowled so black that some of the soldiers cried after me with a jeer.

The priest and Kilbride I found were not at the inn where I had left them, having gone back to the vessel, so I hurried down to the quay after them. The hoy had been moved since morning, and in the throng of other vessels that were in the harbour at the time I lost well-nigh an hour in seeking her. Whether that was well for me or ill would be folly now to guess, but when I had no more than set a foot upon the gunwale of a small boat that was to take me out to her I was clapped upon the shoulder.

I turned, to see Thurot and two officers of marine!

"Pardon, M. Greig, a moment," said Thurot, with not the kindest of tones. "Surely you would not hurry out of Dunkerque without a *congé* for old friends?"

I stammered some sentences that were meant to reassure him. He interrupted me, and—not with any roughness, but with a pressure there was no mistaking and I was not fool enough to resist—led me from the side of the quay.

"*Ma foi!*" said he. "'Tis the most ridiculous thing! I had nearly missed you and could never have forgiven myself. My Swiss has just informed me that you were in the house an hour ago while I was there myself. I fear we must have bored you, M. Albany and I, with our dull affairs. At least there was no other excuse for your unceremonious departure through my back window."

I was never well-equipped to conceal my feelings, and it was plain in my face that I knew all.

He sighed.

"Well, lad," said he, rather sorrowfully, "I'd give a good many *louis d'or* that you had come visiting at another hour of the day, and now there's but one thing left me. My Swiss did not know you, but he has—praise *le bon Dieu !*—a pair of eyes in his head, and he remembered that my visitor wore red shoes. Red shoes and a Scotsman !—the conjunction was unmistakable, and here we are, M. Greig. There are a score of men looking all over Dunkerque at this moment for these same shoes."

"Confound the red shoes !" I cried, unable to conceal my vexation that they should once more have brought me into trouble.

"By no means, M. Greig," said Thurot. "But for them we should never have identified our visitor, and a somewhat startling tale was over the Channel a little earlier than we intended. And now all that I may do for old friendship to yourself and the original wearer of the shoes is to give you a free trip to England in my own vessel. 'Tis not the *Roi Rouge* this time—worse luck !—but a frigate, and we can be happy enough if you are not a fool."

CHAPTER XXXVIII

THUROT'S PRISONER.   MY FRIEND THE WATCH

It was plain from the first that my overhearing of the plot must compel Thurot to the step he took. He was not unkind, but so much depended on the absolute secrecy of the things he had talked to the Prince, that, even at the unpleasant cost of trepanning me, he must keep me from carrying my new-got information elsewhere. For that reason he refused to accede to my request for a few minutes' conversation with the priest or my fellow-countrymen. The most ordinary prudence, he insisted, demanded that he should keep me in a sort of isolation until it was too late to convey a warning across the Channel.

It was for these reasons I was taken that Sabbath afternoon to the frigate that was destined to be in a humble sense his flagship, and was lying in the harbour with none of her crew as yet on board. I was given a cabin; books were furnished to cheer my incarceration, for it was no less. I was to all intents and purposes a prisoner, though enjoying again some of the privileges of the *salle d'épreuves* for the sake of old acquaintance.

All that day I planned escape. Thurot came to

the cabin and smoked and conversed pleasantly, but found me so abstracted that he could scarcely fail to think I meant a counter-sap.

"Be tranquil, my Paul," he advised; "Clancarty and I will make your life on ship-board as little irksome as possible, but it is your own cursed luck that you must make up your mind to a fortnight of it."

But that was considerably longer than I was ready to think of with equanimity. What I wished for was an immediate freedom and a ship to England, and while he talked I reviewed a dozen methods of escape. Here was I with a secret worth a vast deal to the British Government; if I could do my country that service of putting her into possession of it in time to prevent catastrophe, might I not, without presumption, expect some clemency from her laws for the crime I had committed in the hot blood of ignorant and untutored youth? I saw the most cheerful possibilities rise out of that accident that had made me an eavesdropper in Thurot's lodging—freedom, my family perhaps restored to me, my name partly re-established; but the red shoes that set me on wrong roads to start with still kept me on them. Thurot was an amiable enough gaoler, but not his best wine nor his wittiest stories might make me forget by how trivial a chance I had lost my opportunity.

We were joined in the afternoon by Lord Clancarty.

"What, lad!" cried his lordship, pomaded and scented beyond words; fresh, as he told us, from

the pursuit of a lady whose wealth was shortly to
patch up his broken fortunes. "What, lad! Here's
a pretty matter! Pressed, egad! A renegade against
his will! 'Tis the most cursed luck, Captain Thurot,
and wilt compel the poor young gentleman to cut
the throats of his own countrymen?"

"I? Faith, not I!" said Thurot. "I press none
but filthy Swedes. M. Greig has my word for it that
twelve hours before we weigh anchor he may take
his leave of us. *Je le veux bien.*"

"Bah! 'Tis an impolite corsair this. As for me
I should be inconsolable to lose M. Greig to such a
dull country as this England. Here's an Occasion,
M. le Capitaine, for pledging his health in a bottle,
and wishing him well out of his troubles."

"You do not stand sufficiently on your
dignity, Clancarty," laughed Thurot. "Here's the
enemy——"

"Dignity! pooh!" said his lordship. "To stand
on that I should need a year's practice first on the
tight-rope. There's that about an Irish gentleman
that makes the posturings and proprieties and pre-
tences of the fashionable world unnecessary. Sure,
race will show in his face and action if he stood
alone in his shirt-sleeves on a village common juggling balls. I am of the oldest blood that springs
in Irish kings. 'Tis that knowledge keeps my heart
up when circumstances make the world look rotten
like a cheese. But the curst thing is one cannot for
ever be drinking and dining off a pedigree, and here
I am deserted by M. Tête-de-mouche——"

Thurot put up his hand to check one of these

disloyalties to the Pretender that I had long since learned were common with Lord Clancarty.

"Bah!" cried his lordship. "I love you, Tony, and all the other boys, but your Prince is a madman —a sotted madman tied to the petticoat tails of a trollope. This Walkinshaw—saving your presence, Paul Greig, for she's your countrywoman and by way of being your friend, I hear—has ruined Charles and the Cause. We have done what we could to make him send madame back to the place she came from, but he'll do nothing of the kind. 'She has stuck by me through thick and thin, and lost all for me, and now I shall stick by her,' says foolish Master Sentiment."

"Bravo!" cried Thurot. "'Tis these things make us love the Prince and have faith in his ultimate success."

"You were ever the hopeful ass, Tony," said his lordship coolly. "*Il n'est pire sourd que celui qui ne veut pas entendre,* and you must shut your ears against a tale that all the world is shouting at the pitch of its voice. Who knows better than Tony Thurot how his Royal Highness has declined? Why! 'tis manifest in the fellow's nose; I declare he drinks like a fish —another vice he brought back from your mountain land, M. Greig, along with Miss Walkinshaw——"

"There is far too much of Miss Walkinshaw about your lordship's remarks," I cried in an uncontrollable heat that the lady should be the subject of implications so unkind.

He stared, and then kissed his hand to me with laughter and a bow.

"Ha!" he cried, "here's another young gentleman of sentiment. Stap me if I say a word against the lady for your sake, Andy Greig's nephew." And back he went to his bottle.

In this light fashion we spent a day that by rights should have been more profitably and soberly occupied. The frigate lay well out from the quays from which Thurot had conveyed me with none of the indignities that might be expected by a prisoner. There was, as I have said, none of her crew on board save a watch of two men. Beside her quarter there hung a small smuggling cutter that had been captured some days previously. As I sat in the cabin, yawning at the hinder-end over Clancarty's sallies, I could hear now and then the soft thudding of the smuggler's craft against the fenders as the sea rocked us lightly, and it put a mad fancy into my head.

How good it would be, I thought, to be free on board such a vessel and speeding before a light wind to Britain! Was it wholly impossible? The notion so possessed me that I took an occasion to go on deck and see how things lay.

The smuggler's boat had her mast stepped, but no sails in her. Over the bulwark of the frigate leaned one of the watch idly looking at sea-gulls that cried like bairns upon the smuggler's thwarts and gunnels. He was a tarry Dutchman (by his build and colour); I fancy that at the time he never suspected I was a prisoner, for he saluted me with deference.

The harbour was emptier than usual of shipping. Dusk was falling on the town; some lights were twinkling wanly and bells rang in the cordage of the quays. I asked the seaman if he knew where the hoy *Vrijster* of Helvoetsluys lay.

At that his face brightened and he promptly pointed to her yellow hull on the opposite side of the harbour.

"Did my honour know Captain Breuer?" he asked, in crabbed French.

My honour was very pleased to confess that he did, though in truth my acquaintance with the skipper who had taken us round from Helvoetsluys went scarcely further than sufficed me to recall his name.

The best sailor ever canted ship! my Dutchman assured me with enthusiasm. How often have I heard the self-same sentiment from mariners? for there is something jovial and kind in the seaman's manner that makes him ever fond of the free, the brave and competent of his own calling, and ready to cry their merits round the rolling world.

A good seaman certainly!—I agreed heartily, though the man might have been merely middling for all I knew of him.

He would like nothing better than to have an hour with Captain Breuer, said Mynheer.

"And I, too," said I quickly. "But for Captain Thurot's pressing desire that I should spend the evening here I should be in Breuer's cabin now. Next to being with him there I would reckon the privilege of having him here."

There might be very little difficulty about that if my honour was willing, said Mynheer. They were old shipmates; had sailed the Zuyder Sea together, and drunken in a score of ports. Dearly indeed would he love to have some discourse with Breuer. But to take leave from the frigate and cross to the hoy—no! Captain Thurot would not care for him to do that.

"Why not have Breuer come to the frigate?" I asked, with my heart beating fast.

"Why, indeed?" repeated Mynheer with a laugh. "A hail across the harbour would not fetch him."

"Then go for him," said I, my heart beating faster than ever lest he should have some suspicion of my condition and desires.

He reminded me that he had no excuse to leave the frigate, though to take the small boat at the stern and row over to the hoy would mean but a minute or two.

"Well, as for excuses," said I, "that's easily arranged, for I can give you one to carry a note to the care of the captain, and you may take it at your leisure."

At his leisure! He would take it at once and thankfully while we gentlemen were drinking below, for there was no pleasure under heaven he could compare with half an hour of good Jan Breuer's company.

Without betraying my eagerness to avail myself of such an unlooked-for opportunity, I deliberately wrote a note in English intimating that I was a prisoner on the frigate and in pressing humour to get out of her at the earliest moment. I addressed it to Kilbride, judging the Highlander more likely than Father Hamilton to take rational steps for my release if that were within the bounds of possibility.

I assured the seaman that if he lost no time in taking it over I would engage his absence would never be noticed, and he agreed to indicate to me by a whistle when he returned.

With a cheerful assurance that he would have Jan Breuer on this deck in less than twenty minutes the seaman loosed the painter of the small boat and set forth upon his errand, while I returned to the cabin where Thurot and Clancarty still talked the most contrary and absurd politics over their wine. The vast and tangled scheme of French intrigue was set before me; at another time it might have been of the most fascinating interest, but on this particular occasion I could not subdue my mind to matters so comparatively trivial, while I kept my hearing strained for the evidence that the Dutchman had accomplished his mission and got back.

The moments passed; the interest flagged; Clancarty began to yawn and Thurot grew silent. It was manifest that the sooner my Dutchman was back to his ship the better for my plan. Then it was I showed the brightest interest in affairs that an hour earlier failed to engage a second of my attention, and I discovered for the entertainment of my gaoler and his friend a hitherto unsuspected store of reminiscence about my Uncle Andrew and a fund of joke and anecdote whereof neither of them probably had thought me capable.

But all was useless. The signal that the Dutchman had returned was not made when Lord

Clancarty rose to his feet and intimated his intention there and then of going ashore, though his manner suggested that it would have been easy to induce him to wait longer. We went on deck with him. The night was banked with clouds though a full moon was due; only a few stars shone in the spaces of the zenith; our vessel was in darkness except where a lamp swung at the bow.

" *Mon Dieu!* Tony, what a pitchy night! I'd liefer be safe ashore than risking my life getting there in your cockle-shell," said Clancarty.

"'Art all right, Lord Clancarty," said Thurot. "Here's a man will row you to the quay in two breaths, and you'll be snug in bed before M. Greig and I have finished our prayers." Then he cried along the deck for the seaman.

I felt that all was lost now the fellow's absence was to be discovered.

What was my astonishment to hear an answering call, and see the Dutchman's figure a blotch upon the blackness of the after-deck.

"Bring round the small boat and take Lord Clancarty ashore," said the captain, and the seaman hastened to do so. He sprang into the small boat, released her rope, and brought her round.

" *À demain,* dear Paul," cried his lordship with a hiccough. "It's curst unkind of Tony Thurot not to let you ashore on parole or permit me to wait with you."

The boat dropped off into the darkness of the harbour, her oars thudding on the thole-pins.

" There goes a decent fellow though something of

a fool," said Thurot. " 'Tis his kind have made so
many enterprises like our own have an ineffectual
end. And now you must excuse me, M. Greig, if
I lock you into your cabin. There are too few
of us on board to let you have the run of the
vessel."

He put a friendly hand upon the shoulder I
shrugged with chagrin at this conclusion to an
unfortunate day.

"Sorry, M. Greig, sorry," he said humorously.
"*Qui commence mal finit mal,* and I wish to heaven
you had begun the day by finding Antoine Thurot
at home, in which case we had been in a happier
relationship to-night."

CHAPTER XXXIX

DISCLOSES THE MANNER OF MY ESCAPE AND HOW
WE SET SAIL FOR ALBION

THUROT turned the key on me with a pleasantry
that was in no accordance with my mood, and himself retired to the round house on deck where his
berth was situated. I sat on a form for a little,
surrendered all to melancholy, then sought to remove
it by reading, as sleep in my present humour was
out of the question. My reading, though it lasted
for an hour or two, was scarcely worth the name,
for my mind continually wandered from the page.
I wondered if my note to Kilbride had been delivered,
and if any step on his part was to be expected there-
from; the hope that rose with that reflection died at
once upon the certainty that as the Dutch seaman
had not signalled as he had promised he had somehow learned the true nature of my condition in the
frigate. Had he told Thurot? If he had told
Thurot—which was like enough—that I had communicated with any one outside the vessel there was
little doubt that the latter would take adequate steps
to prevent interference by Kilbride or any one else.

We are compact of memories, a mere bundle of

bygone days, childish recollections, ancient impressions, and so an older experience came to me, too, of the night I sat in the filthy cabin of Dan Risk's doomed vessel hearing the splash of illegitimate oars, anticipating with a mind scarcely more disturbed than I had just now the step of the officer from the prison at Blackness and the clutch of the chilly fetters.

There was a faint but rising nor'-east wind. It sighed among the shrouds of the frigate. I could hear it even in the cabin, pensive like the call of the curlew at a great distance. The waves washed against the timbers in curious short gluckings and hissings. On the vessel herself not a sound was to be heard, until of a sudden there came a scratching at my cabin door!

It was incredible! I had heard no footstep on the companion, and I had ceased to hope for anything from the Dutchman!

"Who's there?" I asked softly, and at that the key outside was turned and I was fronted by Kilbride!

He wore the most ridiculous travesty of the Dutchman's tarry breeks and tarpaulin hat and coarse wide jumper, and in the light of my candle there was a humorous twinkle on his face as he entered, closed the door softly after him, and sat down beside me.

"My goodness!" he whispered, "you have a face on you as if you were in a graveyard watching ghosts. It's time you were steeping the withies to go away as we say in the Language, and you may be telling me all the story of it elsewhere."

"Where's the Dutchman that took my letter?" I asked.

"Where," said Kilbride, "but in the place that well befits him—at the lug of an anker of Rotterdam gin taking his honest night's rest. I'm here guizing in his tarry clothes, and if I were Paul Greig of the Hazel Den I would be clapping on my hat gey quick and getting out of here without any more parley."

"You left him in the hoy!" said I astonished.

"Faith, there was nothing better for it!" said he coolly. "Breuer gave him so much of the juniper for old acquaintance that when I left he was so full of it that he had lost the power of his legs and you might as well try to keep a string of fish standing."

"And it was you took Clancarty ashore?"

"Who else? And I don't think it's a great conceit of myself to believe I play-acted the Dutch tarry-breeks so very well, though I was in something of a tremble in case the skipper here would make me out below my guizard's clothes. You may thank your stars the moon was as late of rising this night as a man would be that was at a funeral yesterday."

"And where's the other man who was on this vessel?" I asked, preparing to go.

"Come on deck and I'll show you," said Kilbride, checking a chuckle of amusement at something.

We crept softly on deck into the night now slightly lit by a moon veiled by watery clouds. The ship seemed all our own and we were free to leave her when we chose for the small boat hung at her stern.

"You were asking for the other one," said Kilbride. "There he is," and he pointed to a huddled figure bound upon the waist. "When I came on board after landing Clancarty this stupid fellow discovered I was a stranger and nearly made an outcry; but I hit him on the lug with the loom of an oar. He'll not be observing very much for a while yet, but I was bound all the same to put a rope on him to prevent him disturbing Captain Thurot's sleep too soon."

We spoke in whispers for the night seemed all ear and I was for ever haunted by the reflection that Thurot was divided from us by little more than an inch or two of teak-wood. Now and then the moon peeped through a rift of cloud and lit a golden road-way over the sea, enticing me irresistibly home.

"O God, I wish I was in Scotland!" I said passionately.

"Less luck than that will have to be doing us," said Kilbride, fumbling at the painter of the boat. "The hoy sets sail for Calais in an hour or two, and it's plain from your letter we'll be best to be taking her round that length."

"No, not Calais," said I. "It's too serious a business with me for that. I'm wanting England, and wanting it unco fast."

"*Oh, Dhe!*" said my countryman, "here's a fellow with the appetite of Prince Charlie and as likely to gratify it. What for must it be England, *loachain?*"

"I can only hint at that," I answered hastily, "and that in a minute. Are ye loyal?"

"To a fine fellow called MacKellar first and to my king and country after?"

"The Stuarts?" said I.

He cracked his thumb. "It's all by with that," said he quickly and not without a tone of bitterness.

"The breed of them has never been loyal to me, and if I could wipe out of my life six months of the cursedest folly in Forty-five I would go back to Scotland with the first chance and throw my bonnet for Geordie ever after like the greasiest burgess ever sold a wab of cloth or a cargo of Virginia in Glasgow."

"Then," I said, "you and me's bound for England this night, for I have that in my knowledge should buy the safety of the pair of us," and I briefly conveyed my secret.

He softly whistled with astonishment.

"Man! it's a gey taking idea," he confessed. "But the bit is to get over the Channel."

"I have thought of that," said I. "Here's a smuggler wanting no more than a rag of sail in this wind to make the passage in a couple of days."

"By the Holy Iron it's the very thing!" he interrupted, slapping his leg.

It takes a time to tell all this in writing, but in actual fact our whole conversation together in the cabin and on the deck occupied less than five minutes. We were both of us too well aware of the value of time to have had it otherwise and waste moments in useless conversation.

"What is to be done is this," I suggested, casting a rapid glance along the decks and upwards to the spars. "I will rig up a sail of some sort here and you will hasten over again in the small-boat to the hoy and give Father Hamilton the option of coming with us. He may or he may not care to run the risks involved in the exploit, but at least we owe him the offer."

"But when I'm across at the hoy there, here's you with this dovering body and Captain Thurot. Another knock might settle the one, but you would scarcely care to have knocks going in the case of an old friend like Tony Thurot, who's only doing his duty in keeping you here with such a secret in your charge."

"I have thought of that, too," I replied quickly, "and I will hazard Thurot."

Kilbride lowered himself into the small-boat, pushed off from the side of the frigate, and in silence half-drifted in the direction of the Dutch vessel. My plans were as clear in my head as if they had been printed on paper. First of all I took such provender as I could get from my cabin and placed it along with a breaker of water and a lamp in the cutter. Then I climbed the shrouds of the frigate, and cut away a small sail that I guessed would serve my purpose, letting it fall into the cutter. I made a shift at sheets and halyards and found that with a little contrivance I could spread enough canvas to take the cutter in that weather at a fair speed before the wind that had a blessed disposition towards the coast of England. I worked so fast it was a miracle, dreading at every rustle of the stolen sail—at every creak of the cutter on the fenders, that either the captain or his unconscious seaman would awake.

My work was scarcely done when the small-boat came off again from the hoy, and as she drew cautiously near I saw that MacKellar had with him the bulky figure of the priest. He climbed ponderously, at my signal, into the cutter, and MacKellar joined me for a moment on the deck of the frigate.

" He goes with us then ? " I asked, indicating the priest.

"To the Indies if need be," said Kilbride.   "But the truth is that this accident is a perfect God-send to him, for England's the one place below the firmament he would choose for a refuge at this moment. Is all ready ? "

" If my sail-making's to be relied on she's in the best of trim," I answered.

" And—what do ye call it ?—all found ? "

" A water breaker, a bottle of brandy, a bag of bread——"

" Enough for a foray of fifty men ! " he said heartily. " Give me meal and water in the heel of my shoe and I would count it very good vivers for a fortnight."

He went into the cutter ; I released the ropes that bound her to the frigate and followed him.

" Mon Dieu ! dear lad, 'tis a world of most fantastic happenings," was all the poor old priest said, shivering in the cold night air.

We had to use the oars of the frigate's small-boat for a stroke or two so as to get the cutter round before the wind ; she drifted quickly from the large ship's side almost like a living thing with a crave for freedom at last realised ; up speedily ran her sail, unhandsome yet sufficient, the friendly air filled out the rustling folds and drove her through the night into the open sea.

There is something in a moonlit night at sea that must touch in the most cloddish heart a spring of fancy.   It is friendlier than the dawn that at its most glorious carries a hint of sorrow, or than the bravest sunset that reminds us life is a brief day at the best of it, and the one thing sempiternal yet will be the darkness. We sat in the well of the cutter—three odd adventurers, myself the most silent because I had the double share of dubiety about the enterprise, for who could tell how soon the doomster's hand would be on me once my feet were again on British soil? Yet now when I think of it—of the moonlit sea, the swelling sail above us, the wake behind that shone with fire—I must count it one of the happiest experiences of my life.

The priest looked back at the low land of France receding behind us, with its scattered lights on the harbour and the shore, mere subjects to the queenly moon. "There goes poor Father Hamilton," said he whimsically, "happy schoolboy, foolish lover in Louvain that had never but moonlit eves, parish priest of Dixmunde working two gardens, human and divine, understanding best the human where his bees roved, but loving all men good and ill. There goes the spoiled page, the botched effort, and here's a fat old man at the start of a new life, and never to see his darling France again. Ah! the good mother; *Dieu te bénisse!*"

CHAPTER XL

OF our voyage across the Channel there need be no more said than that it was dull to the very verge of monotony, for the wind, though favourable, was often in a faint where our poor sail shook idly at the mast. Two days later we were in London, and stopped at the Queen's Head above Craig's Court in Charing Cross.

And now I had to make the speediest possible arrangement for a meeting with those who could make the most immediate and profitable use of the tidings I was in a position to lay before them, by no means an easy matter to decide upon for a person who had as little knowledge of London as he had of the Cities of the Plain.

MacKellar—ever the impetuous Gael—was for nothing less than a personal approach to his Majesty.

"The man that is on the top of the hill will always be seeing furthest," he said. "I have come in contact with the best in Europe on that under standing, but it calls for a kind of Hielan' tact that—that——"

"That you cannot credit to a poor Lowlander like myself," said I, amused at his vanity.

"Oh, I'm meaning no offence, just no offence at all," he responded quickly, and flushing at his *faux pas*. "You have as much talent of the kind as the best of us I'm not denying, and I have just the one advantage, that I was brought up in a language that has delicacies of address beyond the expression of the English, or the French that is, in some measure, like it."

"Well," said I, "the spirit of it is obviously not to be translated into English, judging from the way you go on crying up your countrymen at the expense of my own."

"That is true enough," he conceded, "and a very just observe; but no matter, what I would be at is that your news is worth too much to be wasted on any poor lackey hanging about his Majesty's back door, who might either sell it or you on his own behoof, or otherwise make a mull of the matter with the very best intentions. If you would take my way of it, there would be but Geordie himself for you."

"What have you to say to that?" I asked the priest, whose knowledge of the world struck me as in most respects more trustworthy than that of this impetuous Highland chirurgeon.

"A plague of your kings! say I; sure I know nothing about them, for my luck has rubbed me against the gabardine and none of your ermined cloaks. There must be others who know his Majesty's affairs better than his Majesty himself, otherwise what advantage were there in being a king ? "

In fine his decision was for one of the Ministers, and at last the Secretary of State was decided on.

How I came to meet with Mr. Pitt need not here be recorded; 'twas indeed more a matter of good luck than of good guidance, and had there been no Scots House of Argyll perhaps I had never got rid of my weighty secret after all. I had expected to meet a person magnificent in robes of state; instead of which 'twas a man in a blue coat with yellow metal buttons, full round bob wig, a large hat, and no sword-bag nor ruffles that met me—more like a country coachman or a waggoner than a personage of importance.

He scanned over again the letter that had introduced me and received me cordially enough. In a few words I indicated that I was newly come from France, whence I had escaped in a smuggler's boat, and that I had news of the first importance which I counted it my duty to my country to convey to him with all possible expedition.

At that his face changed and he showed singularly little eagerness to hear any more.

"There will be—there will be the—the usual bargain, I presume, Mr. Greig ? " he said, half-smiling. "What are the conditions on which I am to have this vastly important intelligence ? "

"I never dreamt of making any, sir," I answered, promptly, with some natural chagrin, and yet mixed with a little confusion that I should in truth be expecting something in the long run for my story.

"Pardon my stupid pleasantry, Mr. Greig," he said, reddening slightly. "I have been so long one of his Majesty's Ministers, and of late have seen so many urgent couriers from France with prime news to be bargained for, that I have grown something of a cynic. You are the first that has come with a secret not for sale. Believe me, your story will have all the more attention because it is offered disinterestedly."

In twenty minutes I had put him into possession of all I knew of the plans for invasion. He walked up and down the room, with his hands behind his back, intently listening, now and then uttering an exclamation incredulous or astonished.

"You are sure of all this?" he asked at last sharply, looking in my face with embarrassing scrutiny.

"As sure as any mortal man may be with the gift of all his senses," I replied firmly. "At this moment Thurot's vessel is, I doubt not, taking in her stores; the embarkation of troops is being practised daily, troops are assembled all along the coast from Brest to Vannes, and——"

"Oh! on these points we are, naturally, not wholly dark," said the Minister. "We have known for a year of this somewhat theatrical display on the part of the French, but the lines of the threatened invasion are not such as your remarkable narrative suggests. You have been good enough to honour me with your confidence, Mr. Greig; let me reciprocate by telling you that we have our——our good friends in France, and that for six months back I have been in possession of the Chevalier D'Arcy's instructions to Dumont to reconnoitre the English coast, and of Dumont's report, with the chart of the harbours and towns where he proposed that the descent should be made." He smiled somewhat grimly. "The gentleman who gave us the information," he went on, "stipulated for twenty thousand pounds and a pension of two thousand a year as the just reward for his loving service to his country in her hour of peril. He was not to get his twenty thousand, I need scarcely say, but he was to get something in the event of his intelligence proving to be accurate, and if it were for no more than to get the better of such a dubious patriot I should wish his tale wholly disproved, though we have hitherto acted on the assumption that it might be trustworthy. There cannot be alternative plans of invasion; our informant—another Scotsman, I may say—is either lying or has merely the plan of a feint."

"You are most kind, sir," said I.

"Oh," he said, "I take your story first, and as probably the most correct, simply because it comes from one that loves his country and makes no bagman's bargains for the sale of secrets vital to her existence."

"I am much honoured, sir," said I, with a bow.

And then he stopped his walk abruptly and faced me again.

"You have told me, Mr. Greig," he went on, "that Conflans is to descend in a week or two on the coast of Scotland, and that Thurot is to create a diversion elsewhere with the aid of the Swedes.

I have, from the most delicate considerations, refrained from asking you how you know all this ? "

"I heard it from the lips of Thurot himself."

"Thurot! impossible!" he murmured.

"Of Thurot himself, sir."

"You must be much in that pirate's confidence," said Mr. Pitt, for the first time with suspicion.

"Not to that extent that he would tell me of his plans for invading my country," I answered, "and I learned these things by the merest accident. I overheard him speak last Sunday in Dunkerque with the Young Pretender——"

"The Pretender!" cried the Minister, shrugging his shoulders, and looking at me with more suspicion than ever. "You apparently move in the most select and interesting society, Mr. Greig?"

"In this case, sir, it was none of my choosing," I replied, and went on briefly to explain how I had got into Thurot's chamber unknown to him, and unwittingly overhead the Prince and him discuss the plan.

"Very good, very good, and still—you will pardon me—I cannot see how so devout a patriot as Mr. Greig should be in the intimacy of men like Thurot?"

"A most natural remark under the circumstances," I replied. "Thurot saved my life from a sinking British vessel, and it is no more than his due to say he proved a very good friend to me many a time since. But I was to know nothing of his plans of invasion, for he knew very well I had no sympathy with them nor with Charles Edward, and, as I have told you, he made me his prisoner on his ship so that I might not betray what I had overheard."

The Minister made hurried notes of what I had told him, and concluded the interview by asking where I could be communicated with during the next few days.

I gave him my direction at the Queen's Head, but added that I had it in my mind to go shortly to Edinburgh, where my address would be best known to the Lord Advocate.

"The Lord Advocate!" said Mr. Pitt, raising his eyebrows.

"I may as well make a clean breast of it, sir," I proceeded hurriedly, "and say that I left Scotland under circumstances peculiarly distressing. Thurot saved me from a ship called the *Seven Sisters*, that had been scuttled and abandoned with only myself and a seaman on board of her in mid-channel, by a man named Daniel Risk."

"Bless me!" cried Mr. Pitt, "the scoundrel Risk was tried in Edinburgh a month or two ago on several charges, including the one you mention, and he has either been hanged, or is waiting to be hanged at this moment, in the jail at Edinburgh."

"I was nominally purser on the *Seven Sisters*, but in actual fact I was fleeing from justice."

The Minister hemmed, and fumbled with his papers.

"It was owing to a duelling affair, in which I had the misfortune to—to—kill my opponent. I desire, sir, above all, to be thoroughly honest, and I am bound to tell you it was my first intention to make the conveyance of this plan of Thurot's a lever to secure my pardon for the crime of manslaughter which lies at my charge. I would wish now that my loyalty to my country was really disinterested, and I have, in the last half-hour, made up my mind to surrender myself to the law of Scotland."

"That is for yourself to decide on," said the Minister more gravely, "but I should advise the postponement of your departure to Edinburgh until you hear further from me. I shall expect to find you at the inn at Charing Cross during the next week; thereafter——"

He paused for a moment. "Well—thereafter we shall see," he added.

After a few more words of the kindest nature the Minister shook hands with the confessed manslayer (it flashed on me as a curious circumstance), and I went back to join the priest and my fellow country-man.

They were waiting full of impatience.

"Hast the King's pardon in thy pocket, friend Scotland?" cried Father Hamilton; then his face sank in sympathy with the sobriety of my own that was due to my determination on a surrender to justice once my business with the Government was over.

"I have no more in my pocket than I went out with in the morning," said I. "But my object, so far, has been served. Mr. Pitt knows my story and is like to take such steps as may be needful. As for my own affair I have mentioned it, but it has gone no further than that."

"You're not telling me you did not make a bargain

of it before saying a word about the bit plan?" cried MacKellar in surprise, and could scarcely find words strong enough to condemn me for what he described as my stupidity.

"Many a man will sow the seed that will never eat the syboe," was his comment; "and was I not right yonder when I said yon about the tact? If it had been me now I would have gone very canny to the King himself and said: 'Your Majesty, I'm a man that has made a slip in a little affair as between gentlemen, and had to put off abroad until the thing blew by. I can save the lives of many thousand Englishmen, and perhaps the country itself, by intelligence that came to my knowledge when I was abroad; if I prove it, will your Majesty pardon the thing that lies at my charge?'"

"And would have his Majesty's signature to the promise as 'twere a deed of sale!" laughed the priest convulsively. "La! la! la! Paul, here's our Celtic Solon with tact—the tact of the foot-pad. Stand and deliver! My pardon, sire, or your life! *Mon Dieu!* there runs much of the old original cateran in thy methods of diplomacy, good Master MacKellar. Too much for royal courts, I reckon."

MacKellar pshawed impatiently. "I'm asking you what is the Secretary's name, Mr. Greig?" said he. "Fox or Pitt it is all the same—the one is sly and the other is deep, and it is the natures of their names. I'll warrant Mr. Pitt has forgotten already the name of the man who gave him the secret, and the wisest thing Paul Greig could do now would be to go into hiding as fast as he can."

But I expressed my determination to wait in the Queen's Head a week longer, as I had promised, and thereafter (if nothing happened to prevent it) to submit myself at Edinburgh. Though I tried to make as little of that as possible to myself, and indeed would make myself believe I was going to act with a rare bravery, I must confess now that my determination was strengthened greatly by the reflection that my service to the country would perhaps annul or greatly modify my sentence.

CHAPTER XLI

TREATS OF FATHER HAMILTON'S DEATH

It was a gay place, London, in the days I write of, however it may be now, though Father Hamilton was prone occasionally to compare it unfavourably with the Paris of his fancy, the which he held a sample-piece of paradise. The fogs and rains depressed him ; he had an eye altogether unfriendly for the signs of striving commerce in the streets and the greedy haste of clerks and merchants into whose days of unremitting industry so few joys (as he fancied) seemed to enter.

MacKellar soon found company in it among silken bucks that held noisy sederunts in the evenings at a place called White's and another called (if my memory does not fail me) the Cocoa Nut Tree. 'Twas marvellous the number of old friends and fellow countrymen that, by his own account, he found there. And what open hands they had ! But for him that was privileged, for old acquaintance sake, to borrow from them, we had found our week or two in London singularly hungry because (to tell the truth of it) our money was come very nearly to an end. But MacKellar, who had foraged so well in Silesia, was equally good at it in the city of London. From these night escapades he seldom failed to return richer than he went, and it was he who paid the piper with so much of an air of thinking it a privilege, that we had not the heart, even if we had the inclination, to protest.

If I had known then, as I know now, or at least suspect, that the money that fed and boarded us was won through his skill at dice and cards, I daresay I had shifted sooner from London than I did at the last.

Day after day passed, and no word from Mr. Pitt. I dared scarcely leave my inn for an hour's airing lest I should be asked for in my absence. There was, for a while, a hope that though I had refused to make any bargain about the pardon, something— I could not so much as guess what—might happen to avert the scandal of a trial at Edinburgh, and the disgrace that same might bring upon my family. But day after day passed, as I have said, and there came no hint of how matters stood.

And then there came a day when I was to consider it mattered very little whether I heard from Pitt or not; when even my country was forgotten and I was to suffer a loss whose bitterness abides with me yet. It was the death of Father Hamilton, whom I had grown to like exceedingly. Birds have built and sung for many generations since then; children play in the garden still; there is essence at the table, there is sparkle in the wine, and he will never enjoy them any more. Fortune has come to me since then, so that I might have the wherewithal, if I had the wish, to take the road again with him in honesty, and see it even better than when Sin paid the bill for us, but it cannot be with him.

It was a December day of the whitest, the city smothered in snow, its tumult hushed. I had been tempted to wander in the forenoon a good way from our lodging. Coming home in the afternoon I met Kilbride, distracted, setting out to seek for me. He had a face like the clay, and his hands, that grasped my lapels as if I meant to fly from him, were trembling.

"Oh, Paul," said he. "Here's the worst of all," and I declare his cheeks were wet with tears.

"What is it?" I cried in great alarm.

"The priest, the priest," said he. "He's lying yonder at the ebb, and I'm no more use to him than if I were a bairn. I've seen the death-thraws a thousand times, but never to vex me just like this before. He could make two or three of us in bulk, and yet his heart was like a wean's, and there he's crying on you even-on till I was near demented and must run about the streets to seek for you."

"But still you give me no clue!" I cried, hurrying home with him.

He gave me the story by the way. It seemed his reverence had had a notion to see Eastcheap, round which the writer Shakespeare had thrown a glamour for him. He had gone there shortly after I had gone out in the forenoon, and after a space of walking about it had found himself in a mean street where a blackguard was beating a child. 'Twas the man's own child, doubtless, and so he had, I make no doubt, the law of it on his own side, but the drunken wretch outdid all reasonable chastisement, and thrashed her till the blood flowed.

Up ran the priest and took her in his arms, shielding her from the blows of the father's cudgel with his arm. The child nuzzled to his breast, shrieking, and the father tried to pull her away. Between them she fell; the priest stood over her, keeping back the beast that threatened. The man struck at him with his stick; Father Hamilton wrenched it from him, threw it down that he might have no unfair advantage, and flung himself upon the wretch. He could have crushed him into jelly, but the man was armed, and suddenly drew a knife. He thrust suddenly between the priest's shoulders, released himself from the tottering body, and disappeared with his child apparently beyond all chance of identification or discovery.

Father Hamilton was carried home upon a litter.

"O God! Kilbride, and must he die?" I cried in horror.

"He will travel in less than an hour," said the Highlander, vastly moved. "And since he came here his whole cry has been for you and Father Joyce."

We went into the room that seemed unnaturally white and sunny. He lay upon the bed-clothes. The bed was drawn towards the window, through which the domes and towers and roofs of London could be seen, with their accustomed greyness gone below the curtain of the snow. A blotch of blood was on his shirt-front as he lay upon his side. I thought at first it was his own life oozing, but learned a little later that the stricken child had had her face there.

"Paul! Paul!" he said, "I thought thou wouldst blame me for deserting thee again, and this time without so much as a letter of farewell."

What could I do but take his hand, and fall upon my knees beside his bed? He had blue eyes that never aged nor grossened—the eyes of a boy, clear, clean, and brave, and round about them wrinkles played in a sad, sweet smile.

"What, Paul!" he said, "all this for behemoth! for the old man of the sea that has stuck on thy shoulders for a twelvemonth, and spurred thee to infinite follies and perils! I am no more worth a tear of thine than is the ivied ash that falls untimely and decayed, eaten out of essence by the sins he sheltered. And the poor child, Paul!—the poor child with her arms round my neck, her tears brine —sure I have them on my lips—the true *viaticum!* The brute! the brute! Ah no! ah no! poor sinner, we do not know."

"Oh, father!" I cried, "and must we never go into the woods and towns any more?"

He smiled again and stroked my hair.

"Not in these fields, boy," said he, "but perhaps in more spacious, less perplexed. Be good, be simple, be kind! 'Tis all I know."

We heard the steps of Father Joyce upon the stairs.

"All I know!" repeated the priest. "Fifty years to learn it, and I might have found it in my mother's lap. *Chère ange*—the little mother—'twas a good world! And Fanchon that is dead below the snow in Louvain—oh, the sweet world! And the sunny gardens of bees and children——"

His eyes were dull. A pallor was on his countenance. He breathed with difficulty. Kilbride, who stood by, silent, put a finger on his pulse. At that he opened his eyes again, once more smiling, and Father Joyce was at the door.

"Kiss me, Paul," said the dying man, "I hear them singing prime."

When Father Joyce was gone I came into the room again where the priest lay smiling still, great in figure, in the simplicity and sweetness of his countenance like a child.

Kilbride and I stood silent for a little by the bed, and the Highlander was the first to speak.

"I have seen worse," said he, "than Father Hamilton."

It may seem a grudging testimony, but not to me that heard it.

On the day after the priest's funeral Kilbride came to me with that news which sent me north. He had the week's gazette in his hand, "Have you heard the latest?" he cried. "It is just what I expected," he went on. "They have made use of your information and set you aside. Here's the tidings of Conflans' defeat. Hawke came down on him off Brest, drove him back from the point of Quiberon to the coast near the mouth of the Vilaine, sank four ships, captured two, and routed the enemy. The invasion is at an end."

"It is gallant news!" I cried, warm with satisfaction.

"Maybe," said he indifferently, "but the main thing is that Paul Greig, who put the Government in the way of taking proper steps, is here in cheap lodgings with a charge on his head and no better than ever he was. Indeed, perhaps he's worse off than ever he was."

"How is that?"

"Well, they ken where you are, for one thing, and you put yourself in their power. I am one that has small faith in Governments. What will hinder them to clap you in jail and save another reward like the first one Pitt told you about? I would never put it past a Sassenach of the name."

Then I told him it had been in my mind ever since I had seen the Minister to go to Edinburgh and give myself up to the authorities.

"Are ye daft?" he cried, astonished.

I could only shrug my shoulders at that.

"Perhaps you fancy this business of the invasion will help you to get your neck out of the loop? I would not lippen on a Government for ten minutes. You have saved the country—that's the long and the short of it; now you must just be saving your own hide. There's nothing for us but the Continent again, and whether you're in the key for that or not, here's a fellow will sleep uneasy till he has Europe under his head."

Even at the cost of parting with Kilbride I determined to carry out my intention of going to Edinburgh. With the priest gone, no prospect of

Mr. Pitt taking the first step, and Kilbride in the humour for a retreat, I decided that the sooner I brought matters to a head the better.

There was a mail coach that went north weekly. It took a considerable deal of money and a fortnight of time to make the journey between the two capitals, but MacKellar, free-handed to the last, lent me the money (which I sent him six months later to Holland), and I set out one Saturday from the "Bull and Whistle" in a genteel two-end spring machine that made a brisk passage—the weather considered —as far as York on our way into Scotland.

I left on a night of jubilation for the close of the war and the overthrow of Conflans. Bonfires blazed on the river-side and the eminences round the city ; candles were in every window, the people were huzzaing in the streets where I left behind me only the one kent face—that of MacKellar of Kilbride who came to the coach to see the last of me. And everywhere was the snow—deep, silent, apparently enduring.

CHAPTER XLII

I DEPART IN THE MIDST OF ILLUMINATION AND COME
TO A JAIL, BAD NEWS, AND AN OLD ENEMY

WE carried this elation all through England with us.
Whatever town we stopped at flags were flying, and
the oldest resident must be tipsy on the green for the
glory of the British Isles. The seven passengers who
occupied the coach with me found in these rejoicings,
and in the great event which gave rise to them, subjects of unending discourse as we dragged through
the country in the wake of steaming horses. There
was with us a maker of perukes that had found trade
dull in Town (as they call it), and planned to start
business in York; a widow woman who had buried
her second husband and was returning to her parents
in Northumberland with a sprightliness that told she
was ready to try a third if he offered; and a squire
(as they call a laird) of Morpeth.

But for the common interest in the rejoicings it
might have been a week before the company thawed
to each other enough to start a conversation. The
first mile of the journey, however, found us in the
briskest debate on Hawke and his doings. I say us,

but in truth my own share in the conversation was very small as I had more serious reflections.

The perruquier, as was natural to his trade, knew everything and itched to prove it.

"I have it on the very best authority," he would say, "indeed "—with a whisper for all the passengers as if he feared the toiling horses outside might hear him—"indeed between ourselves I do not mind telling that it was from Sir Patrick Dall's man—that the French would have been on top of us had not one of themselves sold the plot for a hatful of guineas."

"That is not what I heard at all," broke in the squire. "I fancy you are mistaken, sir. The truth, as I have every reason to believe, is that one of the spies of the Government—a Scotsman, by all accounts—discovered Conflans' plans, and came over to London with them. A good business too, egad! otherwise we'd soon have nothing to eat at Morpeth George Inn on market days but frogs, and would find the parley-voos overrunning the country by next Lent with their masses and mistresses, and so on. A good business for merry old England that this spy had his English ears open."

"It may be you are right, sir," conceded the perruquier deferentially. "Now that I remember, Sir Patrick's gentleman said something of the same kind, and that it was one of them Scotsmen brought the news. Like enough the fellow found it worth his while. It will be a pretty penny in his pocket, I'll wager. He'll be able to give up spying and start an inn."

I have little doubt the ideal nature of retirement

N

to an inn came to the mind of the peruke maker from the fact that at the moment we were drawing up before "The Crown" at Bawtry. Reek rose in clouds from the horses, as could be seen from the light of the doors that showed the narrow street knee-deep in snow; a pleasant smell of cooking supper and warm cordials came out to us, welcome enough it may be guessed after our long day's stage. The widow clung just a trifle too long on my arm as I gallantly helped her out of the coach; perhaps she thought my silence and my abstracted gaze at her for the last hour or two betrayed a tender interest, but I was thinking how close the squire and the wig-maker had come upon the truth, and yet made one mistake in that part of their tale that most closely affected their silent fellow passenger.

The sea-fight and the war lasted us for a topic all through England, but when we had got into Scotland on the seventh day after my departure from London, the hostlers at the various change-houses yoked fresh horses to the tune of "Daniel Risk."

We travelled in the most tempestuous weather. Snow fell incessantly, and was cast in drifts along the road; sometimes it looked as if we were bound for days, but we carried the mails, and with gigantic toil the driver pushed us through.

The nearer we got to Edinburgh the more we learned of the notorious Daniel Risk, whom no one knew better than myself. The charge of losing his ship wilfully was, it appeared, among the oldest and least heinous of his crimes. Smuggling had engaged his talent since then, and he had murdered a cabin-boy under the most revolting circumstances. He had almost escaped the charge of scuttling the *Seven Sisters*, for it was not till he had been in the dock for the murder that evidence of that transaction came from the seaman Horn, who had been wrecked twice, it appeared, and far in other parts of the world between the time he was abandoned in the scuttled ship and returned to his native land, to tell how the ruffian had left two innocent men to perish.

Even in these days of wild happenings the fame of Risk exceeded that of every malefactor that season, and when we got to Edinburgh the street singers were chanting doleful ballads about him.

I would have given the wretch no thought, or very little, for my own affairs were heavy enough, had not the very day I landed in Edinburgh seen a broad-sheet published with "The Last Words and Warning" of Risk. The last words were in an extraordinarily devout spirit; the homily breathed what seemed a real repentance for a very black life. It would have moved me less if I could have learned then, as I did later, that the whole thing was the invention of some drunken lawyer's clerk in the Canongate, who had probably devised scores of such fictions for the entertainment of the world that likes to read of scaffold repentances and of wicked lives. The condition of the wretch touched me, and I made up my mind to see the condemned man who, by the accounts of the journals, was being visited daily by folks interested in his forlorn case.

With some manœuvring I got outside the bars of his cell.

There was little change in him. The same wild aspect was there though he pretended a humility. The skellie eye still roved with little of the love of God or man in it; his iron-grey hair hung tawted about his temples. Only his face was changed and had the jail-white of the cells, for he had been nearly two months in confinement. When I entered he did not know me; indeed, he scarce looked the road I was on at first, but applied himself zealously to the study of a book wherein he pretended to be rapturously engrossed.

The fact that the Bible (for so it was) happened to be upside down in his hands somewhat staggered my faith in the repentance of Daniel Risk, who, I remembered, had never numbered reading among his arts.

I addressed him as Captain.

"I am no Captain," said he in a whine, "but plain Dan Risk, the blackest sinner under the cope and canopy of heaven." And he applied himself to his volume as before.

"Do you know me?" I asked, and he must have found the voice familiar, for he rose from his stool, approached the bars of his cage, and examined me. "Andy Greig's nephew!" he cried. "It's you; I hope you're a guid man?"

"I might be the best of men—and that's a dead one—so far as you are concerned," I replied, stung a little by the impertinence of him.

"The hand of Providence saved me that last item in my bloody list o' crimes," said he, with a singular mixture of the whine for his sins and of pride in their number. "Your life was spared, I mak' nae doubt, that ye micht repent o' your past, and I'm sorry to see ye in sic fallals o' dress, betokenin' a licht mind and a surrender to the vanities."

My dress was scantily different from what it had been on the *Seven Sisters*, except for some lace, my tied hair, and a sword.

"Indeed, and I am in anything but a light frame of mind, Captain Risk," I said. "There are reasons for that, apart from seeing you in this condition which I honestly deplore in spite of all the wrong you did me."

"I thank God that has been forgiven me," he said, with a hypocritical cock of his hale eye. "I was lost in sin, a child o' the deevil, but noo I am made clean," and much more of the same sort that it is unnecessary here to repeat.

"You can count on my forgiveness, so far as that goes," I said, disgusted with his manner.

"I'm greatly obleeged," said he, "but man's forgiveness doesna coont sae muckle as a preen, and I would ask ye to see hoo it stands wi' yersel'. Daniel Risk has made his peace wi' his Maker, but what way is it wi' the nephew o' Andrew Greig?"

"It ill becomes a man in a condemned cell to be preacher to those outside of it," I told him in some exasperation at his presumption.

He threw up his hands and glowered at me with his gleed eye looking seven ways for sixpence as the saying goes.

"Dinna craw ower crouse, young man," he said. "Whit brings ye here I canna guess, but I ken that you that's there should be in here where I am, for there's blood on your hands."

He had me there! Oh, yes, he had me there! Every vein in my body told me so. But I was not in the humour to make an admission of that kind to this creature.

"I have no conceit of myself in any respect whatever, Daniel Risk," I said slowly. "I came here from France but yesterday after experiences there that paid pretty well for my boy's crime, for I have heard from neither kith nor kin since you cozened me on the boards of the *Seven Sisters*."

He put his hands upon the bars and looked at me. He wore a prison garb of the most horrible colour, and there were round him the foul stenches of the cell.

"Ay!" said he. "New back! And they havena nabbed ye yet! Weel, they'll no' be lang, maybe, o' doin' that, for I'll warrant ye've been advertised plenty aboot the country; ony man that has read a gazette or clattered in a public-hoose kens your description and the blackness o' the deed you're chairged wi'. All I did was to sink a bit ship that was rotten onyway, mak' free trade wi' a few ankers o' brandy that wad hae been drunk by the best i' the land includin' the very lords that tried me, and accidentally kill a lad that sair needed a beltin' to gar him dae his honest wark. But you shot a man deliberate and his blood is crying frae the grund. If ye hurry ye'll maybe dance on naethin' sooner nor mysel'."

There was so much impotent venom in what he

said that I lost my anger with the wretch drawing near his end, and looked on him with pity. It seemed to annoy him more than if I had reviled him.

"I'm a white soul," says he, clasping his hands—the most arrant blasphemy of a gesture from one whose deeds were desperately wicked! "I'm a white soul, praise God! and value not your opinions a docken leaf. Ye micht hae come here to this melancholy place to slip a bit guinea into my hand for some few extra comforts, instead o' which it's jist to anger me."

He glued his cheek against the bars and stared at me from head to foot, catching at the last a glance of my fateful shoes. He pointed at them with a rigid finger.

"Man! man!" he cried, "there's the sign and token o' the lot o' ye—the bloody shoon. They may weel be red for him and you that wore them. Red shoon! red shoon!" He stopped suddenly. "After a'," said he, "I bear ye nae ill-will, though I hae but to pass the word to the warder on the ither side o' the rails. And oh! abin a' repent——" He was off again into one of his blasphemies, for at my elbow now was an old lady who was doubtless come to confirm the conversion of Daniel Risk. I turned to go.

He cast his unaffected eye piously heavenward, and coolly offered up a brief prayer for "this erring young brother determined on the ways of vice and folly."

It may be scarce credible that I went forth from

the condemned cell with the most shaken mind I had had since the day I fled from the moor of Mearns. The streets were thronged with citizens; the castle ramparts rose up white and fine, the bastions touched by sunset fires, a window blazing like a star. Above the muffled valley, clear, silvery, proud, rang a trumpet on the walls, reminding me of many a morning rouse in far Silesia. Was I not better there? Why should I be the sentimental fool and run my head into a noose? Risk, whom I had gone to see in pity, paid me with a vengeance! He had put into the blunt language of the world all the horror I had never heard in words before, though it had often been in my mind. I saw myself for the first time the hunted outlaw, captured at last. "You that's out there should be in where I am!" It was true! But to sit for weeks in that foul hole within the iron rail, waiting on doom, reflecting on my folks disgraced—I could not bear it!

Risk cured me of my intention to hazard all on the flimsy chance of a Government's gratitude, and I made up my mind to seek safety and forgetfulness again in flight to another country.

CHAPTER XLIII

BACK TO THE MOORLAND

I HAD seen yon remnant of a man in the Tolbooth cell, and an immediate death upon the gallows seemed less dreadful than the degradation and the doubt he must suffer waiting weary months behind bars. But gallows or cell was become impossible for the new poltroon of Dan Risk's making to contemplate with any equanimity, and I made up my mind that America was a country which would benefit greatly by my presence, if I could get a passage there by working for it.

Perhaps I would not have made so prompt a decision upon America had not America implied a Clyde ship, and the Clyde as naturally implied a flying visit to my home in Mearns. Since ever I had set foot on Scotland, and saw Scots reek rise from Scots lums, and blue bonnets on Scots heads, and heard the twang of the true North and kindly from the people about me, I had been wondering about my folk. It was plain they had never got the letter I had sent by Horn, or got it only recently, for he himself had only late got home.

To see the house among the trees, then, to get a

reassuring sight of its smoke and learn about my parents, was actually of more importance in my mind than my projected trip to America, though I did not care to confess so much to myself.

I went to Glasgow on the following day; the snow was on the roofs; the students were noisily battling; the bells were cheerfully ringing as on the day with whose description I open this history. I put up at the "Saracen Head," and next morning engaged a horse to ride to Mearns. In the night there had come a change in the weather; I splashed through slush of melted snow, and soaked in a constant rain, but objected none at all because it gave me an excuse to keep up the collar of my cloak, and pull the brim of my hat well forward on my face and so minimise the risk of identification.

There is the lichened root of an ancient fallen saugh tree by the side of Earn Water between Kirkillstane and Driepps that I cannot till this day look on without a deep emotion. Walter's bairns have seen me sitting there more than once, and unco solemn so that they have wondered, the cause beyond their comprehension. It was there I drew up my horse to see the house of Kirkillstane from the very spot where I had rambled with my shabby stanzas, and felt the first throb of passion for a woman.

The country was about me familiar in every dyke and tree and eminence; where the water sobbed in the pool it had the accent it had in my dreams; there was a broken branch of ash that trailed above the fall, where I myself had dragged it once in climbing. The smell of moss and rotten leafage in the dripping rain, the eerie aspect of the moorland in the mist, the call of lapwings—all was as I had left it. There was not the most infinite difference to suggest that I had seen another world, and lived another life, and become another than the boy that wandered here.

I rode along the river to find the smoke rising from my father's house—thank God! but what the better was the outlaw son for that? Dare he darken again the door he had disgraced, and disturb anew the hearts he had made sore?

I pray my worst enemy may never feel torn by warring dictates of the spirit as I was that dreary afternoon by the side of Earn; I pray he may never know the pang with which I decided that old events were best let lie, and that I must be content with that brief glimpse of home before setting forth again upon the roads of dubious fortune. Fortune! Did I not wear just now the very Shoes of Fortune? They had come I knew not whence, from what magic part and artisan of heathendom I could not even guess, to my father's brother; they had covered the unresting foot of him; to me they had brought their curse of discontent, and so in wearing them I seemed doomed to be the unhappy rover, too.

The afternoon grew loud with wind as I sat my horse beside the increasing water; I felt desolate beyond expression.

"Well, there must be an end of it some way!" I said bitterly, and I turned to go.

The storm opposed me as I cantered over Whiggitlaw, and won by Brooms, and Bishops Offerance, and Kilree. Shepherds sheltered in the lee of dykes, and women hurried out and shuttered windows. I saw sheep hastening into the angles of the fields, and the wild white sea-gull beating across the sky. The tempest thrashed on me as though it could not have me go too soon from the country of my shame; I broke the horse to gallop, and fields and dykes flew by like things demented.

Then of a sudden the beast grew lame; I searched for a stone or a cast shoe, but neither ailed him, and plainly the ride to town that night was impossible. Where the beast failed was within half a mile of Newton, and at all hazards I decided I must make for the inn there. I felt there were risks of recognition, but I must run them. I led the horse by a side path, and reached the inn no sooner than the darkness that fell that night with unusual suddenness. Lights were in the house, and the sound of rural merriment in the kitchen, where farm lads drank twopenny ale, and sang.

A man—he proved to be the innkeeper—came to my summons with a lantern in his hand, and held it up to see what wayfarer was this in such a night. He saw as little of me as my hat and cloak could reveal, and I saw, what greatly relieved me, that he was not John Warnock, who had tenanted the inn when I left the country, but a new tenant and one unknown to me. He helped me to unsaddle the horse, discovered with me that the lameness would probably succumb to a night in the stall, and unburdened himself to the questions every unknown traveller in the shire of Renfrew may expect.

"You'll be frae Ayr, maybe, or Irvine?"

No, I was from neither; I was from Glasgow.

"Say ye sae, noo! Dod! it's nae nicht for travellin', and nae wonder your horse is lamed. Ye'll be for ower Fenwick way, noo, i' the mornin'?"

Nor was I for over Fenwick way in the morning. I was for Glasgow again.

He looked from the corners of his eyes at this oddity who travelled like a shuttle in such weather. I was drenched with rain, and my spatter-dashes, with which I had thought to make up in some degree for the inadequate foot-wear of red shoes on horse-back, were foul with clay. He presumed I was for supper?

"No," I answered; "I'm more in the humour for bed, and I will be obliged if you send to my room for my clothes in a little so that they may be dry by the time I start in the morning, and I shall set out at seven if by that time my horse is recovered."

I drank a tankard of ale for the good of the house, as we say, during a few minutes in the parlour, making my dripping clothes and a headache the excuse for refusing the proffered hospitality of the kitchen where the ploughboys sang, and then went to the little cam-ceiled room where a hasty bed had been made for me.

The world outside was full of warring winds and plashing rains, into which the yokels went at last reluctantly, and when they were gone I fell asleep, wakening once only for a moment when my wet clothes were being taken from the room.

CHAPTER XLIV

WHEREIN THE SHOES OF FORTUNE BRING ME HOME

I CAME down from my cam-ceiled room to a breakfast by candle-light in a morning that was yet stormy. The landlord himself waited on me ('twas no other than Ralph Craig that's now retired at the Whinnell), and he had a score of apologies for his servant lass that had slept in too long, as he clumsily set a table with his own hand, bringing in its equipment in single pieces.

There was a nervousness in his manner that escaped me for a little in the candle-light, but I saw it finally with some wonder, rueing I had agreed to have breakfast here at all, and had not taken my horse, now recovered of his lameness, and pushed on out of a neighbourhood where I had no right in common sense to be.

If the meal was slow of coming it was hearty enough, though the host embarrassed me too much with his attentions. He was clearly interested in my personality.

"It's not the first time ye've been in the 'Red Lion,'" said he with an assurance that made me stare.

"And what way should you be thinking that?" I

asked, beginning to feel more anxious about my position.

"Oh, jist a surmise o' my ain," he answered. " Ye kent your way to the stable in the dark, and then— and then there's whiles a twang o' the Mearns in your speech."

This was certainly coming too close! I hastened through my breakfast, paid my lawing, and ordered out my horse. That took so long that I surmised the man was wilfully detaining me. "This fellow has certainly some project to my detriment," I told myself, and as speedily as I might got into the saddle. Then he said what left no doubt :

"They'll be gey glad to see ye at the Hazel Den, Mr. Greig."

I felt a stound of anguish at the words that might in other circumstances have been true but now were so remote from it.

"You seem to have a very gleg eye in your head," I said, "and to have a great interest in my own affairs."

"No offence, Mr. Paul, no offence!" said he civilly, and indeed abashed. "There's a lassie in the kitchen that was ance your mither's servant and she kent your shoes."

"I hope then you'll say nothing about my being here to any one—for the sake of the servant's old mistress—that was my mother."

"That *was* your mither!" he repeated. "And what for no' yet? She'll be prood to see ye hame."

"Is it well with them up there?" I eagerly asked.

"I'll wager it will be the happiest day o' their lives," he protested.

"I thank God if they're well," said I, "but for the rest of it I must be going away at once, and I trust they will not suffer the distress of learning from you or your maid that I have been in the neighbourhood."

The landlord scratched his head and hummed and hawed. The dawn was beginning to show in the east; I was impatient to be gone, and gathered up my reins.

"Hold on a wee," said he. "They'll be expectin' ye hame the day, for the lassie's awa at the Hazel Den noo to tell them ye're here."

"You could not have done me a worse turn than to send her on such an errand," I said, "for there's that between my people and myself that makes my father's honest house no place for me."

"Michty!" cried the landlord, "ye're surely no' in ony mair trouble than ye went awa in?"

"Is it not enough?" I asked bitterly.

"No' enough to keep ye frae your faither's hoose when ye're on the moor o' Mearns," said he boldly.

"You have a very tolerant view of manslaughter," I said.

"Lord keep's!" said he. "Are ye in that notion ye went awa wi' yet? Is it Davie Borland ye mean? The man's nae mair slaughtered than ye are yoursel', and there's blythmeat in his hoose the day, for his wife has just gotten him a son."

For some seconds the meaning of his words failed to find me, for I was too troubled with the knowledge that my people had been apprised of my neighbourhood to grasp the fact that set all else at naught—that David Borland was not dead. When that came home to me I jumped from my horse and seized the innkeeper by the shoulder till he twisted in my grasp.

"What in God's name is this ye're telling me?" I demanded.

"Oh, jist what onybody could hae tauld ye the very day ye took legs for it oot o' the country. Jist that Borland was nane the waur o' your shooting, and was only in a swound because your bullet skimmed his lug."

"And there's nothing wrong with him?" I cried, still incredulous, recalling the circumstantial assurances of Daniel Risk that I had been the object of the hue and cry; finding it ill to believe even of such a wretch that on the brink of the tomb he should concoct so villainous a fiction for my punishment.

"Nae mair nor whit's wrang wi' me," cried the innkeeper. "Am n't I tellin' ye there's blythmeat at his hoose this very mornin'?"

"And he's married since I left?" I said, preparing to mount and ride for home with a pang of some regret at this part of my revelation.

"A twelvemonth syne, to Jean Fortune o' the Kirkillstane," said he.

"You mean her sister Isobel?" said I, feeling a new hope rise.

"No, nor Isobel," said he. "Isobel's yonder yet, and like to be until ye gang for her. It was the ither ane that Borland courted a' the time."

I rode like fury home. The day was come before I reached the dykes of Hazel Den. Smoke was rising from its chimneys; there was a homely sound of lowing cattle, and a horse was saddling for my father who was preparing to ride over to the inn at Newton to capture his errant son. He stood before the door, a little more grey, a little more bent, a little more shrunken than when I had seen him last. When I drew up before him with my hat in my hand and leaped out of the saddle, he scarcely grasped at first the fact that here was his son.

"Father! Father!" I cried to him, and he put his arms about my shoulders.

"You're there, Paul!" said he at last. "Come your ways in; your dear mother is making your breakfast."

I could not have had it otherwise—'twas the welcome I would have chosen!

His eyes were brimming over; his voice was full of sobs and laughter as he cried "Katrine! Katrine!" and my mother came to throw herself into my arms.

My Shoes of Fortune had done me their one good office; they had brought me home.

And now, my dear David, and Quentin, and Jean, my tale is ended, leaving some folks who figured therein a space with their ultimate fortunes unexplained. There is a tomb in Rome that marks the end of Prince Charles Edward's wanderings and

exploits, ambitions, follies, and passions. Of him
and of my countrywoman, Clementina Walkinshaw,
you will by-and-by read with understanding in your
history-books. She died unhappy and disgraced,
yet I can never think of her but as young, beautiful,
kind, the fool of her affections, the plaything of
Circumstance. Clancarty's after career I never
learned, but Thurot, not long after I escaped from
him in Dunkerque, plundered the town of Carrick-
fergus, in Ireland, and was overtaken by three
frigates when he was on his way back to France.
His ships were captured and he himself was killed.
You have seen Dr. MacKellar here on a visit from
his native Badenoch ; his pardon from the Government was all I got, or all I wished for, from Mr. Pitt.
"And where is Isobel Fortune ?" you will ask.
You know her best as your grandmother, my wife.
My Shoes of Fortune, she will sometimes say,
laughing, brought me first and last Miss Fortune;
indeed they did ! I love them for it, but I love you,
too, and hope to keep you from the Greig's tempta-
tion, so they are to the fore no longer.

THE END

Printed in Great Britain by
WILLIAM BLACKWOOD AND SONS.